A Light From Within

Yoga Workbook and Journal

By Miguel J. Latronica, Eryt
Foreward by Mary Farhi, MD, RYT

A Light From Within

Yoga Workbook and Journal

By Miguel J. Latronica, Eryt
Foreward by Mary Farhi, MD, RYT

Yoga Bent, LLC
PO Box 384
Highland Park, Illinois
60035-0384
Tel. 847-831-1515
www.yogabent.com

ISBN 978-0-9886316-1-8
Library of Congress Control Number: 2015908488

Cover: Miguel Latronica
Interior Design: Diana Ramirez and Miguel J.Latronica
Illustrations: Jurek Polanski
Photographer: Miguel Latronica
Models: Mary Farhi, MD and Miguel Latronica

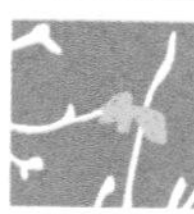

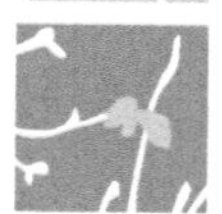

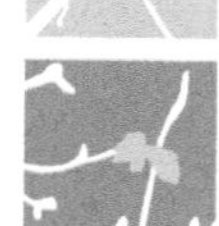

Notice

This book is intended as a reference volume only, not as a medical manual. The information given here is designed to help you make informed decisions about your health. It is not intended as a substitute for any treatment that may have been prescribed by your doctor. If you suspect that you have a medical problem, we urge you to seek competent medical help.

Health Condition Precautions

If you are currently taking medication for, or have risk of, any of the following below, it is imperative that you consult your doctor before first starting the Yoga Bent® Method program.

- High fever (over 100.4°F or 38°C)
- Persons needing convalescence 
- Persons with undiagnosed symptoms of pain
- Persons with undiagnosed depression
- Persons with any spinal injury 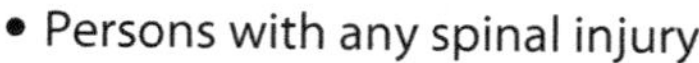
- During any postoperative period
- Pregnant women or postpartum
- Osteoporosis
- Cancer
- Heart disease
- Aneurysm, serious disturbances of blood circulation, thrombosis, etc. 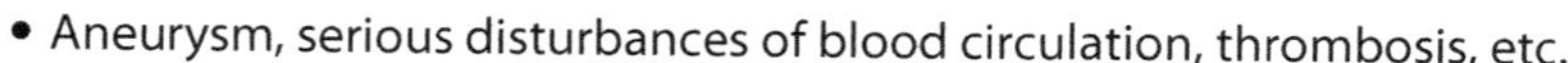
- Uncontrolled high blood pressure 
- Persons with acute injury such as epiphyseal fracture, sprain and muscle strain, etc.
- Glaucoma
- Persons using embedded medical electronic apparatus or device such as a heart pacemaker 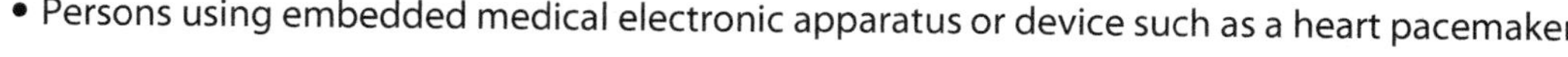

FAMOUS QUOTES

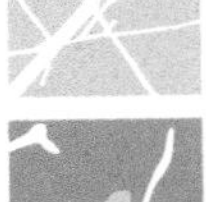

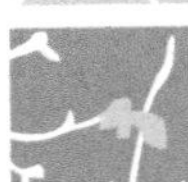

"The soul comes from without into the human body, as into a temporary abode, and it goes out of it anew it passes into other habitations, for the soul is immortal." Ralph Waldo Emerson – American Essayist

"I know of no more encouraging fact than the unquestionable ability of to elevate his life by conscious endeavor." – Henry Thoreau

"Close your eyes and let the mind expand. Let no fear of death or darkness arrest its course. Allow the mind to merge with mind. Let it flow out upon the great curve of consciousness. Let it soar on the wings of the great bird of duration, up to the very Circle of Eternity." - Hermes Trismegistus

"It is not more surprising to be born twice than once; everything in nature is resurrection."
Voltaire French Writer,

"Our birth is but a sleep and a forgetting; The Soul that rises with us, our life's Star, Hath had elsewhere its setting. And cometh from afar." - William Wordsworth

"If for mastering the physical sciences you have to devote a whole lifetime, how many life times may be needed for mastering the greatest spiritual force that mankind has known? For if this is the only permanent thing in life, if this is the only thing that counts, then whatever effort you bestow on mastering it is well spent. Having flung aside the sword, there is nothing except the cup of life which I can offer to those who oppose me. It is by offering that cup that I expect to draw them close to me.
I cannot think of permanent enmity between man and man, and believing as I do in the theory of rebirth, I live in the hope that if not in this birth, in some other birth I shall be able to hug all humanity in friendly embrace. " Mahatma Gandhi Indian Political Leader,

"The nitrogen in our DNA, the calcium in our teeth, the iron in our blood, the carbon in our apple pies were made in the interiors of collapsing stars. We are made of star stuff." Carl Sagan, Cosmos

"Mathematics expresses values that reflect the cosmos, including orderliness, balance, harmony, logic, and abstract beauty." Deepak Chopra

"We are fast moving into something, we are fast flung into something like asteroids cast into space by the death of a planet, we the people of earth are cast into space like burning asteroids and if we wish not to disintegrate into nothingness we must begin to now hold onto only the things that matter while letting go of all that doesn't. For when all of our dust and ice deteriorates into the cosmos we will be left only with ourselves and nothing else. So if you want to be there in the end, today is the day to start holding onto your children, holding onto your loved ones; onto those who share your soul. Harbor and anchor into your heart justice, truth, courage, bravery, belief, a firm vision, a steadfast and sound mind. Be the person of meaningful and valuable thoughts. Don't look to the left, don't look to the right; we simply don't have the time. Never be afraid of fear." C. JoyBell C

ACKNOWLEDGMENTS

Yoga Bent® has been blessed with the support, encouragement and aid from various groups and individuals, both within, and far beyond the yoga community. A special thanks to people like G. Jurek Polanski, J.H. McDonald (1996) who has dedicated countless time to translate and make available to all people the translation of Tao Te Ching, by Lao-Tzu.

CONTRIBUTORS

Special thanks and acknowledgment are due to the following:
Mary Farhi MD, Diana Ramirez, Carla Douros Phd, Per Erez, Jodi Foss, Deborah King, Laura Gannarelli, Nicole Aimiee Macaluso, G. Jurek Polanski, Sarah Polito, Alison Faith (Glazov) and Jayne Alenier

DEDICATION

In the world of yoga there is an old greeting whose name is Namaste. Generally speaking, namaste means the light from within my heart and soul acknowledges and sees the light in yours. But that inherently, the light within in yours reciprocates and observes the light in mine. It can be said out loud or just thought in silence. I would like to dedicate this book to my family, especially my beautiful wife Mary S. Farhi and my 6 wonderful boys (Jeremy Aaron, Alexander Lucca, Matan, Elan, Shai and Barak whose hearts, soul and mind I am forever in awe! Forever in gratitude! Forever in Light with!

To my mother, father, six beautiful siblings and ancestors of the past: I thank you for the gift of Life!

I would also like to thank my friends who have so patiently supported me in my efforts to finish this book. I love each and every one of you. And lastly, I would like to thank all of my teachers in life—I would not be who I am without your beautiful help and insights along the way i.e. of crafting greater meaning, of the importance of helping others, and of course. . . knowing the importance of self-discovery.

Self-discovery is the path to community.

Namaste

TABLE OF CONTENTS

TABLE OF CONTENTS

CHAPTER 4 Theory, Physics and Elements of Your Practice

Part Two

CHAPTER 5 A Guide to the Physical Practice

CHAPTER 6 Appendices

ALFW Anatomical Illustrations

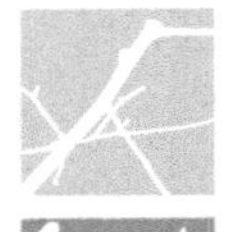

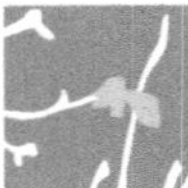

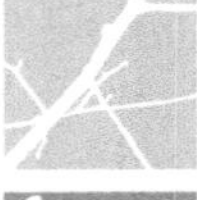

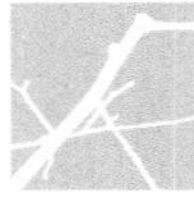

ALFW Alphabetized Yoga Pose Index

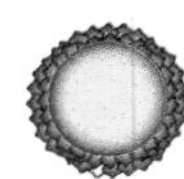

ALFW Pearls of Wisdom Index

Pearls of Wisdom | Page

 ALFW Pearls of Wisdom Index

Pearls of Wisdom Page

Foreward

By Mary Farhi, MD

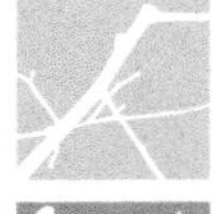

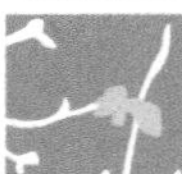

Congratulations on discovering this amazing book. It will be a valuable companion on your journey inward. My personal journey has been blessed with the presence of Miguel Latronica, his expansive wisdom, knowledge and passion for yoga. This book, however, is more than just a book about yoga. It contains an interactive process for healing at all levels: physically, mentally, emotionally and spiritually.

As a physician I have spent more than 20 years exploring wellness. My quest to understand the multidimensional aspects of wellness and healing began in public health and then traditional allopathic medicine. I soon recognized that our traditional model (with its focus on treating diseasewas lacking in helping to create dynamic wellness. This personal paradigm shift has led me to explore yoga, meditation, and ayurvedic medicine. One of the many interesting features of Miguel's workbook and journal is how he incorporates so many aspects of healing and wellness. *A Light From Within* is a beautiful and comprehensive exploration of both yoga and wellness. In the West, many tend to perceive yoga as only the physical practice of postures, or asanas. I am so excited to be able to recommend and share a book, such as Miguel's which explores many aspects of yoga and self-care, ultimately leading to self-healing.

There have been several recent articles in major publications about the increasing popularity of yoga. In general, these focus on the physical practice of yoga-- the asanas. While this is a great doorway into what we call yoga, there are, nonetheless, many other facets (or jewelsof yoga that allow us to shine and experience our "light" more deeply. Miguel's book helps to do just that: He guides us in a process of learning how to cultivate the "jewels" of yoga from within. For example, in addition to the 52 physical yoga poses, we also learn how to blend and incorporate breath work (pranayama, mudras (energy locksand other exercises too. The journaling and workbook exercises allow us to to peel away the unwanted layers of our life. It is through this process that we may learn to become aware of how the words we speak and images we conjure affect who we are.

A Light From Within encourages us to explore the way we think and feel about the things before us. This is what makes this book different from any other yoga book I've ever seen. Its method leads one to the heartfelt process of self-inquiry. It presents a self-guided process based on your personal historical timeline and can therefore be personalized. The method presented here can be beautifully utilized alone, or in small group settings such as yoga teacher trainings. It is very interactive and includes a link to blog for sharing and exchanging your thoughts and ideas with like-minded people. More importantly, it can be used alone and kept private. For those with minimal free time, explore one section of the book at a time. You can start anywhere and explore the book's many options. Just as we are all unique beings, the book can be individualized to provide a unique experience for each and every person.

Becoming whole, healed or well requires attention to not only our physical body but also our othermore subtle layers. Traditionally, the disease-centric model of Western medicine has failed to address this unity of body. We developed "ologies" or separate silos of specialties. Fortunately, I am blessed on my journey as an integrative physician to have discovered functional medicine: a systems biology approach to wellness, understanding that the entire system (mind, body, spirit) functions and cooperates together. Specifically, functional medicine looks upstream at the root causes of disease and illness, in order to create wellness and vitality. It is more than naming a disease and prescribing a medicine. Rather, it is about digging deep to understand causes and individual variability, in order to heal and be well and vital.

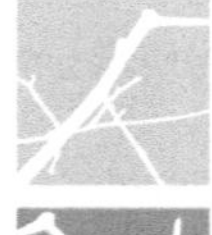
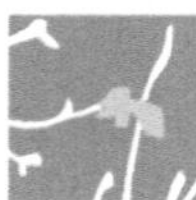

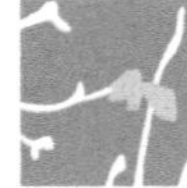

A Light From Within is like a functional method for exploring yoga and wellness. It focuses on the unity of the body, mind and spirit. There are comprehensive directions of each asana, as well as corresponding journal entries, reflective questions, affirmations, mudras and haikus. In this book, you will learn about the subtle aspects of wellness, such as our energetic system, through exploring the power of mudras. The questions for journaling guide us to dig deep and understand the many layers of our subtle being. Each workbook question has a table to rate and explore our emotional imprint or intelligence. When we recognize and rate the parameters of our emotions, we bring more clarity and awareness to our feelings. We all have the ability to heal and turn toward greater health and wellness. In order to heal, we need to understand what role conditioning has played in our lives. In *A Light From Within*, Miguel provides a rich format in which to explore self-awareness and self-acceptance with gratitude and grace.

This book helps us to better see and understand our habits and cultural biases. It actually encourages us to learn to be more present in the moment and develop habits that encourage mindfulness. In our world today, we are rich with opportunities to disconnect from ourselves and our surroundings. We can find endless ways to occupy and distract ourselves from the process of life, from pain and suffering, and ultimately distance ourselves from joy and contentment. Being aware of our breath is one such practice we can cultivate. From our first inhalation to our last, our breath gives us life. In between this first and last are potentially billions of breaths of which we may never take notice, and that we often take for granted.

The section on Pranayama teaches us how to harness the subtle healing potential of prana. We can create a contract with the sublime healing forces of pranic healing from our breath. Traditionally, yoga has eight different limbs or rungs to it. *A Light From Within* focuses on the asanas, mudras, questions and journaling, it includes more than 50 hours of meditative exercises. The entire book is divided into Four Seasons, 52 weeks, or sections of your life. You can begin anywhere. Just begin where you are.

With Light,
Mary Farhi, MD
June 1, 2015

Preface

"The Yoga Journey as it Unfolds" (cont.)

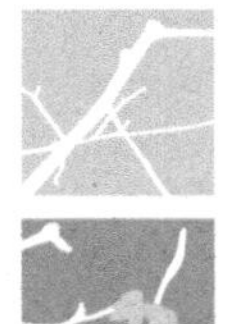

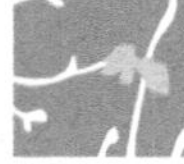

There is an expression: "Take down three walls, but leave the fourth one standing: this is the centerpiece of your being grounded." Welcome to *A Light From Within* (ALFW). I commend you in your desire and willingness to create vibrant health and achieve greater awareness. We all have the ability to transcend our personal experiences, and, it is never too late to live your life in the ray of luminous light: to renew or reconstruct the blueprint(s) of your life. ALFW is based on the seasons of the year and the seasons of your life. It has a common-sense approach to the art of living lighter. It is deeply grounded into the roots and details of your life, your community, friends and family. In many ways, ALFW helps you to become more aware and tuned in to the conscious process of "letting go and holding on." I invite you to think of this book and journal as being your living autobiography. Feel free to explore its many different platforms and possibilities. Have fun with it! Now I'd like to introduce you to some of it's operating principles. First and foremost, unlike a novel, you needn't read and work through the book logically from beginning to end. I encourage you to take your time with it as the purpose is the process.

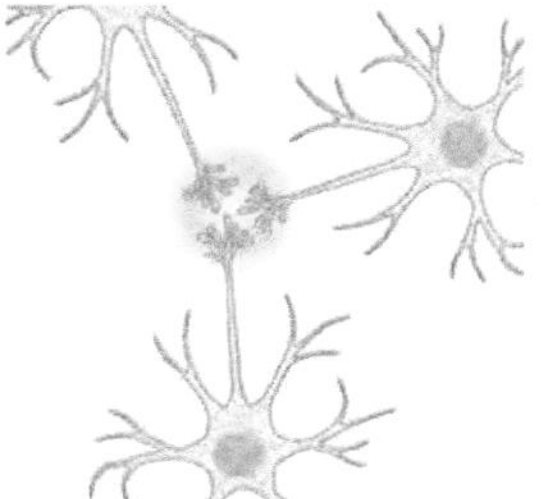

Neurological synapses

The book is 342 pages long, has six chapters, and is divided into two parts. Part One contains 102 workbook questions and journal entries and Part Two contains the physical yoga exercises, anatomical renderings, hand mudra meditations and the miscellaneous pearls of wisdom. Pretty simple. The book is self reporting and, unlike a calendar-based book, there is no expiration date. After interacting with the book for just a short while, you will begin to see and feel difference in your life. Just remember: do not over-edit your responses.

The important thing to keep in mind while working with the book is that as long as you're journaling and answering the workbook questions, you're doing the work. And, as long as you're practicing the physical yoga poses, mudras, and other exercises, again... you're doing the work. When it comes to working through personal change, many of us take an analytical approach, while others may take on a more organic and intuitive approach. No matter what approach you take, it's all good! After all, we're all neurologically wired a little differently. That said, ALFW was specifically designed to be used by the many different kinds of thinkers and learners.

So, whether your learning tends to be linear, spatial, kinetic, intuitive, auditory or any combination thereof, ALFW will work for you!
The workbook and journal helps you to identify many of the blocked energetic patterns that consciously, and even unconsciously work through the various layers of your life. Many of us have seen the picture (right) of the beautiful young woman wearing a hat with a feather on the left side of her head, yet, on second glance, it is now an elderly woman with the feathered hat at the right side of her head. We can only see one image at a time— all by the shifting gears of our perception. This is exactly what we do while working through the exercises of ALFW: we identify and come to terms with so many of the inequalities of our perception. After all, is not the process and quality of our thinking and feeling that give rise and flavor to the many positive and negative emotions? Feelings are subjective and many times mislead us, while the thinking (especially when incorporating critical thinking) is more predictable— it has the capacity to be more objective.

A young or elderly woman?

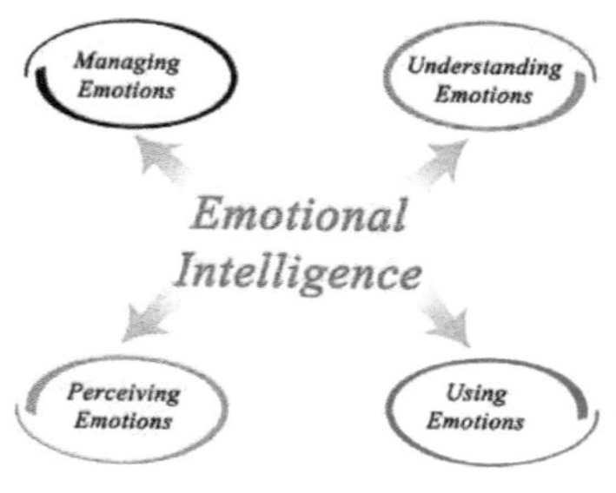

We all know that we feel and experience life differently. So, many of the things that live and express themselves through us *now* are nothing more than mirrored extensions or patterns of our *past*. Living in full awareness requires the ability to transcend these extensions and patterns. When we safely bring to surface the various layers of our past , we also expose the many operating assumptions and preconceived notions that sometimes mislead or dictate the direction of our life. Images, scents, sounds, tastes, intuitions and other expressions (especially from the past) are embedded so very deeply into the fabric of our being that, more often than not, we must find or create another way of looking at what it all means to us in the first place!

ALFW is self-reporting and is based on your life's timeline. What you get out of the book depends entirely on what you put into it. The method demonstrates how often it is that you may have consciously, and even unconsciously chosen to use (or abuse) the various emotional responses that you have. As just mentioned, emotions proceed and are very different than are our feelings. Emotions request an in-the-moment response. They cue us in on the various events from within and around our physical body. They are more concrete and measurable than are our feelings. Emotions can be measured by Galvanic Skin Response (GSR), blood flow, facial expression, body language and brain EEG patterns. And, we must try to remember that we all have an equal opportunity as to how we manage and respond to our sometimes short and long-lived emotions. When we objectively chose to act in response to our emotions, there is greater communication, reciprocity and mindfulness. Most coin have three sides: two large flat sides, otherwise known as heads and tails, and a third side: the edge. I like to tell my students that it is the third side of the coin with which we more optimally manage the relationship between our feelings and emotions. The third side may be said to represent the mind and its ability to execute critical thinking. It is important to understand that through careful analysis or examination, we all have the ability to learn how to better regulate and even down-regulate our out-of-control emotions—this is achieved by re-examining the nature of our everyday habits, thoughts, actions and reactions to the things around us.

Let's face it, we all know what it's like to have experienced insecurity, sadness and rejection. We all know how uncomfortable negative emotions tend make us to feel. However, it is very important to understand the critical importance of not getting caught up in the whirlwind of any single emotion— especially the negative ones. Rather, when we remember to incorporate the tools and skills of critical thinking, we more readily remind ourselves to stay in the moment of mindfulness... of observation. Let's look at this scenario a little differently: hypothetically, if we were to strip away all the continual elements of time such as the past, present and future, what would be left for us to see? I will tell you: a jumbled raw collection of life long learning, conditioning and even out-dated coping mechanisms thereof. These elements often dictate how often it is that we gravitate toward overusing positive and negative emotions—especially knowing how often it is that our so called "accurate" perception misleads us.

Remember, we are looking to balance the beauty and wisdom of our emotions, especially as it relates to our personal feelings— we definitely do not want to suppress or get rid of them. Emotions serve us in such a beautiful way—each has a specific place, a purpose and a valued function. All the various things that have happened to us in throughout our life is exactly what led us to be the wonderful people we are today —We all know this, but how often do we really take the time to appreciate this miraculous-like truth? Let us embrace the gifts that make us unique and more possible. Let us trust to let go of that which no longer serves. Let us do the work: Journal and talk with others about our life. Let us open the doors and windows of our beautiful hearts!

Preface

"The Yoga Journey as it Unfolds" (cont.)

"Never let your negative past steal the beauty of your present."
-Edmond M. Biaka

In life we create goals to achieve the things we need or want to get done. There are countless ways upon which to aim and direct the bow and arrows (intentions) of our life. And, we all know that, until now, there were endless excuses and personal circumstances that, in one way or another, seemed to have justified and validate our beliefs, behaviors and habits. Our intention influences the integrity and clarity of our perceptions' aim. So, again, we must create effective ways with which to feel more safe and secure in expressing ourselves not just intrapersonally, but also interpersonally with others . *A Light From Within* is an inquiry into the heart and wisdom of our being. It is an effective way to explore the various landscapes of our life. This brings us to the subject of yoga: Yoga helps to bridge all the various elements our mental, emotional physical and spiritual life. It is a practice whose integrative process allows for expansive awareness and discernment. Yoga teaches us to become more present and it really fosters community! Throughout the 6 chapters of this book, you will learn how to safely open up to the more sublime components of your being— so that you may more easily see that of which is, and that of which isn't. You will safely learn how to tap into the poetic truth from within your heartfelt being. In many ways, ALFW is a living autobiography. It helps guide you away from fictitious being and more into your truthful self. A famous German poet by the name of Friedrich Hölderlin once said:

"Dichterisch wohnet der Mensch" Poetically man dwells

In many ways, when you read or hear the words "Poetically man dwells,"' please know that this is what I think the author had intended: Every living person is mortal and capable of dying. Therefore, here on earth, over a period of time, one man replaces another. The dwelling place is both you and the earth, to do together the miracles of one only thing: Create a more meaningful perspective by comparing the nature of our existence to that of which is linked and perceived as the greater whole. When we learn to trust and feel more comfortably safe in our skin, we no longer have fear governing our thinking and feeling that we will be rejected for exposing our vulnerabilities, wounds and scars to others. Learning how to open up to ourself (and others) involves a process of deep self-introspection—sometimes what we find is not easy, so it is a lesson of patience and uncanny observation. When work through ALFW workbook and journal, we directly rewire the neural pathways of our mind-body connection. So please bear in mind: feelings are not as easily analyzable as are our emotions. But for sure-- both are conditioned and influenced by the events of our past. So never forget. . . regardless of your past, you always have the choice to reconstruct the neuroplasticity of your brain, therefore life. So, after using this book for just a short while, you should easily begin to tell the difference between an emotion and a feeling— how each solicits and hopes to beg a specific response. Here is a brief distinction:

- **Feeling are mentally based constructs or reactions created by our emotions. They mirror what's going on in our body, especially as it relates to our present "state of mind." Feelings, in part, originate from our conditioned patterns and events of the past—our learned behaviors. Unlike emotions, feelings cannot scientifically be measured.**
- **Emotions are physically based. They are biochemical reactions presented as stimulus-response patterns that take place the subcortical regions of the brain. Emotions alter or change the physical state of our body. Because of our evolutionary history, emotions are programmed deep into genes of our body. They help keep us safe and out of danger.**

Positive personal change is akin to that of a flowing river. A river continuously fills and empties itself. Again, we see a process of *holding on and letting go*. Water continuously morphs. You may know the old saying by Heraclitus, "You can never step into the same river twice." This is also nature's way of assuring Her health and resilience: emptying and filling. This is no different than how we conduct and maintain our daily life. One of the six entry points (portals) into ALFW is Haiku. A haiku, traditionally, is a 17-syllable poem. It was invented in the late 19th century by the Japanese. Haiku has always been deeply rooted into Zen culture. Haikus are arranged in a three-line format of 5, 7 and 5 syllables. Why did I choose to incorporate haiku as an integral part or entry point of this book? Simple: Haiku helps to express our union with nature. Usually, they revolve around the four seasons of the year, and are otherwise timeless. Haiku helps to cultivate simplicity and heightened awareness. They keep us grounded, close to the details and, truly, in the present moment. So, to that end, only you (the observer) and that of which is being observed (object) become one. The following quote was written by Basho describing the "ah-ness" of the haiku moment:

"Go to the pine if you want to learn about the pine, or to the bamboo if you want to learn about the bamboo. And in doing so, you must leave your subjective preoccupation with yourself. Otherwise you impose yourself on the object and do not learn. Your poetry issues of its own accord when you and the object have become one - when you have plunged deep enough into the object to see something like a hidden glimmering there. However well-phrased your poetry may be, if your feeling is not natural - if the object and yourself are separate - then your poetry is not true poetry but merely your subjective counterfeit.[1]

Here is an example of a famous haiku, so famous that a group of Japanese men once carved it into the rocks of the mountains:

stillness--
piercing the rocks
the sound of cicadas
-Basho Matsuo

There is a beautiful moment in time when, every 17 years, cicadas appear seemingly out of nowhere. Their sounds are so piercing and intensely loud that nothing else seems to be of significant importance. Only the listening of the sounds of their celestial song. It is my great hope that ALFW will help you delve more deeply into the essence and nature of you experience your personal experiences that which makes you the beautiful person you are truelycapable.

The six main tenets of this book:

- Social and Self-cognition or awareness
- Self-compassion and compassion for others (empathy)
- Fulfilling your social obligations such as donating and/or volunteering your time for others
- Motivation as it relates to expansive emotional awareness
- Social and cultural tolerance (as a cultivated skill set)
- Nonobjectification of animate and inanimate entities

Elements for creating greater awareness:

- Attentive self-introspection
- Appreciative discrimination
- Confidence
- Sustained effort (will power)
- Integrative movement forward

1 Yussa Nobuyuki (trans.), *Basho: The Narrow Road to the Deep Northand Other Travel Stretches* (Hammondsworth, Midddlesex: Penguin, 1966).

Preface

"The Yoga Journey as it Unfolds" (cont.)

Just below is an illustration of the Caduceus staff. It has somewhat of an esoteric meaning. However, it does have two serpents, each spiraling around a staff (sushumna) from two different directions (ida and pingala). It also has a superimposed set of wings attached toward the top of the staff. Traditionally, the Caduceus relates to one's physical and subtle being. As you can see, there are seven different colored discs known as chakras embedded upon the staff. Chakras are aligned along the axis of our spinal column. They consist of a vortex of oscillating vibrations that regulate the subtle electrical impulses that affect the seven different endocrine glands of the body. Chakras play a critical role in the function and operation of our endocrine system. They have to do with polarities and transmutation of energy. Simply put: Chakras regulate the up and downward flow of energy of the spine via ida and pingala. Ultimately, it is their job to keep the sushmna healthy and resilient. There is an old saying by Hermes Trismegistus: "That which is below is like that which is above and that which is above is like that which is below to do the miracles of one only thing." So you see, the upward moving force of the chakra system is prana and the downward moving force is apana. Each working ". . . to do the miracles of one only thing." Chakras are nothing more than the regulation of a feedback loop. They seek to balance each other, no different than all the other forces of nature: When the earth and atmosphere get too hot, ice caps melt to cool it off! Energy and least resistance.

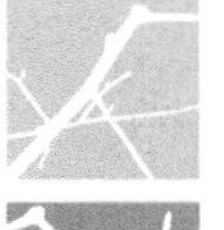
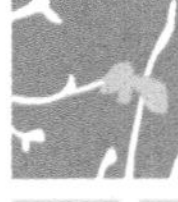

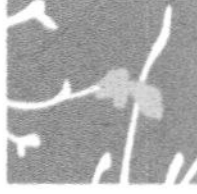

Staff of Caduceus

Three ongoing activities for a continued balanced force include:

- Two or more polarities in aspect to each other
- Observation and acknowledgment thereof
- Mutual change and reciprocity

Now here is the beautiful irony: as Hermes Trismigistus said, there are two elements, one above and one below. The magic is in how the two elements come together to "do the miracles of one only thing." All throughout time, the laws of opposites (or contrasts have existed. For example, let's look at two elements from the periodic table— sodium and chloride— each by themselves, caustic and corrosive. The two together create a stable unit called table salt. The same is true of hydrogen and oxygen, left alone, each has the potential to create great havoc. Yet, united they sustain and create the harmony of the universe as we know it. So you see, in life, it is very important to observe and respect the various laws of nature, that which bind and hold things together as they so do.

In the scientific community there exists three kingdoms of life: Eukarya, Eubacteria and Archaea. While in the yoga community, we say that there are also three kingdoms of Life: Animal, Vegetable and Mineral. Each is a form of life and we must think to ourselves: just because crystals do not have organs, brains or blood running through their "veins" doesn't mean they are devoid of, what is otherwise, scientifically believed to be "life qualifying." In fact, just like plants and animals, crystals grow and belong to the mineral kingdom: they are alive. Through evolution, man is but one of God's many beautiful expressions. In order to live and maintain a healthy planet, we all know, we must learn how to harmoniously coexist. We must learn the importance of knowing how to release strong and unwanted negative psychic and emotional patterns. We should all have the tools of knowing how to balance them with positive, more uplifting habits. To that end, this book is about what binds the space from in between light to dark, life and death and thought and form—I suspect it is awareness. A process of learning how to accept oneself and others without imposed condition. A process that involves forgiving others (and, therefore, yourself) for all the stumbling blocks that may have been placed upon the path of your growth and autonomy. Awareness is, in part, learning to understand and accept why things are the way they are— and not the way we'd like to change them for our own selfish gain.

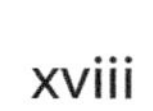

In the parlance of yoga there is a concept known as tapas, or Tapta Marga. Tapas is a spiritual process of rejuvenation. It is a heated-rebirth or renewal of energy. It usually involves giving up (or sacrificing) one thing for the gain of another. In many ways, it is akin to our physical yoga practice—we build up heat which than burns away the many physical and emotional toxins expressing themselves inside and around our mental, physical and subtle bodies. The physical effort is a form of sacrifice for the gain of better health— a simplified explanation. All the five elements of nature have an incredible way of helping to recharge and balance the batteries and flux of our life. However, in order to accept these charges, we must remember to align and keep the nature of our thoughts and body healthy and alert. Remember, while we're still conscious and in our bodies, our potential is never fully exhausted, nor unearthed. For this and the gift of love and volition we must be in great gratitude!

The Two Landscapes of Man: *Invisible and visible*

The *visible-to-the-eye* landscape of our life has its weft and warp in the obvious components of our everyday physical being. Articles of interest such as art, books, cars, houses, music, pictures of family and friends, etc., lend a hand in creating value to the appreciation and heart-felt gifts of our life e.g., I love my children. I love my family and friends. This is a gift of life. Remember... things are neither just good nor bad, right nor wrong: things are layers of variable vibrations ranging from "*invisible*" thoughts to *visible* physical matter. More often than not, the things perceived *outside* the domain of our physical bodies are really nothing more than mirrored projections or representations as to what lay inside. We all possess the the capacity to hone in on greater awareness, we just need to remind ourselves what really matters in the difference we'd like to make in our world—not just for ourselves, but for others too.

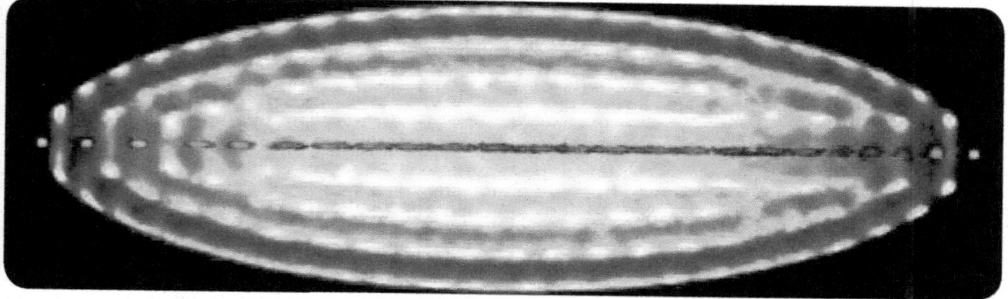

Beauty is in the eye of the beholder—everything is related: there are no separations: God is the string and glue of the universe. God binds all things divine.

The *invisible-to-the-eye* landscape of our being is a bit trickier, and when left unattended has the potential to create a lot of mental confusion and physical disturbance. Any gardener will tell you that when a garden is left unattended, invasive plants and weeds creep in and upset its habitat. So metaphorically, our minds and bodies are not really that different. By learning how to recognize and balance our thought patterns, we pull the weeds (so to speak) of our fields. Cultivating awareness teaches us how to clear and till the land and "stuff" from the habitat of our path. Just remember, awareness requires a lot of upfront work; first physical and then mental. So, what tools do we really possess in helping us to create and maintain expansive spiritual, mental and emotional wellness? How do we access these tools? Do they really help to minimize and eradicate the more invisible negative patterns which often hinder our growth? Yes, we do have theses tools: it's called inner exploration or . And, regardless of ones intellectual capabilities, we all have the same capacity for what is also called transcendental contemplation. And yoga, journaling and meditation help us to get there. We just need to do the weeding—the work. These practices significantly help us to become more focused, emotionally balanced, and even positively more aware as to what our internal and external make-up is. These tools allow us the opportunity for creating integrative health and awareness. Again, we just need to do the work i.e. sow the seeds of our deeper truths.

Preface

"The Journey as it Unfolds" (cont.)

So, when it comes to yoga and self-healing, I wonder, have we relied too much on science and not put enough emphasis on our own personal responsibility to do what we know is right in our hearts and minds? It is through the process of working through this book that we synthesize the tools of yoga, including journaling, workbook questions and other ALFW exercises. ALFW provides a better understanding as to how to create a new possibility: all through simple living and full awareness.

We are all a great lotus, ready to blossom yet another gift. But please remember: both the observer and observed must unite to do the miracles of one only thing. No single entity is a universe unto itself unless, of course we are speaking of God.

Perhaps it is both chance and God that implied universal love and unity. And, so here we are, able to acknowledge each as a gift. Together, you and me, we hold the recipe for change. We can waste our precious time folding into the echoes of some fictitious self, or we can allow ourselves to become a little more humble, more intimate and awakened to the beauty of each other— all in this present moment. Therefore, I declare: I would like to share my findings of the world with you, I would like to hear of yours. For us to share of ourselves to each other is indeed a gift of life. One last thing: Each and every day, we should remind ourselves to commit to memory, and sengrave into all 206 bones of our body, one of the oldest proverbs known to mankind. It is from the Delphi Temple and it reads:

KNOW THYSELF!

Part One

Chapter 1: An Introduction to ALFW Workbook

How to Use ALFW Yoga Workbook and Journal

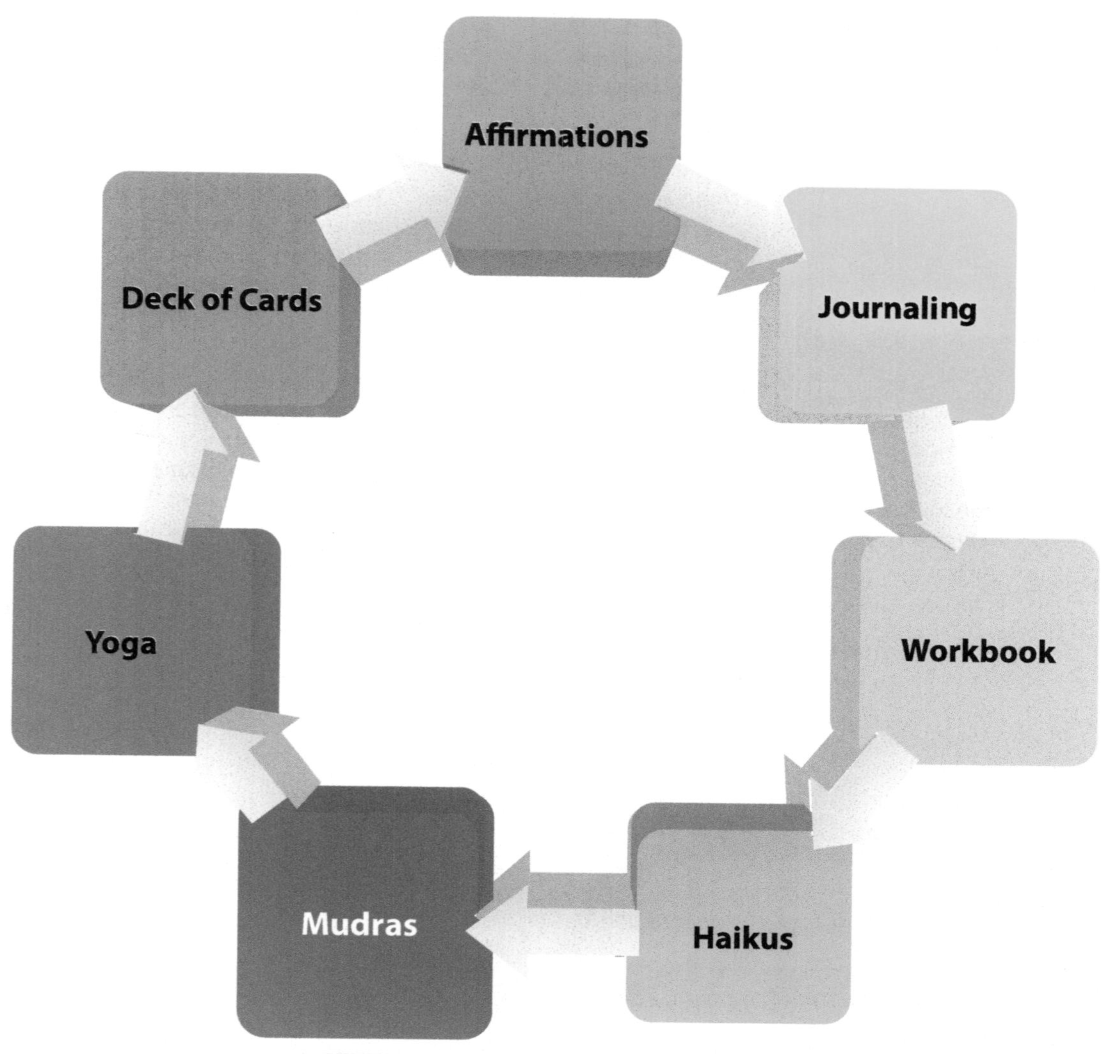

The 7 different portals with which to work *A Light From Within*

Above is a simple diagram outlining the seven different approaches or portals with which to work *A Light From Within*. The purpose of this diagram is, depending on your mood, see which approach or element best works with your present physical, mental and/or emotional state. For example, one day you may want to solicit an affirmation or haiku from the book which acts as the vehicle to drive you more deeply into your journey. Or, you may even prefer to begin with a yoga pose or pull a card from the deck of 52 cards—work from any order you'd like.

Introduction (cont.)

How to use the ALFW

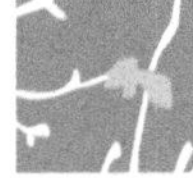

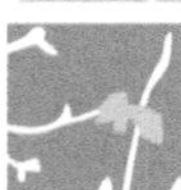

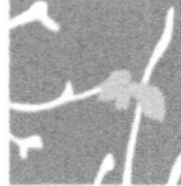

In life, most of us become just a little bit more wise with age. And although our levels of intelligence differs from one person to the next, it's all relative. With our wisdom we learn to listen differently and thus each one of us creates our own reality. So, please when working with this book, remember the purpose is to try and reintegrate the inner workings of our body, mind, emotions and spirit. Please utilize this book as if you were writing your very own autobiography— because, in many ways, you are. As much as possible, conduct your work in first person. If you turn to pages 24-25, you will see the very first workbook question and journal entry spread. There are 52 of them in total. Contained within these spreads are 102 workbook questions journal entries. Each question was carefully structured to be open-ended, and just to the right of all 102 questions are 102 Journal entries. For every question there is a journal entry and together only one is chosen to populate the "Chart of Emotions" (COE). For a more in-depth explanation as to how to properly complete each and every COE, see pages 22-23.

The COE has listed 17 different positive and negative emotions—all of which represent the most commonly experienced. But that because the 17 emotions listed may not fully reflect the entire emotional spectrum, it is important, nonetheless, to chose the next best one. On page 24 you will see a "Scale of Intensity" which ranges from 1 to 10 (10 being the most intensely experienced emotion). So, if you really want to get the most out of ALFW as it pertains to your Personal Emotions Imprint Map (PEIM) or wheel, please be as honest as possible when responding to all your workbook questions and journal entries.

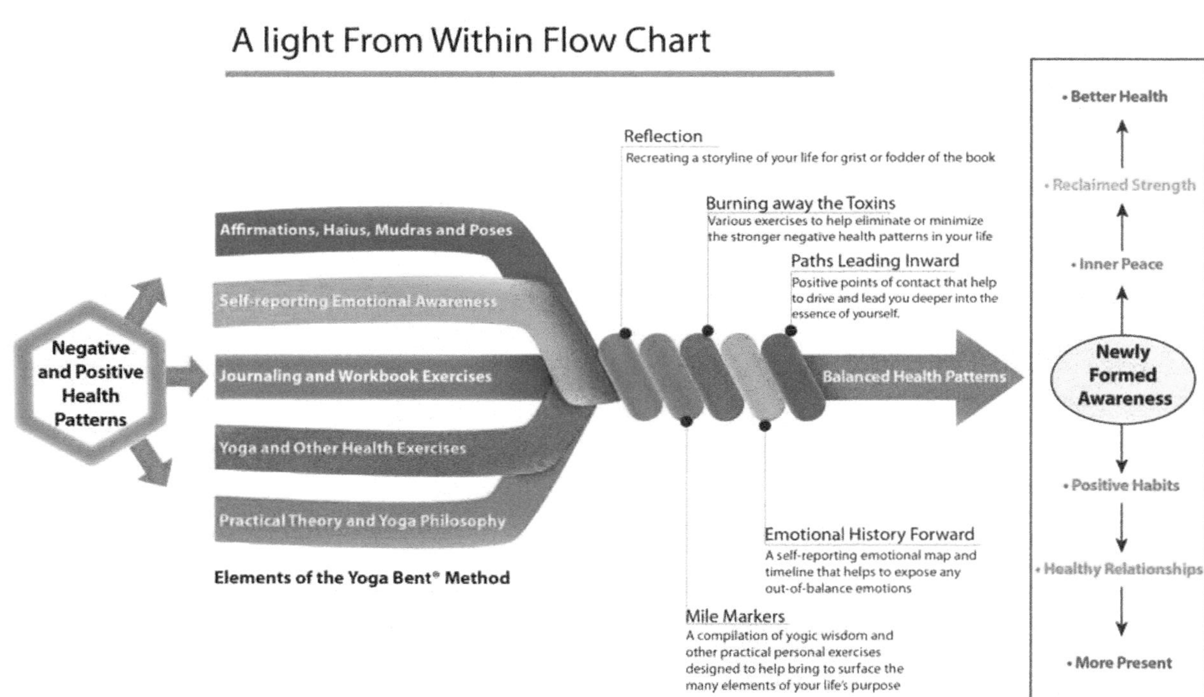

A light From Within Flow Chart
Negative and Positive Health Patterns
Affirmations, Haius, Mudras and Poses
Self-reporting Emotional Awareness
Journaling and Workbook Exercises
Yoga and Other Health Exercises
Practical Theory and Yoga Philosophy
Elements of the Yoga Bent® Method
Reflection
Recreating a storyline of your life for grist or fodder of the book
Burning away the Toxins
Various exercises to help eliminate or minimize the stronger negative health patterns in your life
Paths Leading Inward
Positive points of contact that help to drive and lead you deeper into the essence of yourself.
Balanced Health Patterns
Emotional History Forward
A self-reporting emotional map and timeline that helps to expose any out-of-balance emotions
Mile Markers
A compilation of yogic wisdom and other practical personal exercises designed to help bring to surface the many elements of your life's purpose
• Better Health
• Reclaimed Strength
• Inner Peace
Newly Formed Awareness
• Positive Habits
• Healthy Relationships
• More Present

ALFW flowchart illustrates how the six major elements of the book work together. The first part of the chart (far left) represents many of our overall positive and negative health patterns. The second part (middle) lists the six elements of the book. The third part represents all six elements working together. The fourth part shows an arrow which reads: "Balanced Health Patterns." And, lastly, on the far right side of this chart you will see the end result of having worked through ALFW Book: The Yoga Bent® Method.

Introduction (cont.)

How to use the ALFW

As just mentioned, only one workbook questions or journal entry (of any given spread), should be assigned to populate the COE. To do this, simply circle all associated emotions that belong with that question or journal entry— this is what will ultimately be reflected into your Personal Emotions Imprint Map or wheel. By utilizing this workbook and journal (either partially or in its entirety) you will begin to see a pattern emerge as to how often your sometimes out-of-balance emotions affect your spiritual, mental and physical being. Moreover, you will see how these emotions have affected the way you see yourself and the world around you. Again, it is important to understand that all emotions play a critical role in maintaining balance in our life. One of the goals of *A Light From Within* is to allow you to become a little more integrated and connected not just to yourself, but to all the people around you in your life. In many ways, the path and process of self-inquiry leads us so deeply inward, that at some point, there is nowhere else to go except to come outwards and into the thrust of your community. Again, when working with the workbook questions and journal entries, decide which it is that you would want to enter it into the COE. Take the time to record the date, time, your energy levels and even the weather. Should you choose to not record a journal entry into any given COE, you may use as one long entry— in other words, combine any two journal entries (from the same page only). It is recommended that you take your time and come back to your journaling as many times as you see fit. Just be sure to always complete your thought process. Lastly, at the very top of every journaling page you will see a dialog box titled "*Weekly Random Act of Kindness.*" This dialog box is where you will record any random act of kindness you had performed that was intended to help others. You may notice that after some time, you begin to look forward to help other people. . . and even animals. Now that you fully understand the operating principles of the workbook and journal in Part One, let's take a look at Part Two "A Guide to Your Physical Yoga Practice."

On page 182 and 183, you will see the very first yoga pose spread. Part two holds all 52 spreads, yoga poses on the left side of the page while the anatomy and pearls of wisdom reside on the right hand page. I strongly encourage you to work through all 52 yoga poses. The assumption is that because you purchased this book, you're also interested in working through the physical components of yoga— I suggest that each day (or at least several times a week) you do the physical warm-upsand then work through at least four to five yoga poses. Each practice should last at least 20 minutes. Perhaps you can scroll through the asana thumbnail index to create a nice combination or string of poses. Before you begin doing your warm-ups, read about the anatomy and physiology of each pose. When holding a yoga pose it is important to remember to include the recommended hand mudra. Each yoga pose spread contains a mudra dialogue box with a picture of the mudra and brief meaning. There are 13 slots with which to keep track every time you hold it. After the the 13th time, simply journal your experience in the assigned, preconfigured text box. So whether you take 3 months or a year to complete your ALFW journey, you'll be sure to have formed at least 50 hours (via the mudra) of comprehensive meditation practice.

At the beginning, meditation is not so easy. Its hard to sit for five solid minutes. The more you practice the poses and mudras, the more sensitive you become to their healing properties. I recommend reading and looking over the meridians and mappings of the hand section of the book (located on pages 130-132). It is here that you may visualize and/or intuit the change you're looking for where your alternative health is concerned. In other words, the mappings of the hand section of the book gives a good understanding as to how the meridians of the hand help release any energy blocks in the body. Most importantly, remember that healing, in part, involves the power of belief. After finishing your yoga and mudra exercises, take the time to write and record into your journal all of your different experiences. The last thing to remember is that in the event you feel stuck or short of ideas, please check out our blog at www.alightfromwithin.net. It is here that you may share and read about other people's experience of working with ALFW.

Introduction to the PEIM (Personal Emotions Imprint Map)

House Points
1000
900
800
700
600
500
400
300
200
100
50
Emotion
1 Joy
2 Love
3 Hope
4 Trust
5 Admiration
6 Fear
7 Worried
8 Happy
9 Calm
10 Sad
11 Resentful
12 Generous
13 Disgust
14 Anger
15 Guilt
16 Enthusiastic
17 Shy
(Example Only)

 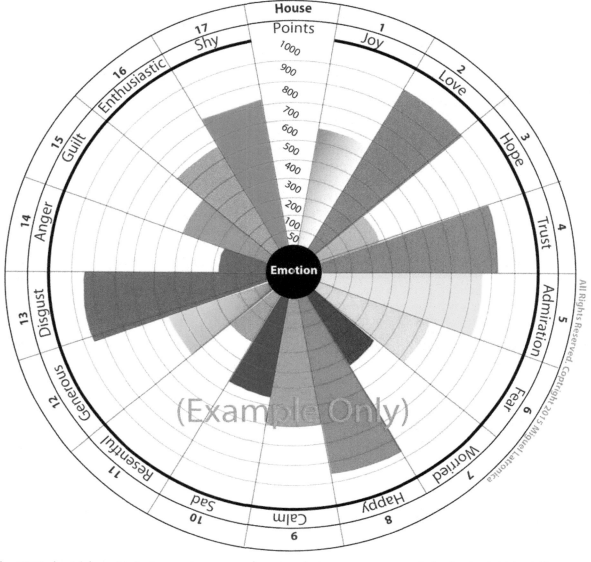
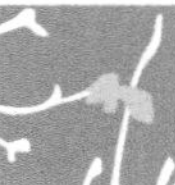

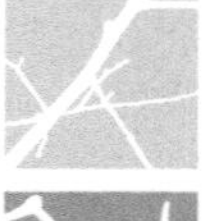
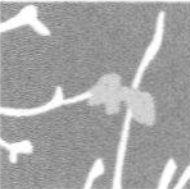

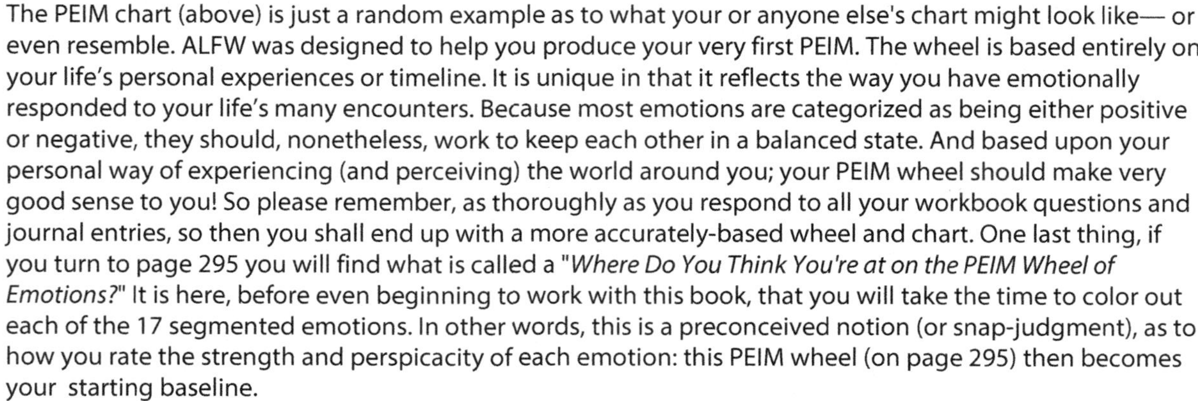

The PEIM chart (above) is just a random example as to what your or anyone else's chart might look like— or even resemble. ALFW was designed to help you produce your very first PEIM. The wheel is based entirely on your life's personal experiences or timeline. It is unique in that it reflects the way you have emotionally responded to your life's many encounters. Because most emotions are categorized as being either positive or negative, they should, nonetheless, work to keep each other in a balanced state. And based upon your personal way of experiencing (and perceiving) the world around you; your PEIM wheel should make very good sense to you! So please remember, as thoroughly as you respond to all your workbook questions and journal entries, so then you shall end up with a more accurately-based wheel and chart. One last thing, if you turn to page 295 you will find what is called a "*Where Do You Think You're at on the PEIM Wheel of Emotions?*" It is here, before even beginning to work with this book, that you will take the time to color out each of the 17 segmented emotions. In other words, this is a preconceived notion (or snap-judgment), as to how you rate the strength and perspicacity of each emotion: this PEIM wheel (on page 295) then becomes your starting baseline.

Introduction to the ALFW Deck of 52 Cards

52 deck of cards

Included in the ALFW book is a deck of 52 index type cards. The cards are printed on pages 297 through 310. They may be cut out or left as is, in place. Just below you can see all 13 spring of hearts cards. The example begins with the Ace of hearts and ends with the King of hearts. The same is true for the other three suits.

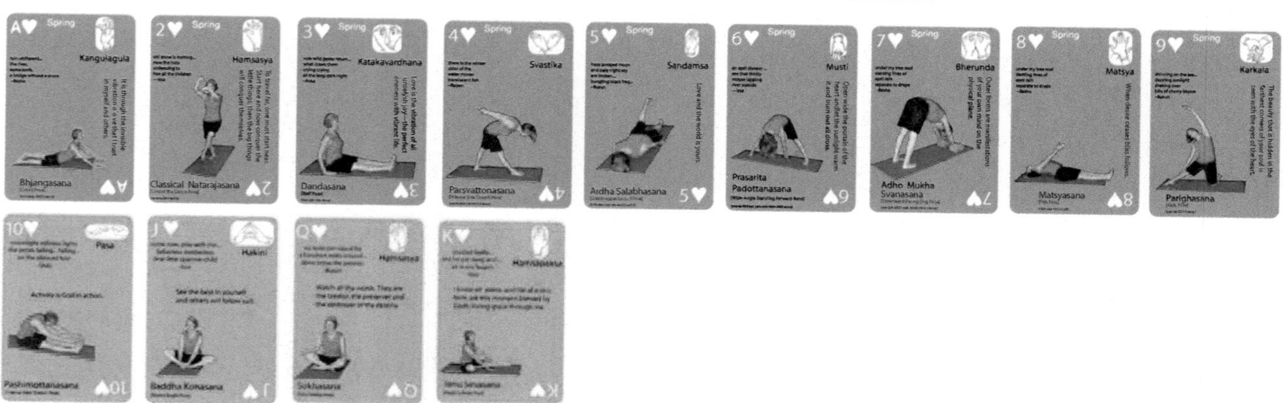

Each card represents one of the 52 poses, mudras, affirmations and haikus as referenced and used throughout this book. The example below illustrates the first card of each season's suit. So, if you look at the first card, it represents summer and is yellow coded. For example, If you turn to pages 76 and 77 and 234 and 235, respectively, you will see that these two spreads correspond to that same card accordingly. The deck of 52 cards can be used for memorization and/or sequencing of yoga poses. Remember, you can use the cards yourself or even in a group setting. Another fun exercise is that, instead of choosing to work with only the five pieces of information contained on each card, choose to answer or interact with any of the corresponding workbook questions and/or journal inquiries. Have fun while learning and connecting to yourself and others as well. The cards contains 5 critical pieces of information:

Card suit and number

Haiku 1

Pose 2

3

Affirmation 4

Mudra 5

Summer Season

Spring Season

Fall Season

Winter Season

Summer
Kilaka
All is good; there is no evil in God's loving eyes.
Marichyasana I

A♥ Spring
Kangulagula
It is through the invisible vibration of love that I trust in myself and others.
Bhjangasana
A♥

A♦ Fall
Balasana
A♦

A♠ Winter
Trisul
God's supply is in abundance now that you accept His gifts.
Tadasana
(Mountain Pose)
A♠

Name of Pose

Personal Affirmation Summary (Winter)

Winter | Card Suit Directory

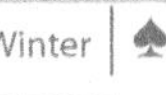

Winter | ♠

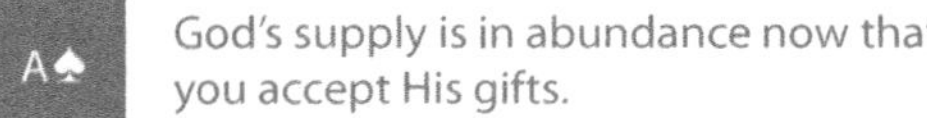

A♠ God's supply is in abundance now that you accept His gifts.

2♠ I have the strength of ten because my heart is filled with the light of truth.

3♠ Be a living temple in which God dwells.

4♠ You are that which you seek.

5♠ You must see the best in others before you see the good in yourself.

6♠ There is no destiny but what you yourself make. All is well because you think it is.

7♠ Great things were never achieved in a day. Their creation was formed by constant toil and thought.

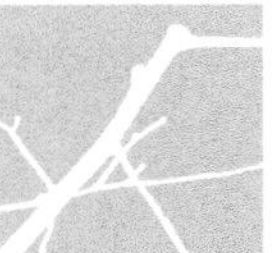

Winter | ♠

8♠ Hate is poison, slowly seeping into the heart, bringing a cruel death its wake.

9♠ Love all alike, free from attachment.

10♠ My body is the outer layer of my mind.

J♠ All craving and seeking for love in a form is the inner urge to find God.

Q♠ Be like a river of supply starting and ending in the same place. From the ocean of life you take, and the ocean of life you give.

K♠ Your tomorrow is the creation of today.

Personal Affirmation Summary (Spring)

Spring | Card Suit Directory

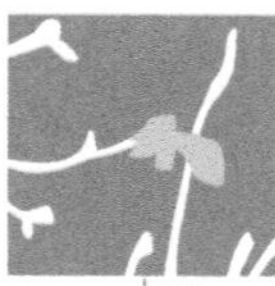

Spring | ♥

A♥ It is through the invisible vibration of love that I trust in myself and others.

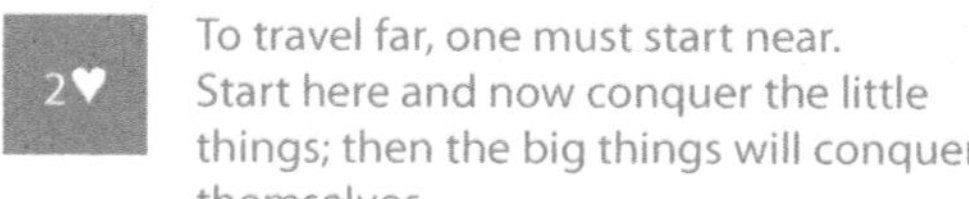

2♥ To travel far, one must start near. Start here and now conquer the little things; then the big things will conquer themselves.

3♥ Love is the vibration of all unselfish joy —the perfect oneness with vibrant life.

4♥ Strength comes from purity of the heart.

5♥ Love and the world is yours.

6♥ Open wide the portals of the heart and let the sunlight warm it and burn out all toxins.

7♥ Outer forms are manifestations of your own mind on the physical plane.

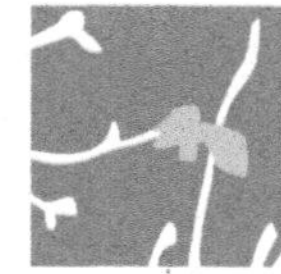

Spring | ♥

8♥ When desire ceases, bliss follows.

9♥ The beauty that is hidden in the farthest corners of your soul is seen with the eyes of the heart.

10♥ Activity is God in action.

J♥ See the best in yourself and others will follow suit.

Q♥ Watch all thy words. They are the creators, the preservers and the destroyers of thy destiny.

K♥ I know all plants and life of every form are this moment blessed by God's loving grace through me.

Personal Affirmation Summary (Summer)

Summer | Card Suit Directory

Summer | ♣

Summer | ♣

A♣	All is good; there is no evil in God's loving eyes.
2♣	You are beyond beginning and beyond end; you are the eternal life.
3♣	I am as weak as my weakest link, but I will never forget that I am as strong as my strongest.
4♣	Wherever there is God, there is beauty, and God is everywhere.
5♣	See beauty in seeming ugliness.
6♣	God moves and has his/her being in every living creature.
7♣	You are as great as you think you are.
8♣	God is the one and only that has the right to judge right or wrong. He and He alone can see the great plan.
9♣	May every creature great and small be free from pain, anguish, despair and a cruel death.
10♣	The only truly wise person is one who feels him or herself one with Nature.
J♣	Love is the joy of sharing others' joyous times, of taking half their burdens on your back and pushing with them until the last steep climb on the road of life is conquered.
Q♣	Vibrations of nature are the very keystone of my heart-felt being
K♣	Don't stop the source of supply by hoarding and thoughts of greed.

Personal Affirmation Summary (Fall)

Fall | Card Suit Directory

Fall | ♦

Self-deprecation is a path running fast down hill into the valley of failure and despair.

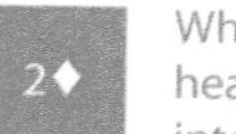

When the dawn of light floods our heart with its beauty, all else fades into nothingness.

You make the destiny which you fear.

Know and feel the joy of living a consecrated life of giving as an open channel to God's gifts.

See God in everything; then separateness falls off, leaving only light.

Fear is a monster killing all true godliness.

Find God and you have found the source of all supply.

Fall | ♦

8♦

Oh, what joy to feel the vibrant pulsating life of God throbbing through the universe and through you in joyous ecstasy.

9♦

In the power of the tongue lies life and death.

10♦

Opulence is God's will for humans. Have faith in God's abundant supply.

J♦

God does not choose those who shall be favored with Her gifts. God puts blessings on all alike. Some are wise and gather in the crops; others leave the fruit of life to wither on the vine.

Q♦

Love God and God alone.

K♦

Open the windows of your soul and perceive God in all his/her glory.

Winter Workbook Questions

Winter | Diretory Questions 1 thru 26

Question#

Winter

Winter

Winter

Winter

1 Having procured and made the choice to work with *A Light From Within*, how does it make you feel?

2 In what way might contentment differ from happiness in your life? Please explain:

3 One goal you have yet to achieve in your life can best be described as:

I think I can move closer toward this goal by:

4 How does your body, mind and spirit tend to affect each other? Give an example from your life:

5 What are some challenges you have where learning is concerned? How does this affect your personal and professional growth and development?

6 How, if at all, might your spirituality separate or make you different from other beings in the world?

7 How might your not-so-strongly-held beliefs affect your interpersonal relationships with other people?

8 Being non-judgmental allows me to experience my life in the following ways:

9 In what ways do you tend to now think differently about some of your childhood memories. Please explain:

10 What I strongly admire about my mom and dad can best be described as:

11 How does the concept of *good and bad* impact or limit your experience to live life in the fullest flavor possible?

12 In what ways do science and spirituality share a creative and/or logical link? How might that notion affect your views in life? Please explain:

13 If you were able to magically just turn off the pain, how would you see your life being different? Please explain:

14 How might your feeling more relaxed in life affect the way you experience Nature's landscape? Please explain:

15 What is the difference between guiding wisdom and guiding logic in your life?

16 There are many ways to turn an impulsive behavior into a constructive exercise. Please list a few examples as to how you have done this for yourself:

17 When looking at the chart of emotions (to the left), you may notice the absence of one very strong emotion: Shame. Please take the time to journal what shame is to you. What role, if any, does it play in your life:

18 When doing yoga, how do the physical and emotional barriers in your body present themselves to you? Is there an overall theme to these barriers or blockages. Please explain:

19 What responsibility do you take for the root cause of stress in your life? How are you working through this problem?

20 Often, when you are alone, is there anything that you tend to think and/or feel over and over again? Please explain:

21 How is your body and mind like a sponge in that it clings and holds on to the impressions from the outside world?

22 How might the repetitive use (or thought) of certain words affect your emotional being? Please explain:

23 How in your efforts to care for yourself, might you make a difference in the lives of other people?

24 Whenever you are hard on yourself, how does the world around you seem to appear or change?

25 The last time something really took your breath away could best be described as having had what kind of effect on you:

26 In life, we all seem to have insecurities. Is there an insecurity in your life that you're willing to share and let go of for good? Please explain:

Spring Workbook Questions

Spring | Directory Questions 27 thru 52

Question#

Spring | ♥

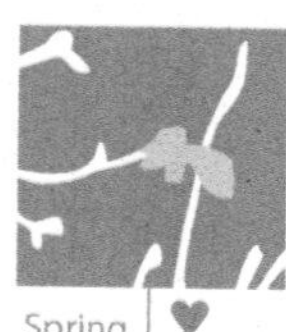

Spring | ♥

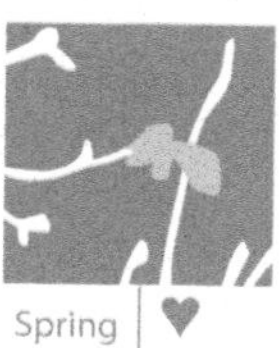

Spring | ♥

Spring | ♥

27 Please list one or two things about yoga and how it has made a difference in your life today:

28 Three things that bring me joy and peace this day can best be described as:

29 Briefly describe how it is that your purchasing power affects your world and the people around you:

30 Think of some special person who you love to be with, someone whose presence fills your heart and soul and love. In what ways are you capable of sharing these similar feelings with a stranger, or even someone with joy with whom you might not like?

31 If the universe is a spiral, where do you see yourself in the unfolding of that space?

32 A big distraction to the renewal of awareness in my life these days could best be described as:

33 How might being more aware of your dreaming-state (sleep) allow you to be more conscious in your waking state? Try and give a specific example as to how dreams affect your very awareness?

34 When you are not feeling strong and at rest, how does the world around you appear or seem to change? Please explain: Was there ever a difficult situation that changed the way you see the world around you?

35 How can you best describe the difference between the feelings and sensations of your body while doing yoga as compared to other activities?

36 The process of having overcome one of the greatest obstacles of my life thus far may best be described as:

37 In what way's might you see your expression(s) reflected through Nature's landscape? Please explain:

38 How, within the barriers of your body do you resist or attract joy or pain. Please explain:

39 Through what activity do you tend to tap into your more creative side? How does this affect your more logical side?

40 How has the process of acquiring your identity mislead or distracted you from the core source and space of who you really are?

41 What do you think people's opinions about other people's "good or bad" behavior(s) say about them?

42 Think of one thing that you may NEVER have shared or told anyone else. Do you agree that there may be at least one thing Are you now ready to journal and/or share that with family and friends now? Please explain:

43 In what way has art ever been therapeutic for you in your life? Explain.

44 If you were not in this world, how do you think things would be different? How does this statement make you feel?

45 How are you beginning a new cycle today?

46 How are you ending an old cycle today?

47 How do you experience the five elements (space, fire, air, water and earth) living through you in life today?

48 What does surrendering mean to you? In what way(s) have you surrendered today?

49 How do your expectations of other people affect your relationship with them?

50 How would you best describe the gift and blessing of being able to be at peace with everything in the universe?

51 Let's imagine that you were pure water. At times you would be as wet as water, as light as a gas or vapor, and, sometimes even frozen as a solid. Let's now say, just like water, that you were able to freely move around the universe, but maintain all of your humanly senses. Now, imagine what it would feel like, if that after two years of having been water, you'd want to share with others in this journal?

52 What elements are already contained within you for greater spiritual awareness?

Summer Workbook Questions

Summer | Directory Questions 53 thru 76

Question#

Summer ♣

Summer ♣

Summer ♣

Summer ♣

53 In what way has forgiveness played a role in your life? Give an example of having to forgive someone for something they had done to you. How has that forgiveness set you free? What has that forgiveness done for them

54 In a research study by Norman Cousins and UCLA, actors were called in to have their blood drawn. Immediately after, they were given an index card with a single emotion written on it. They then acted out that single emotion. After twenty minutes their blood was drawn a second time. Research shows that negative emotions decreased the immune system while, positive emotions improved it. Please journal how you think out of balance emotions affect you.

55 Thoughts are subtle forms of energy. They are held and/or released into the ether at large. Is it possible that one person may pick up on the thoughts of another, and maybe even execute its very intention? How do you release and let go of any negative thoughts in your life?

56 How mindfully aware are you in observing how other's habits and/or behaviors take root even expressing themselves through you? Have you ever noticed another person's mannerism or peculiarity somehow taking root or expressing itself through you? Explain;

57 If money were no issue at all in your life, how do you think you'd live your life differently? Please explain:

58 How accepting do you think you'd be if you could foresee your death? What does that mean to you here and now?

59 Please write and develop a mission statement as to what Life is to you:

60 List five things that you absolutely love about your life. What have you recently done to support what you love?

61 If there were just one day that you could eliminate or erase from your life, which day would that be? In what way has that day benefited you?

62 At this part of my life, one of my greatest strengths can best be described as:

63 What do you think you would learn about yourself were you suddenly transplanted to live in an entirely different culture?

64 One hundred years from now, how do you think the world will have been changed or affected by your life?

65 How can you learn to create new meaning in the otherwise, everyday mundane things you do? Please explain:

66 When your mind is clear, centered and focused, how would you describe the state of your emotions? What elements help create this mindset for you?

67 When your mind is NOT clear, centered and focused, how would you describe the state of your emotions? What elements help to create this mindset for you?

68 Sit comfortably for five minutes and repeat this mantra 108 times: "Om Namha Shivaha." (Mala beads optional)

69 Can feelings of being unconditionally loved and accepted be felt without ever having used (or heard) words to express it?

70 If you were able to create an internationally recognized holiday, what it would be, why would you want it to exist?

71 Have you ever been so deep into a yoga pose that you actually found a hidden mind-body connection?

72 Please name one person with whom you have had some falling-out, and have consequently severed that relationship. How today might you respond differently to that or even a similar situation? Explain the falling out and what you've learned from it.

73 In what ways might your deep-rooted beliefs be holding you back form advancing yourself in the world?

74 The word fear is an acronym: False. Experiences. Acting. Real. In what way does fear play a role in your life?

75 This is an exercise in what is called idiokinetic visualization. Sit comfortably, take five full minutes to visualize yourself doing a single yoga pose. Be as detailed as possible in your efforts. Please journal your experience.

76 If possible, get a photograph of yourself from between the age of five and eight. Become very relaxed and look deep into the face of your photo. Imagine what you were like at that age Is there a common denominator of who you were then and who you are now? Does the same element of your soul speak to you? Is there a creative connection? Please spend an ample amount of time contemplating this exercise. Journal your results.

Fall Workbook Questions

Fall | Directory Questions 77 thru 102

Question#

77 In what areas of your life are you too confident, or conversely, not confident enough? Please explain:

78 The unconscious mind really has no concept of time. What do you think your life would be like if all the parts and pieces of who you are were randomly rearranged? What do you think the overall picture would look like?

79 Think about some conflict in your life right now. Through the process of journaling how might you find more resolve?

80 When you are in the presence of children, what do you think they feel about you?

81 What images run through your mind? Describe a common recurring thought (or thought process) that always seems to work through your mind:

82 In this moment when I close my eyes to center myself, the colors and feelings within me can best be described as having this kind of effect on me:

83 If I were a tree, I would describe the roots of my existence as...

84 If I were a tree, I would like my trunk to consist of...

85 If I were a tree, my limbs and branches would...

86 If I were a tree, the "fruit" I would bear could be described as tasting and having this kind of effect on me (and everyone else):

87 You know that you have the ability to end any habit, but is there any one habit that seems almost impossible to get rid of? Please explain:

88 In life, we sometimes learn or find out things about other people for which, we would never have believed otherwise. Is there anything about you that you think other people would probably never believe?

89 Gather one raisin or one nut of some sort and find a quiet and comfortable place to sit. Carefully examine the physical characteristics of the raisin or nut and then feel and observe the texture and temperature. Hold it in your left hand and feel the quantum vibration. Put it in your mouth and again feel its texture and temperature with your tongue and mouth. Take one bite and then stop. Repeat by taking one bite every 30 seconds or so until the nut or raisin has completely melted into liquid form. You should not have anything physical to swallow. The raisin or nut completely dissolves with the saliva of the mouth. Once dissolved, feel its pranic energy radiating throughout your body. What was this experience like for you?

90 In what way, if any, has your religion and/or your godhead helped to make you the beautiful person you are today?

91 If you could write a letter to one person with whom you have experienced conflict, but never worked it out, to whom would you address this letter, and what would you say? (Please see the Unsaid Things exercise on page 155).

92 Sometimes our most painful experiences can yield unexpected benefits. One such experience can best be described as:

93 When it comes to being confronted with conflict, this is how I see myself evolving:

94 Of the many gifts in your life, which do you hold in high esteem? Please explain

95 If it is true that we attract thoughts, people and animals in our lives, how have these attractions impacted your life? Explain:

96 Many of the things we perceive in life are nothing more than our own projections. One example of this might be:

97 What kinds of behaviors provoke and leave you with the feeling of guilt? Where do you think this strong emotion comes from?

98 Three advantages of allowing myself to be open and vulnerable to others might include:

99 List three things that you hold to be true about money. What are your strengths and perceived issues with money?

100 For whom, if anyone are you (or would you like to be) a role model? What three important values or traits would you like to impart? Who was one of your role models as a child?

101 Our minds are like a filmstrip, sometimes being played over and over again. If, in that non-stop filmstrip, you could insert three motivating words that would remind you to just bring yourself back to your home base what would those words be and why?

102 How, if at all, are the objects to your senses a universe unto themselves? What role do you play in the unfolding journey of the universe?

Winter Haiku Summary

Winter | Directory

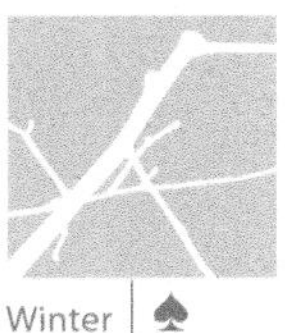

Winter | ♠

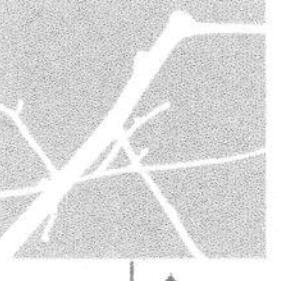

Winter | ♠

A♠

overy the wintry
bold sparrow
companies fly
scarecrow to scarecrow

–Sazanami

2♠

my very bone-ends
made contact with
the icy quilts
of deep december

–Busun

3♠

in my dark winter
lying ill...
at last i ask
how fares my neighbor

–Basho

4♠

a thousand roof-tops
a thousand
market voices...
winter-morning mist

–Busun

5♠

first snow last night...
there across the
morning bay
sudden mountain-white

–Shiki

6♠

there in the winter
color of the
water moves
translucent fish

–Raizen

7♠

see the red berries...
fallen like little
footprints
on the garden snow

–Shiki

8♠

midnight wanderer
walking through
the snowy street...
echoing dog-bark

–Shiki

9♠

blinding wild
snow blows, whirls
and drifts about
me... in this world
alone

-Chora

10♠

from my tiny roof
smooth...soft...
still-white snow
melts in melody

-Issa

J♠

look at that stray cat
sleeping...snug
under the eaves
in the whistling snow

-Taigi

Q♠

solitary crow...
companioning
my progress
over snowy fields
-Senna

K♠

poet nightingale...
will i hear your
later verses
in the vale of death

–Anon

Spring Haiku Summary

Spring | Directory

Spring | ♥

rain-obliterated...
the river,
some roofs,
a bridge without a shore

–Basho

old snow is melting...
now the huts
unfreezing to
free all the children

—Issa

now wild geese return...
what draws them crying
all the long dark night

–Roka

cold morning rainfall...
mingling all their
gleaming horns
oxen at the fence

–Ranko

hazy ponded moon and
pale night sky
are broken...
bungling black frog...

–Busun

an april shower ...
see that thirsty
mouse lapping
river sumida

-Issa

under my tree roof
slanting lines of
april rain
separate to drops

–Basho

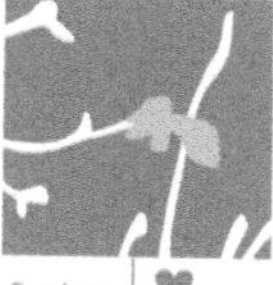

Spring | ♥

bird droppings
pattern the purples
and the yellows
of my iris petals

–Busun

shining on the sea...
dazzling sunlight
shaking over
hills of cherry-bloom

–Busun

moonlight stillness
lights the petals
falling...falling...
on the silenced lute

–Shiki

come now, play with me...
fatherless
motherless dear
little sparrow-child

-Issa

no bold rain-cloud for
a hundred miles
around...dares
brave the peonies

-Busun

the first firefly...
but he got away
and i...
air in my fingers

-Issa

Summer Haiku Summary

Summer | Directory

Summer | ♣

Summer | ♣

A♣

with that new clothing
alas...spring
has been buried
in that wooden chest

–Saikaku

2♣

an old tree was felled...
echoing,
dark echoing
thunder in the hills

–Meisetu

3♣

rainy afternoon...
little daughter
you will never
teach that cat to dance

-Issa

4♣

squads of frogs jumped in
when they heard the
plaunk-plash
of a single frog

–Wakyu

5♣

moon-in-the-water
turned a white
sumersault...yes
and went floating off

–Ryota

6♣

windy-web spider
what is your
silient speaking...
your unsung song

–Basho

7♣

experimenting ....
i hung the moon
on various
branches of the pine

–Hokushi

8♣

on his garden path
this sparrow
scatters pebbles...
man forgotten

-Shoha

9♣

sad twilight cricket...
yes, i have wasted
once again
those daylight hours

–Kikaku

10♣

the night was hot...
stripped to the waist
the snail
enjoyed the moonlight

-Issa

J♣

with the new clothes
remember... the
crow stays black
and the heron white

-Chora

Q♣

a summer shower...
along all the
street, servants
slapping shut shutters

–Shiki

K♣

suddenly you light
and as suddenly
go dark...
fellow firefly
–Chine

Fall Haiku Summary

Fall | Directory

Fall | ♦

A♦

again coolness comes...
silver undersides
of leaves
evening-breeze blown

–Shiki

2♦

we stand still to hear
tinkle of far
temple bell...
willow-leaves fallen

–Basho

3♦

night long in the cold
that monkey sits
conjecturing
how to catch the moon

–Shiki

4♦

supper in autumn
flat light through
an open door
from a setting sun

-Chora

5♦

on a leafless bough
a crow is perched
the Autumn dusk

-Basho

6♦

a windblown grass...
hovering mid-air
in vain
an autumn dragonfly

–Basho

7♦

now the old scarecrow
looks just like
other people...
drenching autumn rain

–Seibi

Fall | ♦

8♦

here is the dark tree
denuded now
of leafage...
but a million stars

-Seibi

9♦

white chrysanthemums
making all else
about them
reflected riches

-Chora

10♦

from the temple steps i
lift to the
autumn moon
my veritable face
–Basho

J♦

nights are getting
cold... not a single
insect now attacks
the candle

–Shiki

Q♦

swallows flying south...
my house too
of sticks and paper only
a stopping-place

–Kyorai

K♦

autumn breezes shake
the scarlet flowers
my poor child
could not wait to pick

-Issa

Winter Asana

(J) Journal & (P) Pose Directory

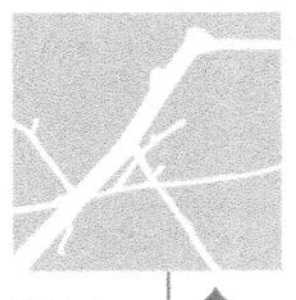

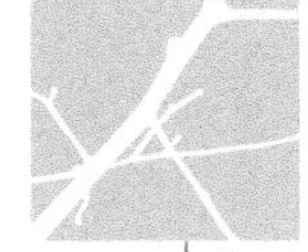

Winter ♠ Winter ♠

(J)	(P)	Asana	Card
25	182	Tadasana	A ♠
39	196	Utthita Tadasana	8 ♠
27	184	Virabhadrasana II	2 ♠
41	198	Utthita Parsvaskonasana	9 ♠
29	186	Virabhadrasana I	3 ♠
43	200	Garudasana	10 ♠
31	188	Virabhadrasana III	4 ♠
45	202	Uttanasana	J ♠
33	190	Utkatasana	5 ♠
47	204	Utthita Trikonasana	Q ♠
35	192	Tadasana Urdhva Hastasana	6 ♠
49	206	Privritti Trikonasana	K ♠
37	194	Vrkshasana	7 ♠

Spring Asana

(J) Journal & (P) Pose Directory

Spring ♥ Spring ♥

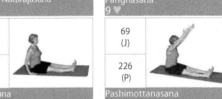

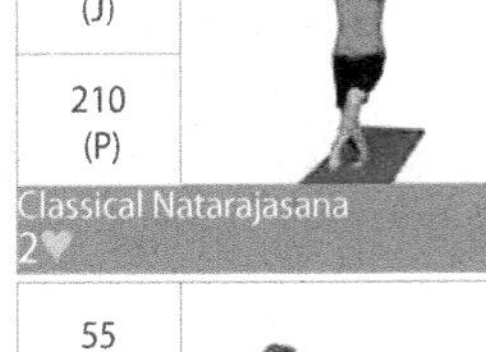

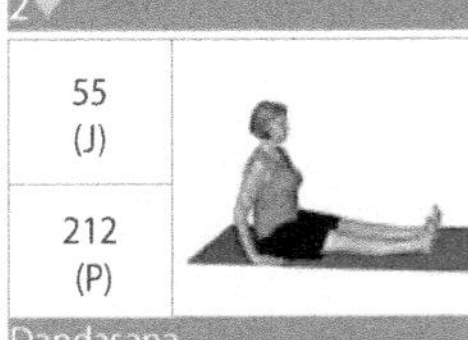

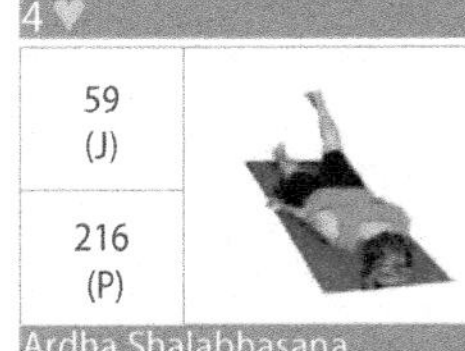

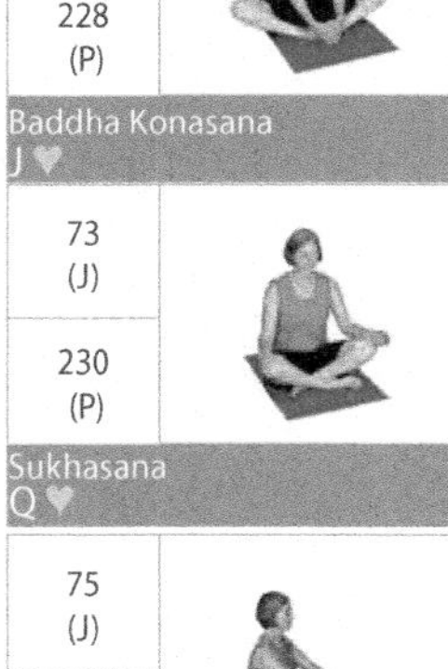

(J)	(P)	Asana	Card
51	208	Bhjangasana	A ♥
65	222	Matsyasana	8 ♥
53	210	Classical Natarajasana	2 ♥
67	224	Parighasana	9 ♥
55	212	Dandasana	3 ♥
69	226	Pashimottanasana	10 ♥
57	214	Parsvattonasana	4 ♥
71	228	Baddha Konasana	J ♥
59	216	Ardha Shalabhasana	5 ♥
73	230	Sukhasana	Q ♥
61	218	Prasarita Padottanasana	6 ♥
75	232	Janu Sirsasana	K ♥
63	220	Adho Mukha Svanasana	7 ♥

Summer Asana

(J) Journal & (P) Pose Directory

Summer ♣ Summer ♣

77 (J) 234 (P)
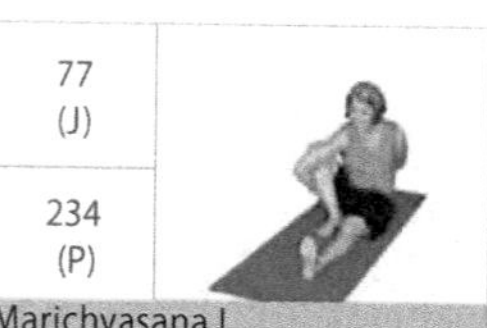
Marichyasana I
A ♣

79 (J) 236 (P)
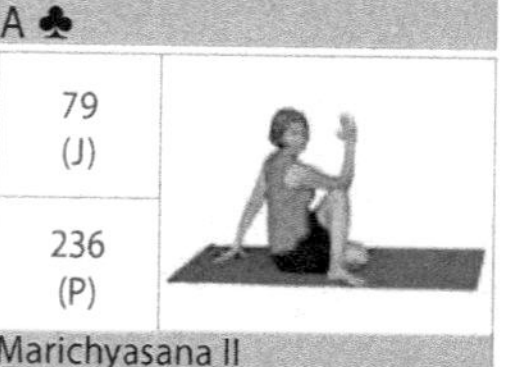
Marichyasana II
2 ♣

81 (J) 238 (P)
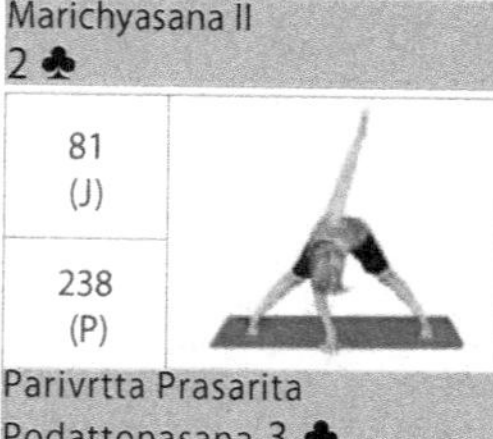
Parivrtta Prasarita Podattonasana 3 ♣

83 (J) 240 (P)

Gumakasana
4 ♣

85 (J) 242 (P)
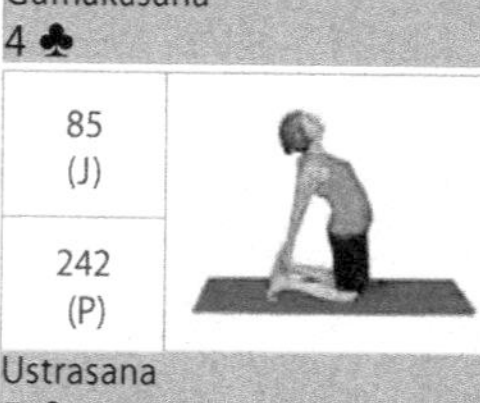
Ustrasana
5 ♣

87 (J) 244 (P)
Eka Pada RajaKapotasana
6 ♣

89 (J) 246 (P)
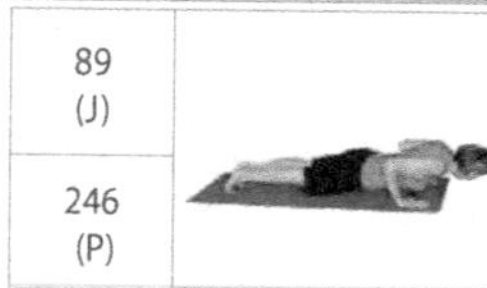
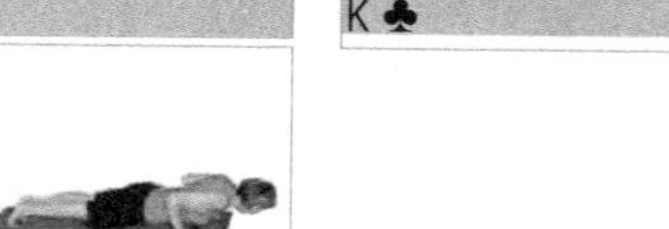
Chaturanga Dandasana
7 ♣

91 (J) 248 (P)
Urdvha Mukha Svanasana
8 ♣

93 (J) 250 (P)
Paripurna Navasana
9 ♣

95 (J) 252 (P)
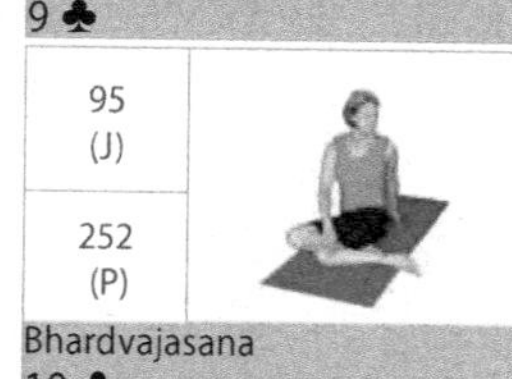
Bhardvajasana
10 ♣

97 (J) 254 (P)

Yoga Mudra
J ♣

99 (J) 256 (P)
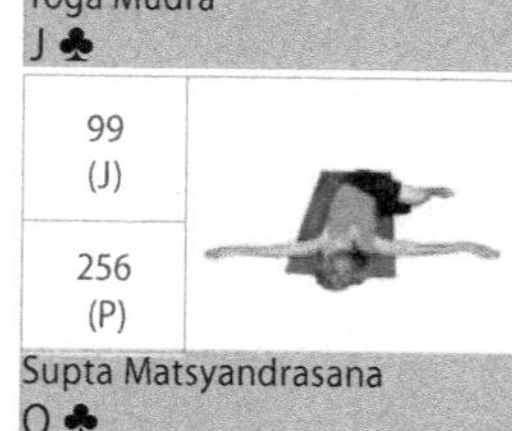
Supta Matsyandrasana
Q ♣

101 (J) 258 (P)
Dandayamana Ardha Chandrasana
K ♣

Fall Asana

(J) Journal & (P) Pose Directory

Fall ♦ Fall ♦

103 (J) 260 (P)
Garbasana
A ♦

105 (J) 262 (P)
Virasana
2 ♦

107 (J) 264 (P)
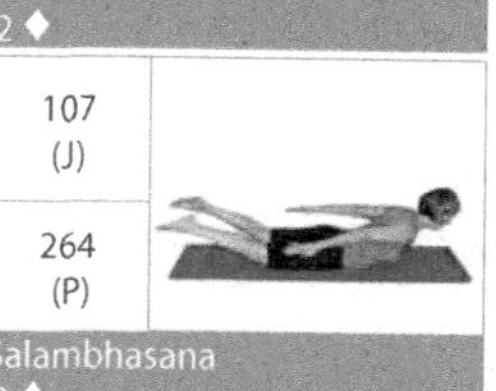
Salambhasana
3 ♦

109 (J) 266 (P)

Setu Bhandasana
4 ♦

111 (J) 268 (P)
Halasana
5 ♦

113 (J) 270 (P)
Pawan Muktasana
6 ♦

115 (J) 272 (P)
Viparita Karani
7 ♦

117 (J) 274 (P)
Sarvangasana
8 ♦

119 (J) 276 (P)
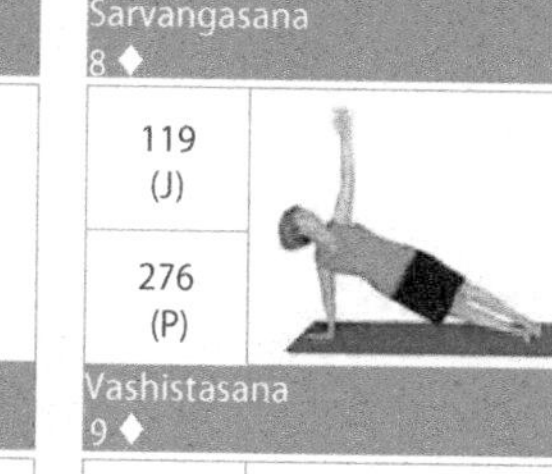
Vashistasana
9 ♦

121 (J) 278 (P)

Urdvha Dhanurasana 10 ♦

123 (J) 280 (P)

Adho Mukha Vrksasana
J ♦

125 (J) 282 (P)

Salamba Sirsasana
Q ♦

127 (J) 284 (P)
Shavasana
K ♦

Winter Mudra

(J) Journal & (P) Pose Directory

Winter | ♠

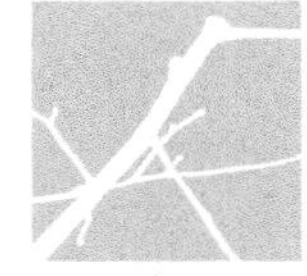

Winter | ♠

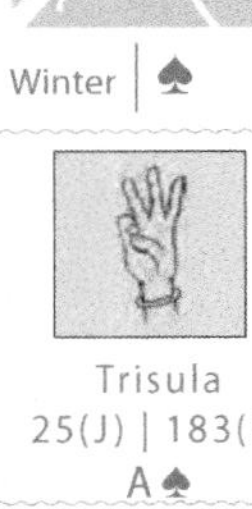

Trisula
25(J) | 183(P)
A♠

Sikhara
27(J) | 185(P)
2♠

Candrakala
29(J) | 187(P)
3♠

Katarimukha
31(J) | 189(P)
4♠

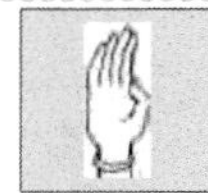

Pataka
33(J) | 191(P)
5♠

Ardha Chandra
35(J) | 193(P)
6♠

Anjali
37(J) | 195(P)
7♠

Suci
39(J) | 197(P)
8♠

Tamracuda
41(J) | 199(P)
9♠

Guruda
43(J) | 201(P)
10♠

Mrgasirsa
45(J) | 203(P)
J♠

Ardhapataka
47(J) | 205(P)
Q♠

Padmakosa
49(J) | 207(P)
K♠

Spring Mudra

(J) Journal & (P) Pose Directory

Spring | ♥

Spring | ♥

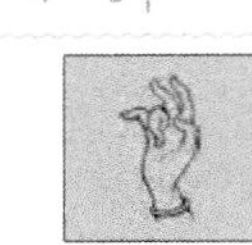

Kangula
51(J) | 209(P)
A♥

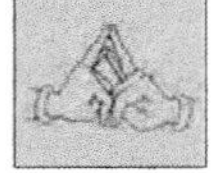

Shakti
53(J) | 211(P)
2♥

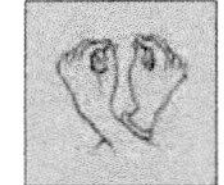

Katakavardhana
55(J) | 213(P)
3♥

Svastika
57(J) | 215(P)
4♥

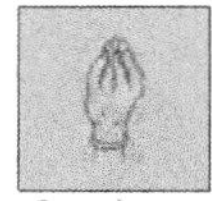
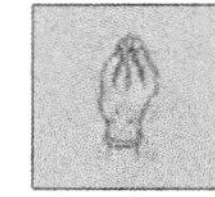

Sandamsa
59(J) | 217(P)
5♥

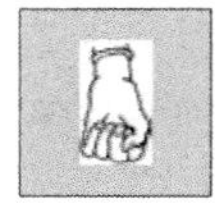

Musti
61(J) | 219(P)
6♥

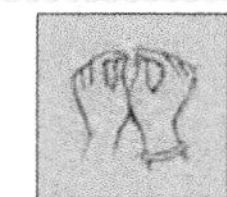
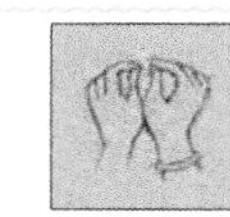

Bherunda
63(J) | 221(P)
7♥

Matsya
65(J) | 223(P)
8♥

Karkala
67(J) | 225(P)
9♥

Pasa
69(J) | 227(P)
10♥

Hakini
71(J) | 229(P)
J♥

Hamsasya
73(J) | 231(P)
Q♥

Hamsapaksa
75(J) | 233(P)
K♥

Summer Mudra

(J) Journal & (P) Pose Directory

Summer | ♣ Summer | ♣

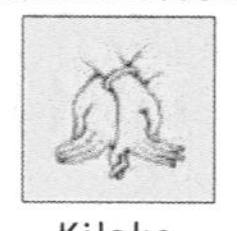
Kilaka
77(J) | 235(P)
A ♣

Bharmaram
79(J) | 237(P)
2 ♣

Katakamukha
81(J) | 239(P)
3 ♣

Ganesha
83(J) | 241(P)
4 ♣

Makara
85(J) | 243(P)
5 ♣

Cakra
87(J) | 245(P)
6 ♣

Nagabandha
89(J) | 247(P)
7 ♣

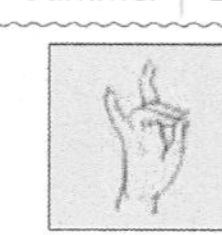
Simhamukha
91(J) | 249(P)
8 ♣

Tripataka
93(J) | 251(P)
9 ♣

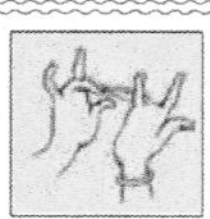
Khatva
95(J) | 253(P)
10 ♣

Sakata
97(J) | 255(P)
J ♣

Puspaputa
99(J) | 257(P)
Q ♣

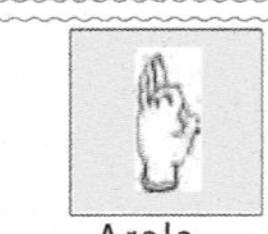
Arala
101(J) | 259(P)
K ♣

Fall Mudra

(J) Journal & (P) Pose Directory

Fall | ♦ Fall | ♦

Catura
103(J) | 261(P)
A ♦

Sivalinga
105(J) | 263(P)
2 ♦

Sarpasirsa
107(J) | 265(P)
3 ♦

Kapitta
109(J) | 267(P)
4 ♦

Mahasir
111(J) | 269(P)
5 ♦

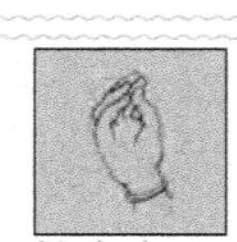
Mukalam
113(J) | 271(P)
6 ♦

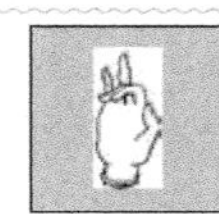
Sukatunda
115(J) | 273(P)
7 ♦

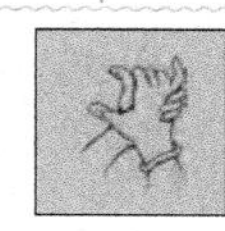
Kurma
117(J) | 275 (P)
8 ♦

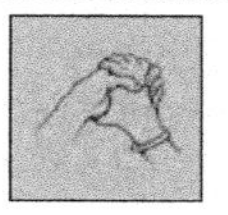
Samputa
119(J) | 277(P)
9 ♦

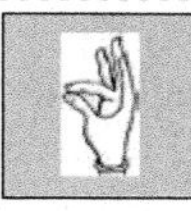
Mayura
121(J) | 279(P)
10 ♦

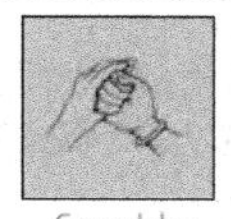
Samkha
123(J) | 281(P)
J ♦

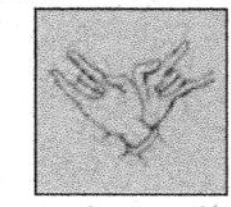
Kartarisvastika
125(J) | 283(P)
Q ♦

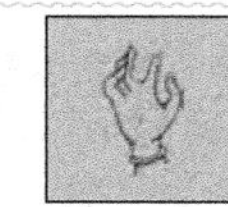
Alapadma
127(J) | 285(P)
K ♦

Chapter 2:
Workbook and Journaling Your Way to Wellness
Instructions for Working with the Workbook Questions and Journal Entry Spreads

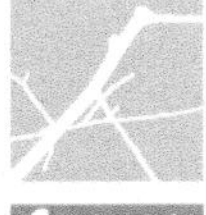

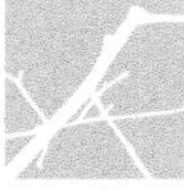

Journaling and taking field notes have long been critical components to self-love, self-reflection and personal and technological development. Philosophers, writers, artists and scientists such as Dante, Anaïs Nin, Leonardo Di Vinci, John Dewey and Nikola Tesla all kept personal journals. They also kept very accurate field notes, which have reflected their views on life. That said, there is a beautiful, yet mysterious side to us all. There is an energy potential waiting to surface, unfold and express itself— all through the efforts and variables of our being true to our self. So please, use and work with ALFW on your own terms! Make sense of it in such a way that it becomes an uplifting experience— something you look forward to do on a regular basis. You may share all or just some of its parts with others . . . or even keep it as a personal diary. It's all good no matter what you choose to do. Please note that while *A Light From Within* is a very effective tool for personal growth and development, it does not in any way substitute the need for professional counseling and/or psychotherapy. If you feel that many of the things in your life are just a little too much to handle, please consult a mental health professional. You may also reach out to like-minded people by interacting with our ALFW blog at www.alightfromwithin.net

Very often when people take the necessary time for themselves for healing to occur they feel guilty, selfish and even self-centered! Let me dispel this ill-perception: Truly the only way for you (or anyone else) to stay sharp, healthy and skillful is to take the time you need to maintain your health. We all know that we must care for ourself to be mindfully more effective and helpful to others. It really is this simple. Moreover, we must understand the critical importance of teaching our children (all children) this very same thing: to love themselves as they are— again, this should never be confused with selfishness or being self-centered. Individuality is a basic human right and not a privilege. The right to be different is the fundamental backdrop of being healthy! So, with this in mind, remember to be as light and playful as possible when working this workbook and journal. Do not take any of this material too seriously.

One last important thing to keep in mind when working with the workbook questions and journal entries: as you can see from the example on page 23, the spread consists of one workbook page and one journal entry page. There are 52 spreads in all. Most always, there are two questions and two journal entries prompts— residing on each spread. This particular spread belongs to the Winter Ace of spades, which explains just how easy it is to work through and complete this and all other spreads. It shows you how to properly fill in or populate all 102 of the Chart of Emotions (COE). Thus, each COE is associated, belongs and mirrors to it's counterpart question(s) or journal entry prompt— but remember, you must choose only one to populate the COE. In this same example, you can see that I had chosen to use workbook question #1 to populate the first COE #1. Whereas for COE #2, I chose to use journal entry #2 (instead of question #2) to populate its correlating COE #2— for simplification, you can see that I have red-lined the entire work flow process. You can also see, that just to the left of every COE there are three gray-shaded labels or words that read: "Workbook", "Journal" and "Entered." Each is followed by an underscored line— These exist so that you can more easily determine which it is (the question or journal entry) that belongs to the COE. For example, to the left of COE #1, you can see that I have put a red "X" after "Workbook." Why? Because this "X" tells me that this particular COE belongs to the correlating workbook question— not its correlating journal entry. The same is true and applies to COE#2: it also has a red "X" mark after "Journal." Get it?

Please note: Should you find yourself needing a bit more writing space for any given journal entry, simply use the lower journal entry (from only the same spread) as if they were just one larger entry so that you may complete your journaling work.-- in this case one full page. Whenever this is technique is used, just be sure to cross out the lower journal entry so that there is no future confusion regarding its relevance as it pertains to the COE. This way you will always know that it was, in fact, a conscious effort to combine the 2 two journal entries. ALFW is extremely versatile and very easy to use. It takes the notion and principles of a personal journal to a new level. Enjoy your Journey!

Workbook Questions and Journal Entry Spread

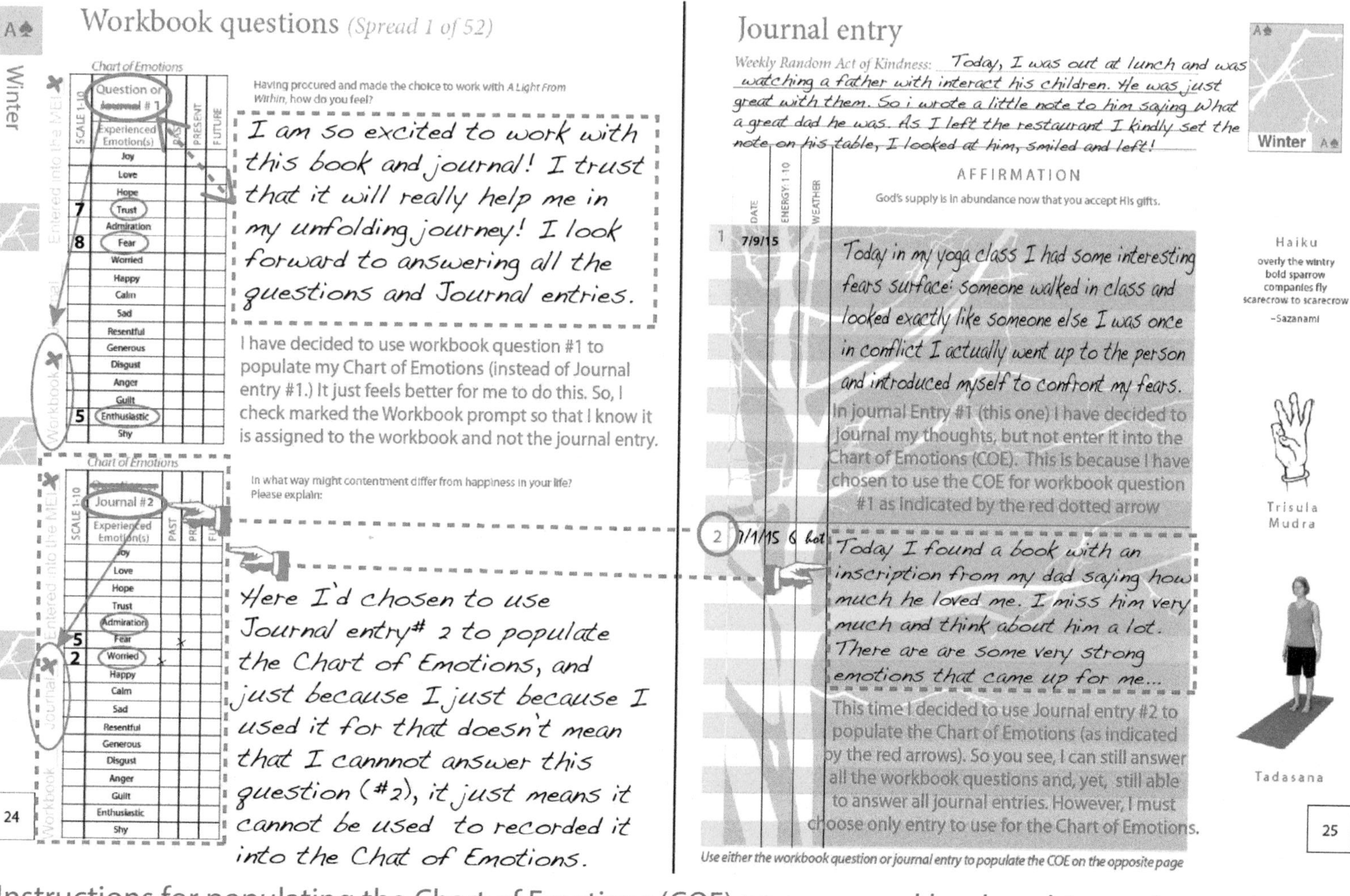

Workbook questions (Spread 1 of 52)

Winter

Chart of Emotions

SCALE 1-10	Question or ~~Journal~~ # 1 Experienced Emotion(s)	PAST	PRESENT	FUTURE
	Joy			
	Love			
	Hope			
7	Trust			
	Admiration			
8	Fear			
	Worried			
	Happy			
	Calm			
	Sad			
	Resentful			
	Generous			
	Disgust			
	Anger			
	Guilt			
5	Enthusiastic			
	Shy			

Entered into the MEI / Journal / Workbook

Having procured and made the choice to work with *A Light From Within*, how do you feel?

I am so excited to work with this book and journal! I trust that it will really help me in my unfolding journey! I look forward to answering all the questions and Journal entries.

I have decided to use workbook question #1 to populate my Chart of Emotions (instead of Journal entry #1.) It just feels better for me to do this. So, I check marked the Workbook prompt so that I know it is assigned to the workbook and not the journal entry.

Chart of Emotions

SCALE 1-10	~~Question~~ or Journal #2 Experienced Emotion(s)	PAST	PRESENT	FUTURE
	Joy			
	Love			
	Hope			
	Trust			
	Admiration			
5	Fear		x	
2	Worried	x		
	Happy			
	Calm			
	Sad			
	Resentful			
	Generous			
	Disgust			
	Anger			
	Guilt			
	Enthusiastic			
	Shy			

Entered into the MEI / Journal / Workbook

In what way might contentment differ from happiness in your life? Please explain:

Here I'd chosen to use Journal entry# 2 to populate the Chart of Emotions, and just because I just because I used it for that doesn't mean that I cannot answer this question (#2), it just means it cannot be used to recorded it into the Chat of Emotions.

24

Journal entry

Weekly Random Act of Kindness: Today, I was out at lunch and was watching a father with interact his children. He was just great with them. So i wrote a little note to him saying What a great dad he was. As I left the restaurant I kindly set the note on his table, I looked at him, smiled and left!

AFFIRMATION

God's supply is in abundance now that you accept His gifts.

	DATE	ENERGY 1-10	WEATHER	
1	7/9/15			Today in my yoga class I had some interesting fears surface: Someone walked in class and looked exactly like someone else I was once in conflict I actually went up to the person and introduced myself to confront my fears. In journal Entry #1 (this one) I have decided to journal my thoughts, but not enter it into the Chart of Emotions (COE). This is because I have chosen to use the COE for workbook question #1 as indicated by the red dotted arrow
2	7/1/15	6	hot	Today I found a book with an inscription from my dad saying how much he loved me. I miss him very much and think about him a lot. There are are some very strong emotions that came up for me... This time I decided to use Journal entry #2 to populate the Chart of Emotions (as indicated by the red arrows). So you see, I can still answer all the workbook questions and, yet, still able to answer all journal entries. However, I must choose only entry to use for the Chart of Emotions.

Use either the workbook question or journal entry to populate the COE on the opposite page

Winter

Haiku

overly the wintry
bold sparrow
companies fly
scarecrow to scarecrow
–Sazanami

Trisula Mudra

Tadasana

25

Instructions for populating the Chart of Emotions (COE) on every workbook and Journal spread

The workbook questions and journal entries above should help you to better understand how to optimize all 52 workbook spreads. I have outlined (in red) all the necessary steps required to populate each of the said spreads, which .collectively, contain 102 Chart of Emotions (COE). As earlier mentioned, there are many You Tube videos that easily walk you through all the different components and elements of ALFW. These videos can be found on our blog at www.alightfromwithin.net. I would strongly recommend that you take full advantage of all it has to offer. It is a great way to meet and work with other like-minded people. Thank you and Namaste!

Winter

Workbook questions

Chart of Emotions (COE)

ENTERED INTO THE MEI__ JOURNAL__ WORKBOOK__

Scale 1 - 10	Question or Journal Entry 1 Experienced Emotions	Past	Present	Future
	JOY			
	LOVE			
	HOPE			
	TRUST			
	ADMIRATION			
	FEAR			
	WORRIED			
	HAPPY			
	CALM			
	SAD			
	RESENTFUL			
	GENEROUS			
	DISGUST			
	ANGER			
	GUILT			
	ENTHUSIASTIC			
	SHY			

Having procured and made the choice to work with *A Light From Within*, how do you feel?

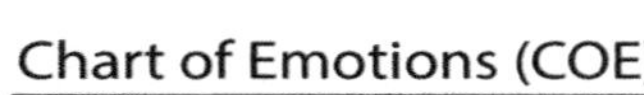

Chart of Emotions (COE)

ENTERED INTO THE MEI__ JOURNAL__ WORKBOOK__

Scale 1 - 10	Question or Journal Entry 2 Experienced Emotions	Past	Present	Future
	JOY			
	LOVE			
	HOPE			
	TRUST			
	ADMIRATION			
	FEAR			
	WORRIED			
	HAPPY			
	CALM			
	SAD			
	RESENTFUL			
	GENEROUS			
	DISGUST			
	ANGER			
	GUILT			
	ENTHUSIASTIC			
	SHY			

In what way might contentment differ from happiness in your life? Please explain:

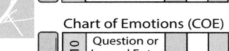

Journal entry

Weekly Random Act of Kindness: ______________________________

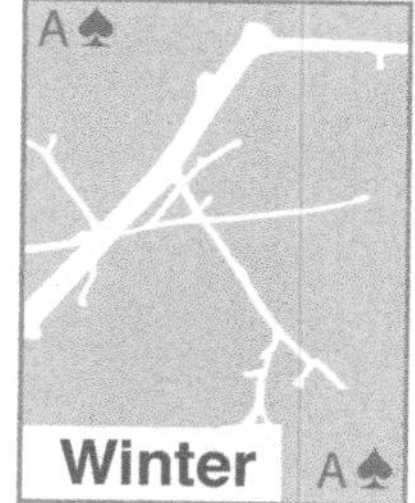

DATE	ENERGY: 1-10	WEATHER	AFFIRMATION God's supply is in abundance now that you accept His gifts.
1			
2			

Haiku

overly the wintry
bold sparrow
companies fly
scarecrow to scarecrow

–Sazanami

Trisula
Mudra

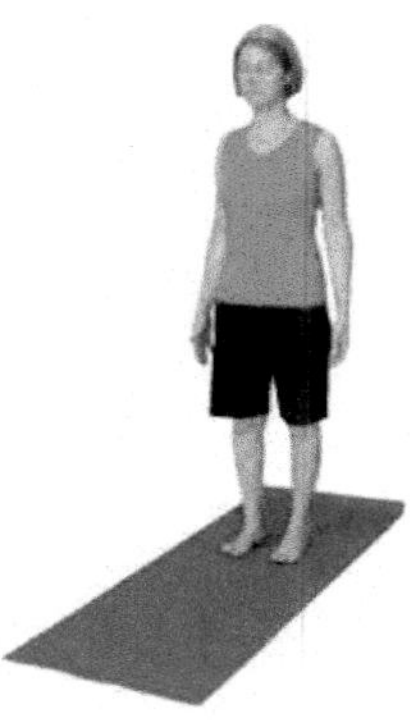

Tadasana

Use either the workbook question or journal entry to populate the COE on the opposite page

Workbook questions

ENTERED INTO THE MEI___ JOURNAL___ WORKBOOK___

Chart of Emotions (COE)

Scale 1 - 10	Question or Journal Entry 3 / Experienced Emotions	Past	Present	Future
	JOY			
	LOVE			
	HOPE			
	TRUST			
	ADMIRATION			
	FEAR			
	WORRIED			
	HAPPY			
	CALM			
	SAD			
	RESENTFUL			
	GENEROUS			
	DISGUST			
	ANGER			
	GUILT			
	ENTHUSIASTIC			
	SHY			

One goal you have yet to achieve in your life can best be described as:

I think I can move closer toward this goal by:

ENTERED INTO THE MEI___ JOURNAL___ WORKBOOK___

Chart of Emotions (COE)

Scale 1 - 10	Question or Journal Entry 4 / Experienced Emotions	Past	Present	Future
	JOY			
	LOVE			
	HOPE			
	TRUST			
	ADMIRATION			
	FEAR			
	WORRIED			
	HAPPY			
	CALM			
	SAD			
	RESENTFUL			
	GENEROUS			
	DISGUST			
	ANGER			
	GUILT			
	ENTHUSIASTIC			
	SHY			

How do your body, mind and spirit tend to affect each other?
Give an example from your life:

Journal entry

Weekly Random Act of Kindness: ______________________

DATE	ENERGY: 1-10	WEATHER	AFFIRMATION I have the strength of ten because my heart is filled with the light of truth.
3			
4			

Haiku

my very bone-ends
made contact with
the icy quilts
of deep december

Buson

Sikhara Mudra

Virabhadrasana II

Use either the workbook question or journal entry to populate the COE on the opposite page

Workbook questions

Chart of Emotions (COE)

Scale 1 - 10	Question or Journal Entry 5 / Experienced Emotions	Past	Present	Future
	JOY			
	LOVE			
	HOPE			
	TRUST			
	ADMIRATION			
	FEAR			
	WORRIED			
	HAPPY			
	CALM			
	SAD			
	RESENTFUL			
	GENEROUS			
	DISGUST			
	ANGER			
	GUILT			
	ENTHUSIASTIC			
	SHY			

ENTERED INTO THE MEI ___ JOURNAL ___ WORKBOOK ___

What are some challenges you have where learning is concerned? How does this affect your personal and professional growth and development?

Chart of Emotions (COE)

Scale 1 - 10	Question or Journal Entry 6 / Experienced Emotions	Past	Present	Future
	JOY			
	LOVE			
	HOPE			
	TRUST			
	ADMIRATION			
	FEAR			
	WORRIED			
	HAPPY			
	CALM			
	SAD			
	RESENTFUL			
	GENEROUS			
	DISGUST			
	ANGER			
	GUILT			
	ENTHUSIASTIC			
	SHY			

ENTERED INTO THE MEI ___ JOURNAL ___ WORKBOOK ___

How, if at all, might your spirituality separate you or make you different from other beings in the world?

Journal entry

Weekly Random Act of Kindness: ______________________________

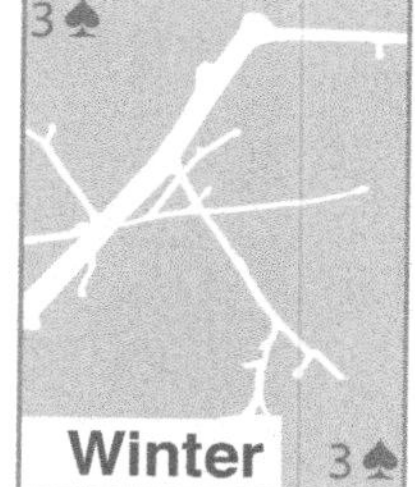

DATE	ENERGY: 1-10	WEATHER	AFFIRMATION Be a living temple in which God dwells.
5			
6			

Use either the workbook question or journal entry to populate the COE on the opposite page

Haiku

in my dark winter
lying ill...
at last i ask
how fares my neighbor

–Basho

Candrakala Mudra

Virabhadrasana I

Winter

Workbook questions

Chart of Emotions (COE)

ENTERED INTO THE MEI ___ JOURNAL ___ WORKBOOK ___

Scale 1 - 10	Question or Journal Entry 7 Experienced Emotions	Past	Present	Future
	JOY			
	LOVE			
	HOPE			
	TRUST			
	ADMIRATION			
	FEAR			
	WORRIED			
	HAPPY			
	CALM			
	SAD			
	RESENTFUL			
	GENEROUS			
	DISGUST			
	ANGER			
	GUILT			
	ENTHUSIASTIC			
	SHY			

How might your not-so-strongly-held beliefs affect your relationships with other people?

Chart of Emotions (COE)

ENTERED INTO THE MEI ___ JOURNAL ___ WORKBOOK ___

Scale 1 - 10	Question or Journal Entry 8 Experienced Emotions	Past	Present	Future
	JOY			
	LOVE			
	HOPE			
	TRUST			
	ADMIRATION			
	FEAR			
	WORRIED			
	HAPPY			
	CALM			
	SAD			
	RESENTFUL			
	GENEROUS			
	DISGUST			
	ANGER			
	GUILT			
	ENTHUSIASTIC			
	SHY			

Being nonjudgmental allows me to experience my life in the following ways:

Journal entry

Weekly Random Act of Kindness: ______________________________

DATE	ENERGY: 1-10	WEATHER	AFFIRMATION You are that which you seek.
7			
8			

Haiku

a thousand roof-tops
a thousand
market voices...
winter-morning mist

–Busun

Katakamukha Mudra

Virabhadrasana III

Use either the workbook question or journal entry to populate the COE on the opposite page

Winter

Workbook questions

Chart of Emotions (COE)

ENTERED INTO THE MEI ___ JOURNAL ___ WORKBOOK ___

Scale 1 - 10	Question or Journal Entry 9 / Experienced Emotions	Past	Present	Future
	JOY			
	LOVE			
	HOPE			
	TRUST			
	ADMIRATION			
	FEAR			
	WORRIED			
	HAPPY			
	CALM			
	SAD			
	RESENTFUL			
	GENEROUS			
	DISGUST			
	ANGER			
	GUILT			
	ENTHUSIASTIC			
	SHY			

In what ways do you tend to now think differently about some of your childhood memories? Please explain:

Chart of Emotions (COE)

ENTERED INTO THE MEI ___ JOURNAL ___ WORKBOOK ___

Scale 1 - 10	Question or Journal Entry 10 / Experienced Emotions	Past	Present	Future
	JOY			
	LOVE			
	HOPE			
	TRUST			
	ADMIRATION			
	FEAR			
	WORRIED			
	HAPPY			
	CALM			
	SAD			
	RESENTFUL			
	GENEROUS			
	DISGUST			
	ANGER			
	GUILT			
	ENTHUSIASTIC			
	SHY			

What I strongly admire about my mom and dad can best be described as:

Journal entry

Weekly Random Act of Kindness: ______________________________

DATE	ENERGY: 1-10	WEATHER	AFFIRMATION You must see the best in others before you see the good in yourself.
9			
10			

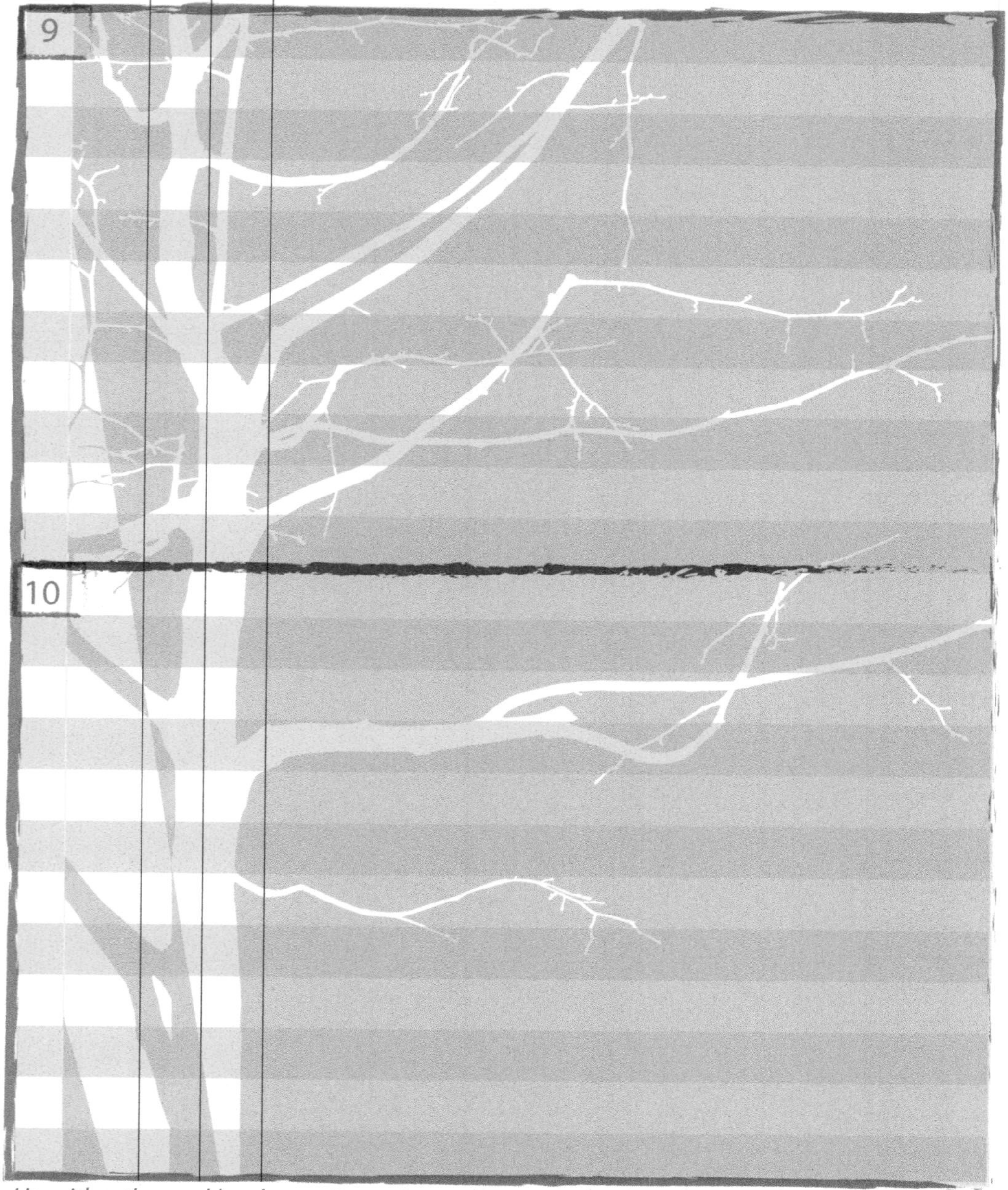

Haiku

first snow last night...
there across the
morning bay
sudden mountain-white

–Shiki

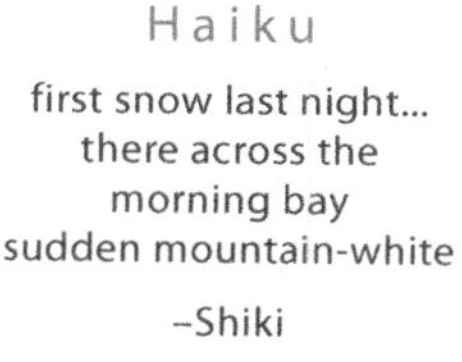

Pataka Mudra

Utkatasana

Use either the workbook question or journal entry to populate the COE on the opposite page

Workbook questions

Winter

Chart of Emotions (COE)

ENTERED INTO THE MEI ___

JOURNAL ___

WORKBOOK ___

Scale 1 - 10	Question or Journal Entry 11 Experienced Emotions	Past	Present	Future
	JOY			
	LOVE			
	HOPE			
	TRUST			
	ADMIRATION			
	FEAR			
	WORRIED			
	HAPPY			
	CALM			
	SAD			
	RESENTFUL			
	GENEROUS			
	DISGUST			
	ANGER			
	GUILT			
	ENTHUSIASTIC			
	SHY			

How does the concept of good and bad impact or limit your experience to live life in the fullest flavor possible?

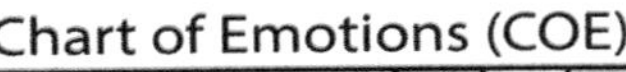

Chart of Emotions (COE)

ENTERED INTO THE MEI ___

JOURNAL ___

WORKBOOK ___

Scale 1 - 10	Question or Journal Entry 12 Experienced Emotions	Past	Present	Future
	JOY			
	LOVE			
	HOPE			
	TRUST			
	ADMIRATION			
	FEAR			
	WORRIED			
	HAPPY			
	CALM			
	SAD			
	RESENTFUL			
	GENEROUS			
	DISGUST			
	ANGER			
	GUILT			
	ENTHUSIASTIC			
	SHY			

In what ways do science and spirituality share a creative and/or logical link? How might that notion affect your views in life? Please explain:

Journal entry

Weekly Random Act of Kindness: ______________________

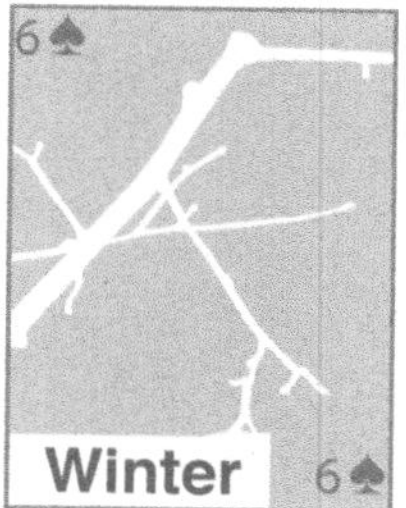

DATE	ENERGY: 1-10	WEATHER	AFFIRMATION There is no destiny but what you yourself make. All is well because you think it is.
11			
12			

Haiku

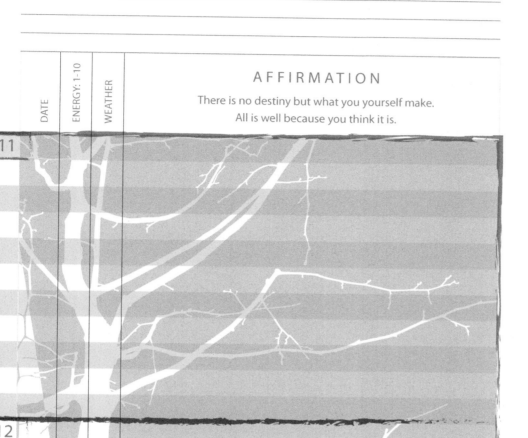

there in the winter
color of the
water moves
transluscent fish

–Raizen

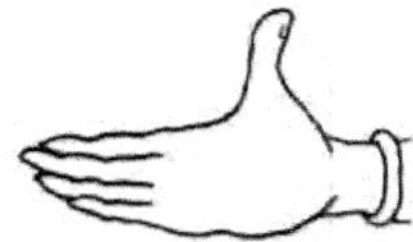

Ardha Chandra
Mudra

Tadasana
Urdvha
Hastasana

Use either the workbook question or journal entry to populate the COE on the opposite page

Workbook questions

Chart of Emotions (COE)

ENTERED INTO THE MEI ___ JOURNAL ___ WORKBOOK ___

Scale 1 - 10	Question or Journal Entry 13 Experienced Emotions	Past	Present	Future
	JOY			
	LOVE			
	HOPE			
	TRUST			
	ADMIRATION			
	FEAR			
	WORRIED			
	HAPPY			
	CALM			
	SAD			
	RESENTFUL			
	GENEROUS			
	DISGUST			
	ANGER			
	GUILT			
	ENTHUSIASTIC			
	SHY			

If you were able to magically just *turn off the pain*, how would you see your life being different? Please explain:

Chart of Emotions (COE)

ENTERED INTO THE MEI ___ JOURNAL ___ WORKBOOK ___

Scale 1 - 10	Question or Journal Entry 14 Experienced Emotions	Past	Present	Future
	JOY			
	LOVE			
	HOPE			
	TRUST			
	ADMIRATION			
	FEAR			
	WORRIED			
	HAPPY			
	CALM			
	SAD			
	RESENTFUL			
	GENEROUS			
	DISGUST			
	ANGER			
	GUILT			
	ENTHUSIASTIC			
	SHY			

How might your feeling more relaxed in life affect the way you experience Nature's landscape? Please explain:

Journal entry

Weekly Random Act of Kindness: ___

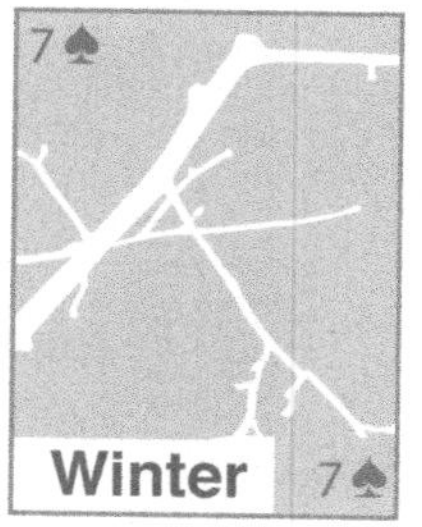

DATE	ENERGY: 1-10	WEATHER	AFFIRMATION
			Great things were never achieved in a day. Their creation was formed by constant toil and thought.
13			
14			

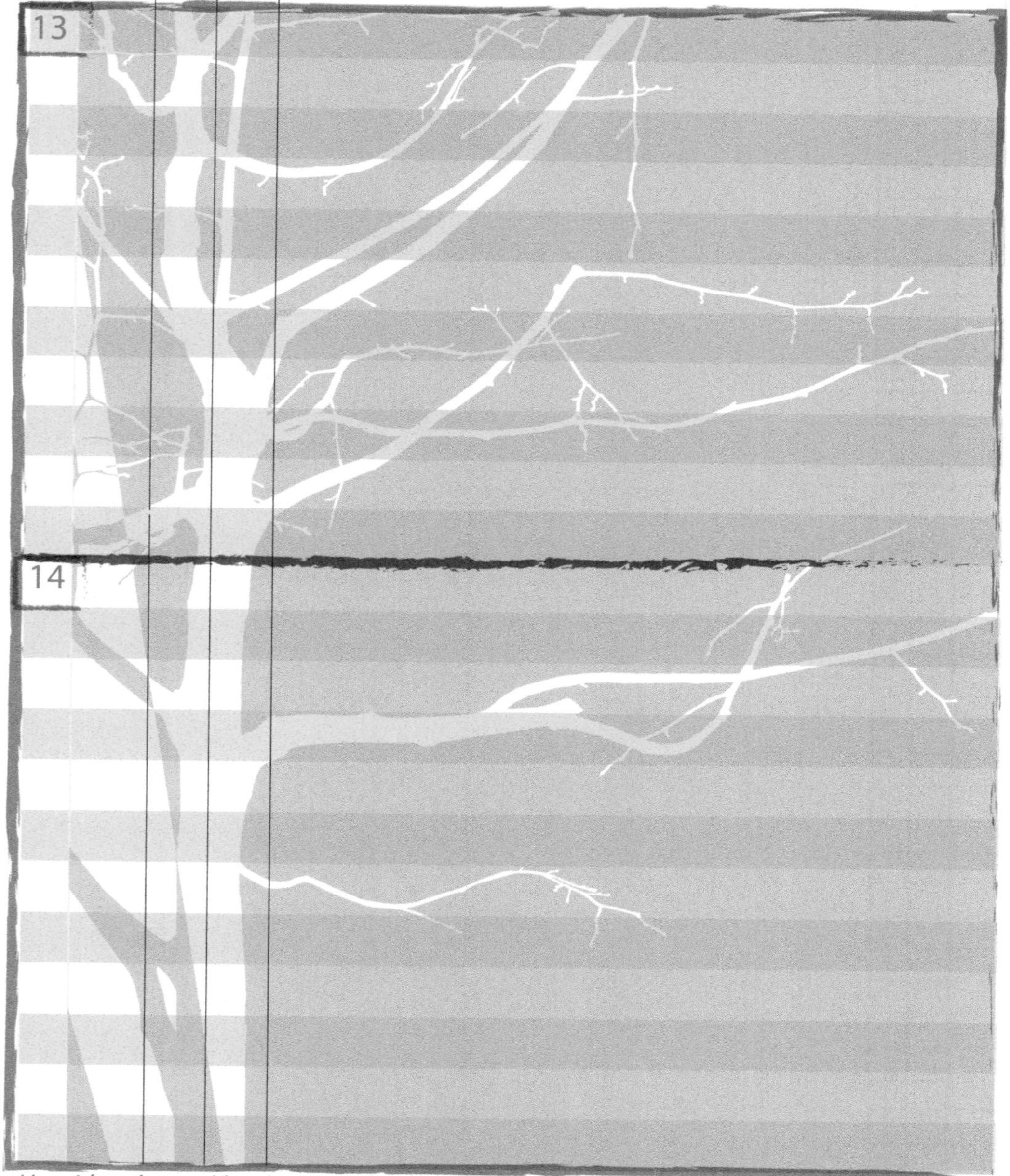

Haiku

see the red berries...
fallen like little
footprints
on the garden snow

–Shiki

Anjali Mudra

Vrkshasana

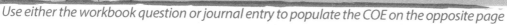

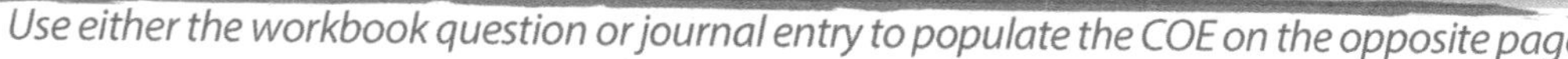

Use either the workbook question or journal entry to populate the COE on the opposite page

Winter

Workbook questions

Chart of Emotions (COE)

ENTERED INTO THE MEI___ JOURNAL___ WORKBOOK___

Scale 1 - 10	Question or Journal Entry 15 / Experienced Emotions	Past	Present	Future
	JOY			
	LOVE			
	HOPE			
	TRUST			
	ADMIRATION			
	FEAR			
	WORRIED			
	HAPPY			
	CALM			
	SAD			
	RESENTFUL			
	GENEROUS			
	DISGUST			
	ANGER			
	GUILT			
	ENTHUSIASTIC			
	SHY			

What is the difference between *guiding wisdom* and *guiding logic* in your life?

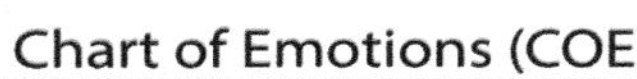

Chart of Emotions (COE)

ENTERED INTO THE MEI___ JOURNAL___ WORKBOOK___

Scale 1 - 10	Question or Journal Entry 16 / Experienced Emotions	Past	Present	Future
	JOY			
	LOVE			
	HOPE			
	TRUST			
	ADMIRATION			
	FEAR			
	WORRIED			
	HAPPY			
	CALM			
	SAD			
	RESENTFUL			
	GENEROUS			
	DISGUST			
	ANGER			
	GUILT			
	ENTHUSIASTIC			
	SHY			

There are many ways to turn an impulsive behavior into a constructive exercise. Please list a few examples as to how you have done this for yourself:

Journal entry

Weekly Random Act of Kindness: ______________________________

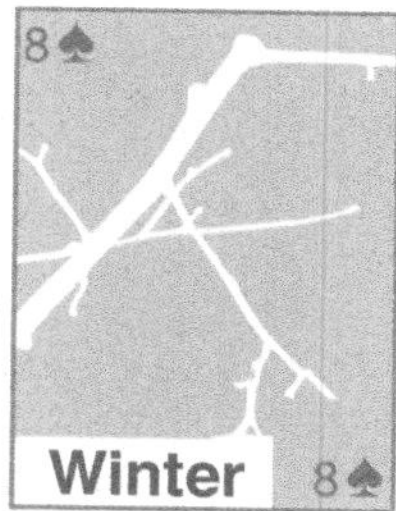

DATE	ENERGY: 1-10	WEATHER	AFFIRMATION Hate is poison, slowly seeping into the heart, bringing a cruel death in its wake.
15			
16			

Haiku

midnight wanderer
walking through
the snowy street...
echoing dog-bark

–Shiki

Suci Mudra

Utthita Tadasana

Use either the workbook question or journal entry to populate the COE on the opposite page

Workbook questions

Winter

ENTERED INTO THE MEI ___ JOURNAL ___ WORKBOOK ___

Chart of Emotions (COE)

Scale 1 - 10	Question or Journal Entry 17 / Experienced Emotions	Past	Present	Future
	JOY			
	LOVE			
	HOPE			
	TRUST			
	ADMIRATION			
	FEAR			
	WORRIED			
	HAPPY			
	CALM			
	SAD			
	RESENTFUL			
	GENEROUS			
	DISGUST			
	ANGER			
	GUILT			
	ENTHUSIASTIC			
	SHY			

When looking at the chart of emotions (to the left), you may notice the absence of one very strong emotion: shame. Please take the time to journal what shame is to you. What role, if any, does it play in your life?

Chart of Emotions (COE)

ENTERED INTO THE MEI ___ JOURNAL ___ WORKBOOK ___

Scale 1 - 10	Question or Journal Entry 18 / Experienced Emotions	Past	Present	Future
	JOY			
	LOVE			
	HOPE			
	TRUST			
	ADMIRATION			
	FEAR			
	WORRIED			
	HAPPY			
	CALM			
	SAD			
	RESENTFUL			
	GENEROUS			
	DISGUST			
	ANGER			
	GUILT			
	ENTHUSIASTIC			
	SHY			

When doing yoga, how do the physical and emotional barriers in your body present themselves to you? Is there an overall theme to these barriers or blockage? Please explain:

Journal entry

Weekly Random Act of Kindness: ______________________________

DATE	ENERGY: 1-10	WEATHER	AFFIRMATION Love all alike, free from attachment.
17			
18			

Use either the workbook question or journal entry to populate the COE on the opposite page

Haiku

blinding wild
snow blows, whirls
and drifts about
me... in this world
alone

- Chora

Tamracuda Mudra

Utthita Parsvaskonsana

Winter

Workbook questions

Chart of Emotions (COE)

ENTERED INTO THE MEI___ JOURNAL___ WORKBOOK___

Scale 1 - 10	Question or Journal Entry 19 Experienced Emotions	Past	Present	Future
	JOY			
	LOVE			
	HOPE			
	TRUST			
	ADMIRATION			
	FEAR			
	WORRIED			
	HAPPY			
	CALM			
	SAD			
	RESENTFUL			
	GENEROUS			
	DISGUST			
	ANGER			
	GUILT			
	ENTHUSIASTIC			
	SHY			

What responsibility do you take for the root cause of stress in your life? How are you working through this problem?

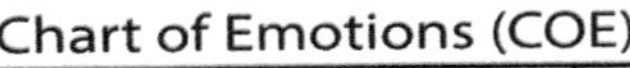

Chart of Emotions (COE)

ENTERED INTO THE MEI___ JOURNAL___ WORKBOOK___

Scale 1 - 10	Question or Journal Entry 20 Experienced Emotions	Past	Present	Future
	JOY			
	LOVE			
	HOPE			
	TRUST			
	ADMIRATION			
	FEAR			
	WORRIED			
	HAPPY			
	CALM			
	SAD			
	RESENTFUL			
	GENEROUS			
	DISGUST			
	ANGER			
	GUILT			
	ENTHUSIASTIC			
	SHY			

Often, when you are alone, is there anything that you tend to think and/or feel over and over again? Please explain:

Journal entry

Weekly Random Act of Kindness: ______________________________

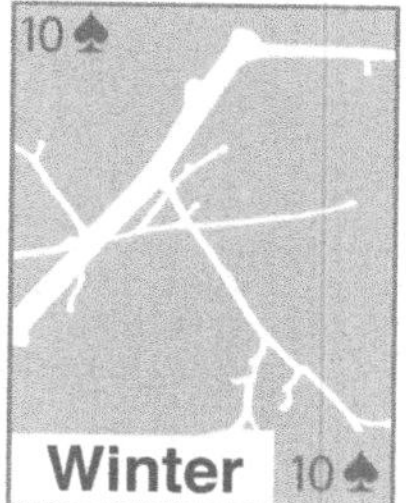

DATE	ENERGY: 1-10	WEATHER	AFFIRMATION My body is the outer layer of my mind.
19			
20			

Haiku

from my tiny roof
smooth...soft...
still-white snow
melts in melody

- Issa

Guruda Mudra

Garudasana

Use either the workbook question or journal entry to populate the COE on the opposite page

Winter

Workbook questions

ENTERED INTO THE MEI___ JOURNAL___ WORKBOOK___

Chart of Emotions (COE)

Scale 1 - 10	Question or Journal Entry 21 / Experienced Emotions	Past	Present	Future
	JOY			
	LOVE			
	HOPE			
	TRUST			
	ADMIRATION			
	FEAR			
	WORRIED			
	HAPPY			
	CALM			
	SAD			
	RESENTFUL			
	GENEROUS			
	DISGUST			
	ANGER			
	GUILT			
	ENTHUSIASTIC			
	SHY			

How is your body and mind like a sponge in that it clings and holds on to impressions from the outside world?

ENTERED INTO THE MEI___ JOURNAL___ WORKBOOK___

Chart of Emotions (COE)

Scale 1 - 10	Question or Journal Entry 22 / Experienced Emotions	Past	Present	Future
	JOY			
	LOVE			
	HOPE			
	TRUST			
	ADMIRATION			
	FEAR			
	WORRIED			
	HAPPY			
	CALM			
	SAD			
	RESENTFUL			
	GENEROUS			
	DISGUST			
	ANGER			
	GUILT			
	ENTHUSIASTIC			
	SHY			

How might the repetitive use (or thought) of certain words affect your emotional being? Please explain:

Journal entry

Weekly Random Act of Kindness: ______________________________

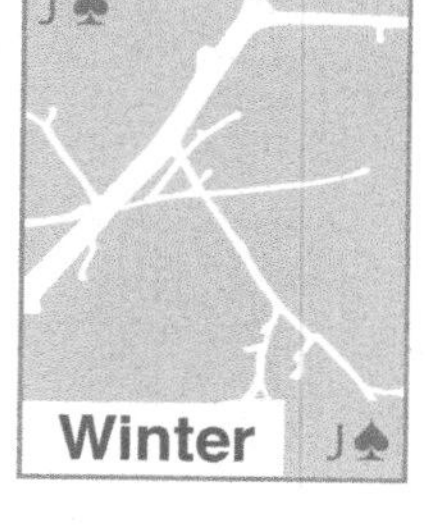

DATE	ENERGY: 1-10	WEATHER	AFFIRMATION All craving and seeking for love in a form is the inner urge to find God.
21			
22			

Haiku

look at that stray cat
sleeping...snug
under the eaves
in the whistling snow

- Taigi

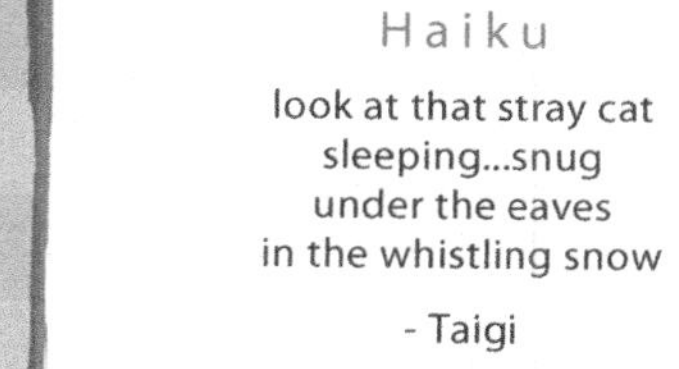

Mrgasirsa
Mudra

Uttanasana

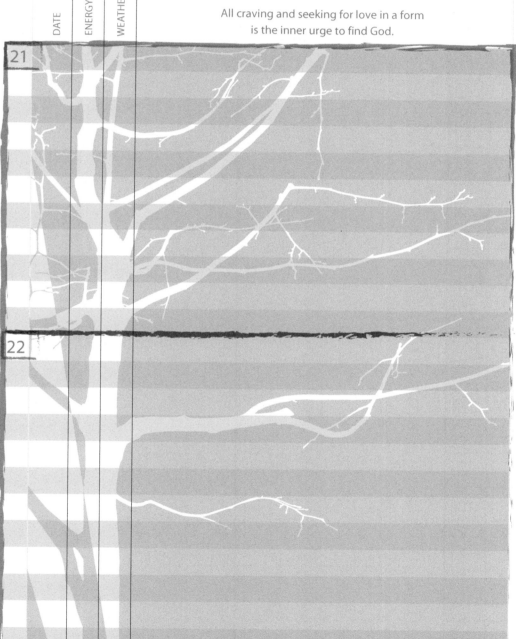

Use either the workbook question or journal entry to populate the COE on the opposite page

Winter

Workbook questions

Chart of Emotions (COE)

ENTERED INTO THE MEI ___ JOURNAL ___ WORKBOOK ___

Scale 1 - 10	Question or Journal Entry 23 / Experienced Emotions	Past	Present	Future
	JOY			
	LOVE			
	HOPE			
	TRUST			
	ADMIRATION			
	FEAR			
	WORRIED			
	HAPPY			
	CALM			
	SAD			
	RESENTFUL			
	GENEROUS			
	DISGUST			
	ANGER			
	GUILT			
	ENTHUSIASTIC			
	SHY			

How in your efforts to care for yourself might you make a difference in the lives of other people?

Chart of Emotions (COE)

ENTERED INTO THE MEI ___ JOURNAL ___ WORKBOOK ___

Scale 1 - 10	Question or Journal Entry 24 / Experienced Emotions	Past	Present	Future
	JOY			
	LOVE			
	HOPE			
	TRUST			
	ADMIRATION			
	FEAR			
	WORRIED			
	HAPPY			
	CALM			
	SAD			
	RESENTFUL			
	GENEROUS			
	DISGUST			
	ANGER			
	GUILT			
	ENTHUSIASTIC			
	SHY			

Whenever you are hard on yourself, how does the world around you seem to appear or change?

Journal entry

Weekly Random Act of Kindness: ______________________________

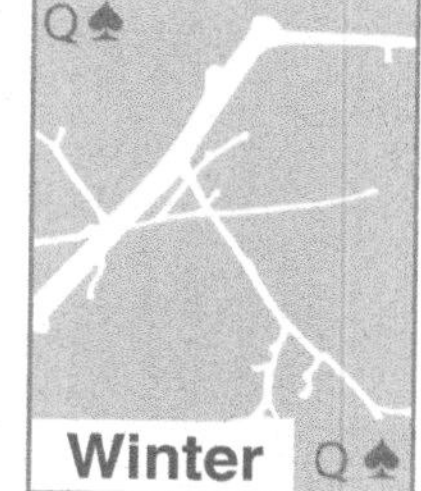

DATE	ENERGY: 1-10	WEATHER	AFFIRMATION Be like a river of supply starting and ending in the same place from the ocean of life you take, and the ocean of life you give.
23			
24			

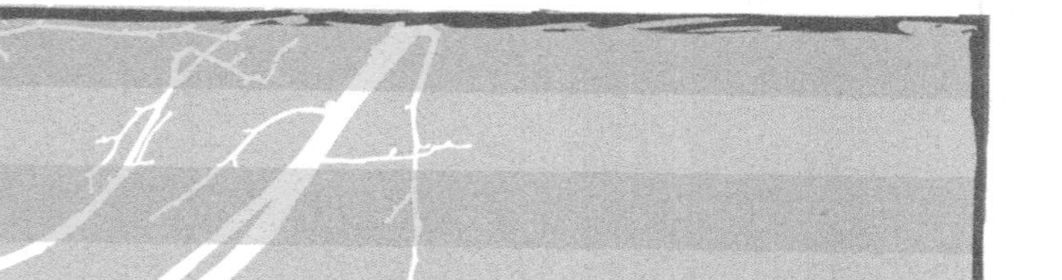

Haiku

solitary crow...
companioning my
progress over
snowy fields -
Senna

Ardhapataka Mudra

Utthita Trikonasana

Use either the workbook question or journal entry to populate the COE on the opposite page

Winter

Workbook questions

Chart of Emotions (COE)

ENTERED INTO THE MEI ___ JOURNAL ___ WORKBOOK ___

Scale 1 - 10	Question or Journal Entry 25 / Experienced Emotions	Past	Present	Future
	JOY			
	LOVE			
	HOPE			
	TRUST			
	ADMIRATION			
	FEAR			
	WORRIED			
	HAPPY			
	CALM			
	SAD			
	RESENTFUL			
	GENEROUS			
	DISGUST			
	ANGER			
	GUILT			
	ENTHUSIASTIC			
	SHY			

The last time something really *took your breath away* could best be described as having had what kind of effect on you:

Chart of Emotions (COE)

ENTERED INTO THE MEI ___ JOURNAL ___ WORKBOOK ___

Scale 1 - 10	Question or Journal Entry 26 / Experienced Emotions	Past	Present	Future
	JOY			
	LOVE			
	HOPE			
	TRUST			
	ADMIRATION			
	FEAR			
	WORRIED			
	HAPPY			
	CALM			
	SAD			
	RESENTFUL			
	GENEROUS			
	DISGUST			
	ANGER			
	GUILT			
	ENTHUSIASTIC			
	SHY			

In life, we all seem to have insecurities. Is there an one in your life that you're willing to share and let go of for good? Please explain:

Journal entry

Weekly Random Act of Kindness: ______________________

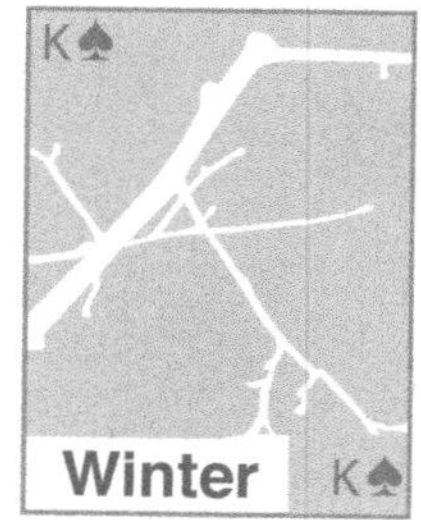

DATE	ENERGY: 1-10	WEATHER	AFFIRMATION Your tomorrow is the creation of today.
25			
26			

Haiku

poet nightingale...
will i hear your
later verses
in the vale of death

–Anon

Padmakosa Mudra

Parivrtti Trikonasana

Use either the workbook question or journal entry to populate the COE on the opposite page

Spring

Workbook questions

Chart of Emotions (COE)

ENTERED INTO THE MEI ___ JOURNAL ___ WORKBOOK ___

Scale 1 - 10	Question or Journal Entry 27 / Experienced Emotions	Past	Present	Future
	JOY			
	LOVE			
	HOPE			
	TRUST			
	ADMIRATION			
	FEAR			
	WORRIED			
	HAPPY			
	CALM			
	SAD			
	RESENTFUL			
	GENEROUS			
	DISGUST			
	ANGER			
	GUILT			
	ENTHUSIASTIC			
	SHY			

Please list one or two things about yoga and how it has made a difference in your life today:

Chart of Emotions (COE)

ENTERED INTO THE MEI ___ JOURNAL ___ WORKBOOK ___

Scale 1 - 10	Question or Journal Entry 28 / Experienced Emotions	Past	Present	Future
	JOY			
	LOVE			
	HOPE			
	TRUST			
	ADMIRATION			
	FEAR			
	WORRIED			
	HAPPY			
	CALM			
	SAD			
	RESENTFUL			
	GENEROUS			
	DISGUST			
	ANGER			
	GUILT			
	ENTHUSIASTIC			
	SHY			

Three things that bring me joy and peace this day can best be described as:

Journal entry

Weekly Random Act of Kindness: ______________________________

DATE	ENERGY: 1-10	WEATHER	AFFIRMATION It is through the invisible vibration of love that I trust in myself and others.
27			
28			

Use either the workbook question or journal entry to populate the COE on the opposite page

Haiku

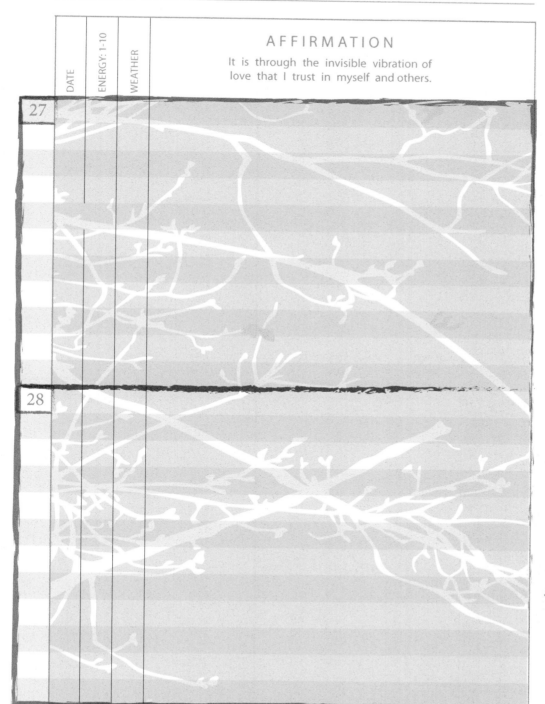

rain-obliterated...
the river,
some roofs,
a bridge without a shore

–Basho

Kangula Mudra

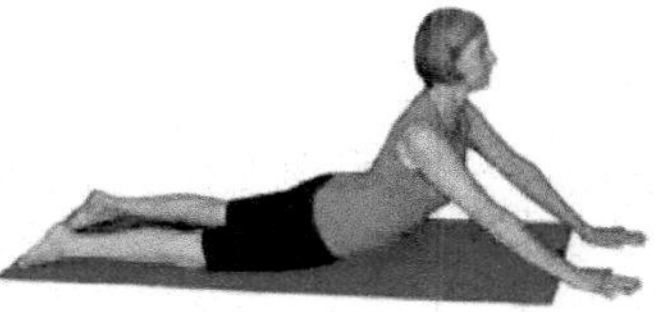

Bhujangasana

Workbook questions

Chart of Emotions (COE)

ENTERED INTO THE MEI ___ JOURNAL ___ WORKBOOK ___

Scale 1 - 10	Question or Journal Entry 29 / Experienced Emotions	Past	Present	Future
	JOY			
	LOVE			
	HOPE			
	TRUST			
	ADMIRATION			
	FEAR			
	WORRIED			
	HAPPY			
	CALM			
	SAD			
	RESENTFUL			
	GENEROUS			
	DISGUST			
	ANGER			
	GUILT			
	ENTHUSIASTIC			
	SHY			

Briefly describe how it is that your purchasing power affects your world and the people around you:

Chart of Emotions (COE)

ENTERED INTO THE MEI ___ JOURNAL ___ WORKBOOK ___

Scale 1 - 10	Question or Journal Entry 30 / Experienced Emotions	Past	Present	Future
	JOY			
	LOVE			
	HOPE			
	TRUST			
	ADMIRATION			
	FEAR			
	WORRIED			
	HAPPY			
	CALM			
	SAD			
	RESENTFUL			
	GENEROUS			
	DISGUST			
	ANGER			
	GUILT			
	ENTHUSIASTIC			
	SHY			

Think of some special person who you love to be with, someone whose presence fills your heart and soul with joy and love. In what ways are you capable of sharing these similar feelings with a stranger, even someone who you might not like?

Journal entry

Weekly Random Act of Kindness: ____________________

DATE	ENERGY: 1-10	WEATHER	AFFIRMATION To travel far, one must start near. Start here and now conquer the little things; then the big things will conquer themselves.
29			
30			

Use either the workbook question or journal entry to populate the COE on the opposite page

Haiku

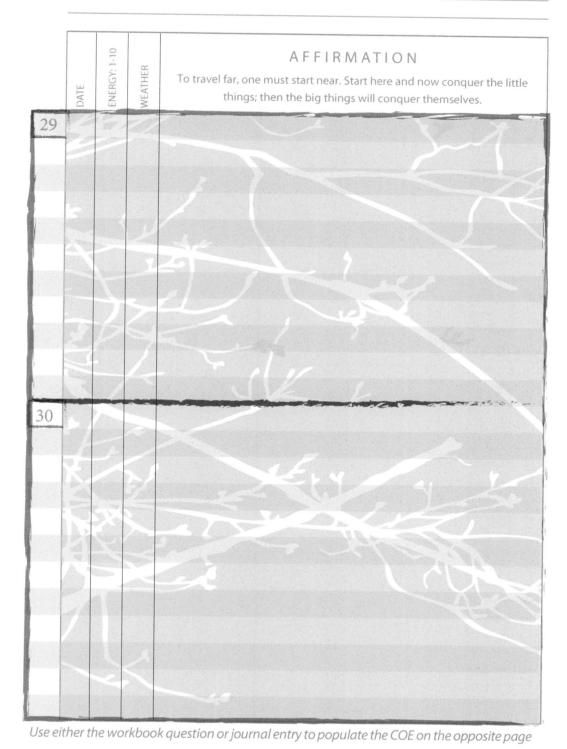

old snow is melting...
now the huts
unfreezing to
free all the children

- Issa

Shakti Mudra

Classical Natarajnasana

Workbook questions

ENTERED INTO THE MEI ___ JOURNAL ___ WORKBOOK ___

Chart of Emotions (COE)

Scale 1 - 10	Question or Journal Entry 31 / Experienced Emotions	Past	Present	Future
	JOY			
	LOVE			
	HOPE			
	TRUST			
	ADMIRATION			
	FEAR			
	WORRIED			
	HAPPY			
	CALM			
	SAD			
	RESENTFUL			
	GENEROUS			
	DISGUST			
	ANGER			
	GUILT			
	ENTHUSIASTIC			
	SHY			

If the universe is a spiral, where do you see yourself in the unfolding of that space?

ENTERED INTO THE MEI ___ JOURNAL ___ WORKBOOK ___

Chart of Emotions (COE)

Scale 1 - 10	Question or Journal Entry 32 / Experienced Emotions	Past	Present	Future
	JOY			
	LOVE			
	HOPE			
	TRUST			
	ADMIRATION			
	FEAR			
	WORRIED			
	HAPPY			
	CALM			
	SAD			
	RESENTFUL			
	GENEROUS			
	DISGUST			
	ANGER			
	GUILT			
	ENTHUSIASTIC			
	SHY			

A big distraction to the renewal of awareness in my life these days could best be described as:

Journal entry

Weekly Random Act of Kindness: ______________________________

DATE	ENERGY: 1-10	WEATHER	AFFIRMATION Love is the vibration of all unselfish joy— the perfect oneness with vibrant life.
31			
32			

Haiku

now wild geese return...
what draws them
crying all the long
dark night

–Roka

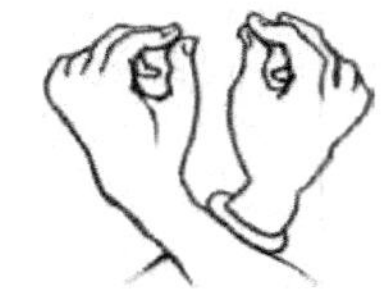

Katakavardhana Mudra

Dandasana

Use either the workbook question or journal entry to populate the COE on the opposite page

Workbook questions

ENTERED INTO THE MEI___ JOURNAL___ WORKBOOK___

Chart of Emotions (COE)

Scale 1 - 10	Question or Journal Entry 33 / Experienced Emotions	Past	Present	Future
	JOY			
	LOVE			
	HOPE			
	TRUST			
	ADMIRATION			
	FEAR			
	WORRIED			
	HAPPY			
	CALM			
	SAD			
	RESENTFUL			
	GENEROUS			
	DISGUST			
	ANGER			
	GUILT			
	ENTHUSIASTIC			
	SHY			

How might being more aware of your dreaming state (sleep) allow you to be more conscious in your waking state? Try and give a specific example as to how dreams affect your very awareness:

ENTERED INTO THE MEI___ JOURNAL___ WORKBOOK___

Chart of Emotions (COE)

Scale 1 - 10	Question or Journal Entry 34 / Experienced Emotions	Past	Present	Future
	JOY			
	LOVE			
	HOPE			
	TRUST			
	ADMIRATION			
	FEAR			
	WORRIED			
	HAPPY			
	CALM			
	SAD			
	RESENTFUL			
	GENEROUS			
	DISGUST			
	ANGER			
	GUILT			
	ENTHUSIASTIC			
	SHY			

When you are not feeling strong or at rest, how does the world around you appear or seem to change? Please explain:

Journal entry

Weekly Random Act of Kindness: ______________________________

DATE	ENERGY: 1-10	WEATHER	AFFIRMATION Strength comes from purity of the heart.
33			
34			

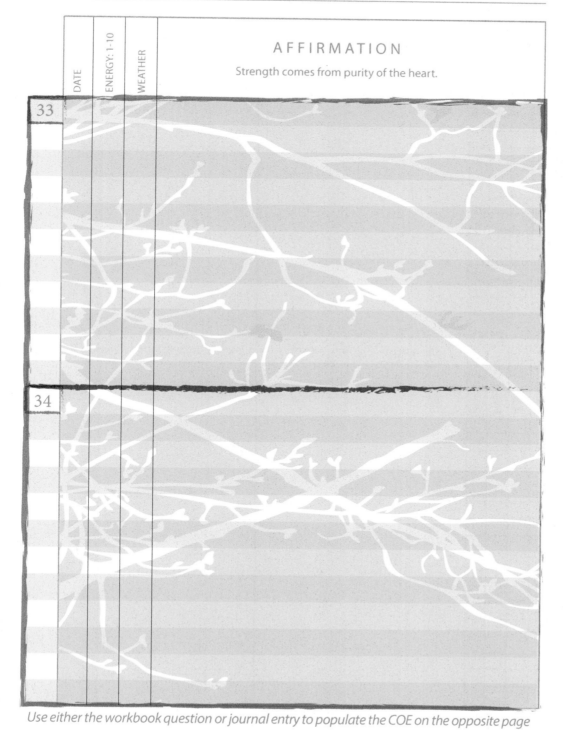

Use either the workbook question or journal entry to populate the COE on the opposite page

Haiku

cold morning rainfall...
mingling all their
gleaming horns
oxen at the fence

–Ranko

Svastika Mudra

Parsvattonasana

Workbook questions

Chart of Emotions (COE)

ENTERED INTO THE MEI ___

JOURNAL ___

WORKBOOK ___

Scale 1 - 10	Question or Journal Entry 35 / Experienced Emotions	Past	Present	Future
	JOY			
	LOVE			
	HOPE			
	TRUST			
	ADMIRATION			
	FEAR			
	WORRIED			
	HAPPY			
	CALM			
	SAD			
	RESENTFUL			
	GENEROUS			
	DISGUST			
	ANGER			
	GUILT			
	ENTHUSIASTIC			
	SHY			

How can you best describe the difference between the feelings and sensations of your body while doing yoga as compared to other activities?

Chart of Emotions (COE)

ENTERED INTO THE MEI ___

JOURNAL ___

WORKBOOK ___

Scale 1 - 10	Question or Journal Entry 36 / Experienced Emotions	Past	Present	Future
	JOY			
	LOVE			
	HOPE			
	TRUST			
	ADMIRATION			
	FEAR			
	WORRIED			
	HAPPY			
	CALM			
	SAD			
	RESENTFUL			
	GENEROUS			
	DISGUST			
	ANGER			
	GUILT			
	ENTHUSIASTIC			
	SHY			

The process of having overcome one of the greatest obstacles of my life (thus far) can best be described as:

Journal entry

Weekly Random Act of Kindness: ______________________________

DATE	ENERGY: 1-10	WEATHER	AFFIRMATION Love and the world is yours.
35			
36			

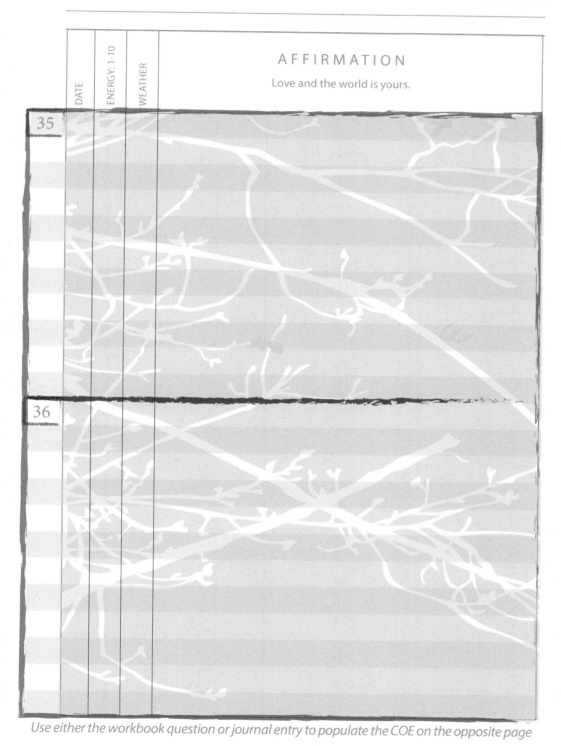

Use either the workbook question or journal entry to populate the COE on the opposite page

Haiku

hazy ponded moon
and pale night sky
are broken...
bungling black frog...

–Busun

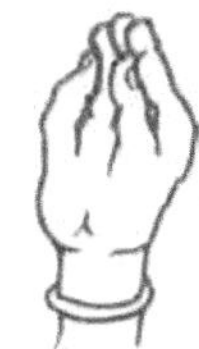

Sandamsa Mudra

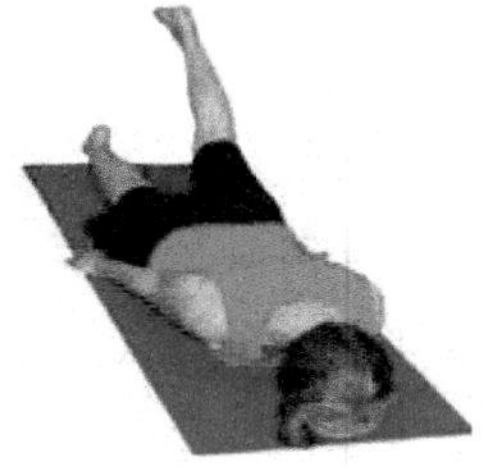

Ardha Shalambhasana

Workbook questions

Chart of Emotions (COE)

ENTERED INTO THE MEI ___ JOURNAL ___ WORKBOOK ___

Scale 1 - 10	Question or Journal Entry 37 / Experienced Emotions	Past	Present	Future
	JOY			
	LOVE			
	HOPE			
	TRUST			
	ADMIRATION			
	FEAR			
	WORRIED			
	HAPPY			
	CALM			
	SAD			
	RESENTFUL			
	GENEROUS			
	DISGUST			
	ANGER			
	GUILT			
	ENTHUSIASTIC			
	SHY			

In what ways might you see your expression(s) reflected through Nature's landscape? Please explain:

Chart of Emotions (COE)

ENTERED INTO THE MEI ___ JOURNAL ___ WORKBOOK ___

Scale 1 - 10	Question or Journal Entry 38 / Experienced Emotions	Past	Present	Future
	JOY			
	LOVE			
	HOPE			
	TRUST			
	ADMIRATION			
	FEAR			
	WORRIED			
	HAPPY			
	CALM			
	SAD			
	RESENTFUL			
	GENEROUS			
	DISGUST			
	ANGER			
	GUILT			
	ENTHUSIASTIC			
	SHY			

How, within the barriers of your body do you resist or attract joy or pain? Please explain:

Journal entry

Weekly Random Act of Kindness: ______________________________

DATE	ENERGY: 1-10	WEATHER	AFFIRMATION Open wide the portals of the heart and let the sunlight warm it and burn out all toxins.
37			
38			

Use either the workbook question or journal entry to populate the COE on the opposite page

Haiku

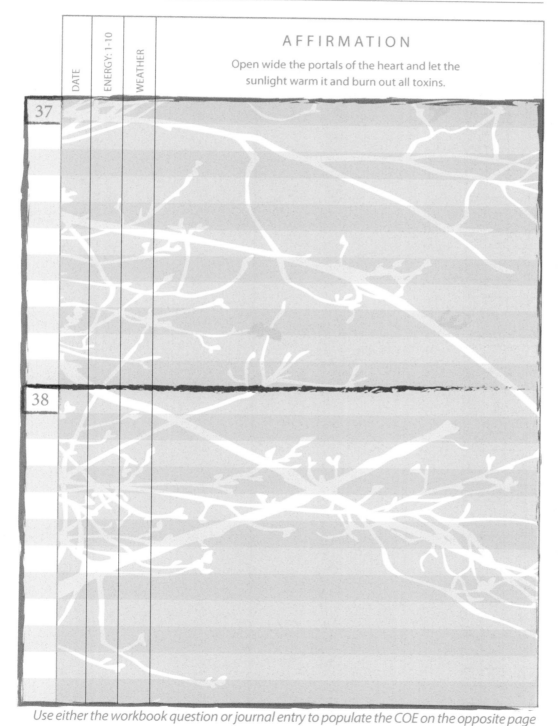

an april shower ...
see that thirsty
mouse lapping
river sumida

-Issa

Musti Mudra

Prasarita Padottanasana

Workbook questions

Chart of Emotions (COE)

ENTERED INTO THE MEI___ JOURNAL___ WORKBOOK___

Scale 1 - 10	Question or Journal Entry 39 Experienced Emotions	Past	Present	Future
	JOY			
	LOVE			
	HOPE			
	TRUST			
	ADMIRATION			
	FEAR			
	WORRIED			
	HAPPY			
	CALM			
	SAD			
	RESENTFUL			
	GENEROUS			
	DISGUST			
	ANGER			
	GUILT			
	ENTHUSIASTIC			
	SHY			

Through what activity do you tend to tap into your more creative side? How does this affect your more logical side?

Chart of Emotions (COE)

ENTERED INTO THE MEI___ JOURNAL___ WORKBOOK___

Scale 1 - 10	Question or Journal Entry 40 Experienced Emotions	Past	Present	Future
	JOY			
	LOVE			
	HOPE			
	TRUST			
	ADMIRATION			
	FEAR			
	WORRIED			
	HAPPY			
	CALM			
	SAD			
	RESENTFUL			
	GENEROUS			
	DISGUST			
	ANGER			
	GUILT			
	ENTHUSIASTIC			
	SHY			

How has the process of acquiring your identity misled or distracted you from the core source and space of who you really are?

Journal entry

Weekly Random Act of Kindness: ____________________

DATE	ENERGY: 1-10	WEATHER	AFFIRMATION Outer forms are manifestations of your own mind on the physical plane.
39			
40			

Haiku

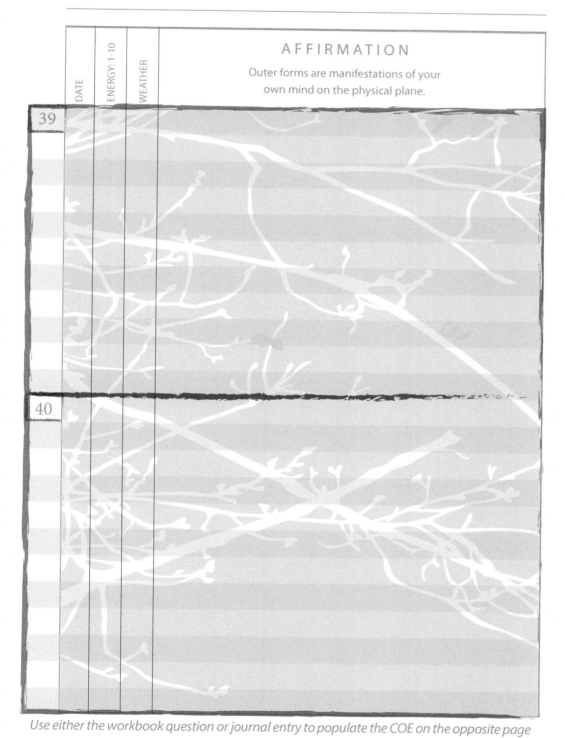

under my tree roof
slanting lines of
april rain
separate to drops

–Basho

Bherunda Mudra

Adho Mukha Svanasana

Use either the workbook question or journal entry to populate the COE on the opposite page

Workbook questions

Chart of Emotions (COE)

ENTERED INTO THE MEI___ JOURNAL___ WORKBOOK___

Scale 1 - 10	Question or Journal Entry 41 / Experienced Emotions	Past	Present	Future
	JOY			
	LOVE			
	HOPE			
	TRUST			
	ADMIRATION			
	FEAR			
	WORRIED			
	HAPPY			
	CALM			
	SAD			
	RESENTFUL			
	GENEROUS			
	DISGUST			
	ANGER			
	GUILT			
	ENTHUSIASTIC			
	SHY			

What do you think people's opinions about other people's "good or bad" behavior(s) say about them?

Chart of Emotions (COE)

ENTERED INTO THE MEI___ JOURNAL___ WORKBOOK___

Scale 1 - 10	Question or Journal Entry 42 / Experienced Emotions	Past	Present	Future
	JOY			
	LOVE			
	HOPE			
	TRUST			
	ADMIRATION			
	FEAR			
	WORRIED			
	HAPPY			
	CALM			
	SAD			
	RESENTFUL			
	GENEROUS			
	DISGUST			
	ANGER			
	GUILT			
	ENTHUSIASTIC			
	SHY			

Think of one thing that you may NEVER have shared or told anyone else. Do you agree that there may be at least one thing? Are you now ready to journal and/or share that with family and friends now? Please explain:

Journal entry

Weekly Random Act of Kindness: ______________________________

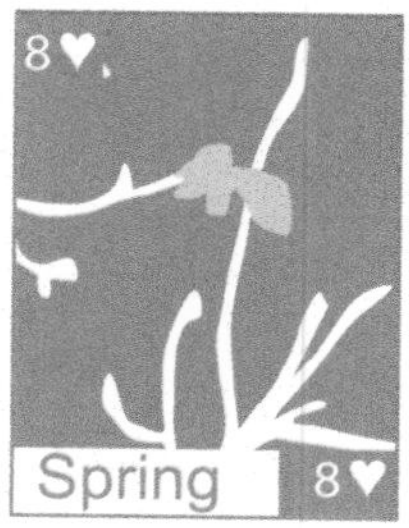

DATE	ENERGY: 1-10	WEATHER	AFFIRMATION When desire ceases bliss follows.
41			
42			

Use either the workbook question or journal entry to populate the COE on the opposite page

Haiku

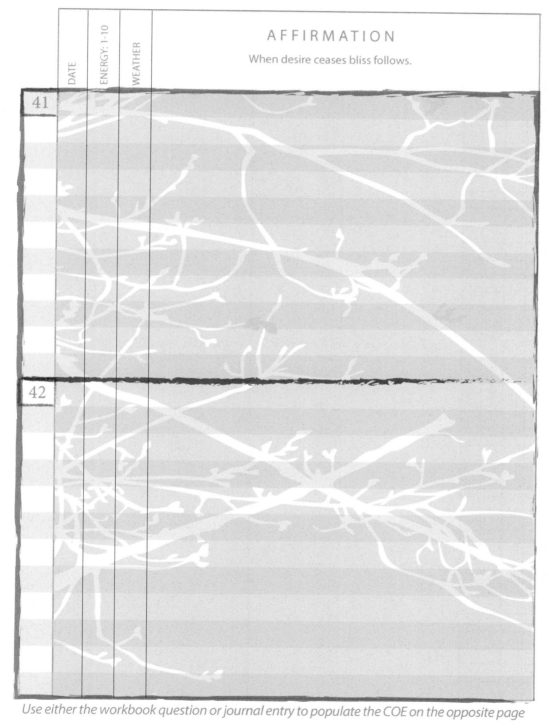

bird droppings
pattern the purples
and the yellows
of my iris petals

–Busun

Matsya Mudra

Matsyasana

Workbook questions

ENTERED INTO THE MEI ___ JOURNAL ___ WORKBOOK ___

Chart of Emotions (COE)

Scale 1 - 10	Question or Journal Entry 43 / Experienced Emotions	Past	Present	Future
	JOY			
	LOVE			
	HOPE			
	TRUST			
	ADMIRATION			
	FEAR			
	WORRIED			
	HAPPY			
	CALM			
	SAD			
	RESENTFUL			
	GENEROUS			
	DISGUST			
	ANGER			
	GUILT			
	ENTHUSIASTIC			
	SHY			

In what way has art ever been therapeutic for you in your life? Please explain:

ENTERED INTO THE MEI ___ JOURNAL ___ WORKBOOK ___

Chart of Emotions (COE)

Scale 1 - 10	Question or Journal Entry 44 / Experienced Emotions	Past	Present	Future
	JOY			
	LOVE			
	HOPE			
	TRUST			
	ADMIRATION			
	FEAR			
	WORRIED			
	HAPPY			
	CALM			
	SAD			
	RESENTFUL			
	GENEROUS			
	DISGUST			
	ANGER			
	GUILT			
	ENTHUSIASTIC			
	SHY			

If you were not in this world, how do you think things would be different? How does this statement make you feel? Please explain:

Journal entry

Weekly Random Act of Kindness: ____________________

DATE	ENERGY: 1-10	WEATHER	AFFIRMATION The beauty that is hidden in the farthest corners of your soul is seen with the eyes of the heart.
43			
44			

Use either the workbook question or journal entry to populate the COE on the opposite page

Haiku

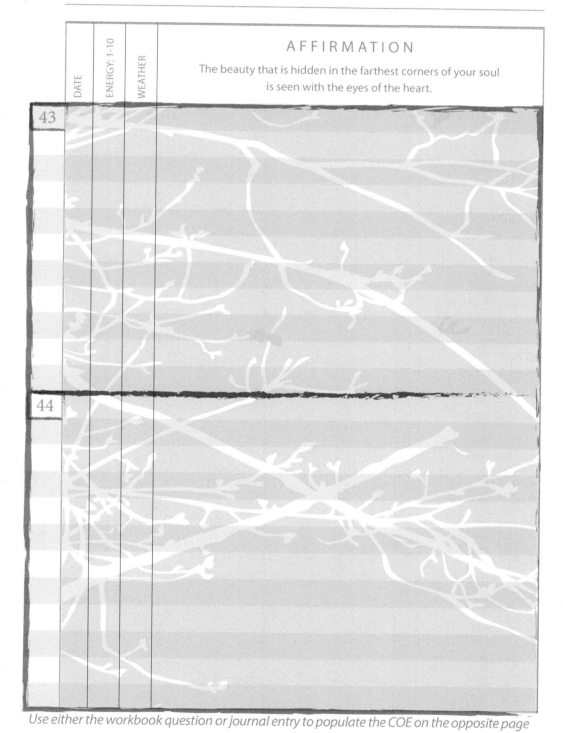

shining on the sea...
dazzling sunlight
shaking over
hills of cherry-bloom

–Busun

Karkala Mudra

Parighasana

Workbook questions

ENTERED INTO THE MEI ___ JOURNAL ___ WORKBOOK ___

Chart of Emotions (COE)

Scale 1 - 10	Question or Journal Entry 45 / Experienced Emotions	Past	Present	Future
	JOY			
	LOVE			
	HOPE			
	TRUST			
	ADMIRATION			
	FEAR			
	WORRIED			
	HAPPY			
	CALM			
	SAD			
	RESENTFUL			
	GENEROUS			
	DISGUST			
	ANGER			
	GUILT			
	ENTHUSIASTIC			
	SHY			

How are you beginning a new cycle today?

ENTERED INTO THE MEI ___ JOURNAL ___ WORKBOOK ___

Chart of Emotions (COE)

Scale 1 - 10	Question or Journal Entry 46 / Experienced Emotions	Past	Present	Future
	JOY			
	LOVE			
	HOPE			
	TRUST			
	ADMIRATION			
	FEAR			
	WORRIED			
	HAPPY			
	CALM			
	SAD			
	RESENTFUL			
	GENEROUS			
	DISGUST			
	ANGER			
	GUILT			
	ENTHUSIASTIC			
	SHY			

How are you ending an old cycle today?

Journal entry

Weekly Random Act of Kindness:

DATE	ENERGY: 1-10	WEATHER	AFFIRMATION Activity is God in action.
45			
46			

Haiku

moonlight stillness
lights the petals
falling...falling...
on the silenced lute

–Shiki

Pasa Mudra

Pashimottanasana

Use either the workbook question or journal entry to populate the COE on the opposite page

Spring

Workbook questions

ENTERED INTO THE MEI___ JOURNAL___ WORKBOOK___

Chart of Emotions (COE)

Scale 1 - 10	Question or Journal Entry 47 / Experienced Emotions	Past	Present	Future
	JOY			
	LOVE			
	HOPE			
	TRUST			
	ADMIRATION			
	FEAR			
	WORRIED			
	HAPPY			
	CALM			
	SAD			
	RESENTFUL			
	GENEROUS			
	DISGUST			
	ANGER			
	GUILT			
	ENTHUSIASTIC			
	SHY			

How do you experience the five elements (space, fire, air, water and earth) living through you in life today?

ENTERED INTO THE MEI___ JOURNAL___ WORKBOOK___

Chart of Emotions (COE)

Scale 1 - 10	Question or Journal Entry 48 / Experienced Emotions	Past	Present	Future
	JOY			
	LOVE			
	HOPE			
	TRUST			
	ADMIRATION			
	FEAR			
	WORRIED			
	HAPPY			
	CALM			
	SAD			
	RESENTFUL			
	GENEROUS			
	DISGUST			
	ANGER			
	GUILT			
	ENTHUSIASTIC			
	SHY			

What does surrendering mean to you? In what ways have you surrendered today?

Journal entry

Weekly Random Act of Kindness: ______________________________

DATE	ENERGY: 1-10	WEATHER	AFFIRMATION See the best in yourself and others will follow suit.
47			
48			

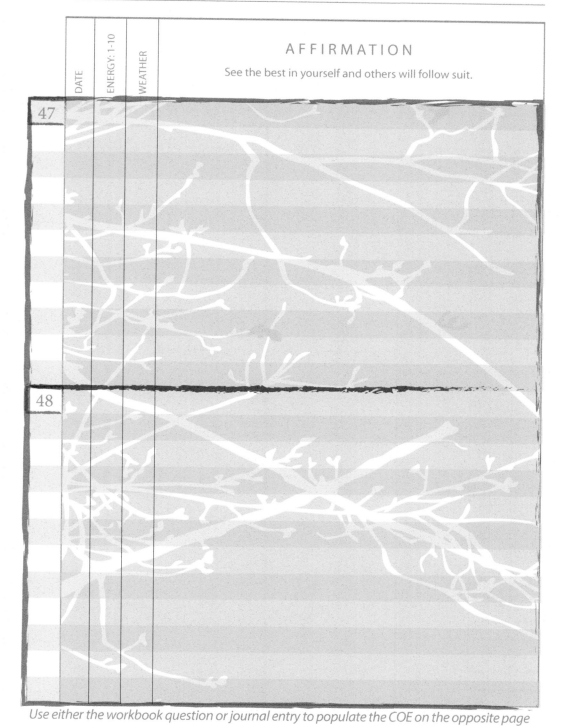

Haiku

come now, play with me...
fatherless
motherless dear
little sparrow-child

-Issa

Hakini Mudra

Baddha Konasana

Use either the workbook question or journal entry to populate the COE on the opposite page

Spring

Workbook questions

ENTERED INTO THE MEI ___ JOURNAL ___ WORKBOOK ___

Chart of Emotions (COE)

Scale 1 - 10	Question or Journal Entry 49 / Experienced Emotions	Past	Present	Future
	JOY			
	LOVE			
	HOPE			
	TRUST			
	ADMIRATION			
	FEAR			
	WORRIED			
	HAPPY			
	CALM			
	SAD			
	RESENTFUL			
	GENEROUS			
	DISGUST			
	ANGER			
	GUILT			
	ENTHUSIASTIC			
	SHY			

How do your expectations of other people affect your relationship with them?

ENTERED INTO THE MEI ___ JOURNAL ___ WORKBOOK ___

Chart of Emotions (COE)

Scale 1 - 10	Question or Journal Entry 50 / Experienced Emotions	Past	Present	Future
	JOY			
	LOVE			
	HOPE			
	TRUST			
	ADMIRATION			
	FEAR			
	WORRIED			
	HAPPY			
	CALM			
	SAD			
	RESENTFUL			
	GENEROUS			
	DISGUST			
	ANGER			
	GUILT			
	ENTHUSIASTIC			
	SHY			

How would you best describe the gift and blessing of being able to be at peace with everything in the universe?

Journal entry

Weekly Random Act of Kindness: ______________________________

	DATE	ENERGY: 1-10	WEATHER	AFFIRMATION Watch all thy words. They are the creator, the preserver and the destroyer of thy destiny.
49				
50				

Haiku

no bold rain-cloud for
a hundred miles
around...dares
brave the peonies

–Busun

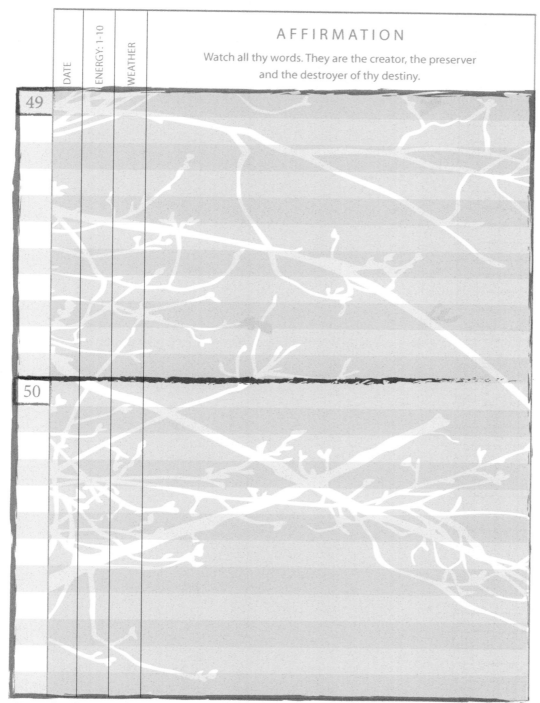

Hamsasya Mudra

Sukhasana

Use either the workbook question or journal entry to populate the COE on the opposite page

Spring

Workbook questions

ENTERED INTO THE MEI ___ JOURNAL ___ WORKBOOK ___

Chart of Emotions (COE)

Scale 1 - 10	Question or Journal Entry 51 / Experienced Emotions	Past	Present	Future
	JOY			
	LOVE			
	HOPE			
	TRUST			
	ADMIRATION			
	FEAR			
	WORRIED			
	HAPPY			
	CALM			
	SAD			
	RESENTFUL			
	GENEROUS			
	DISGUST			
	ANGER			
	GUILT			
	ENTHUSIASTIC			
	SHY			

Let's imagine that you were pure water. At times you would be as wet as water, as light as a gas or vapor, and, sometimes even frozen as a solid. Let's now say, just like water, you were able to freely move around the universe, but maintain all of your humanly senses. Now, imagine what it would feel like if that after two years of having been water, you'd want to share with others in this journal.

ENTERED INTO THE MEI ___ JOURNAL ___ WORKBOOK ___

Chart of Emotions (COE)

Scale 1 - 10	Question or Journal Entry 52 / Experienced Emotions	Past	Present	Future
	JOY			
	LOVE			
	HOPE			
	TRUST			
	ADMIRATION			
	FEAR			
	WORRIED			
	HAPPY			
	CALM			
	SAD			
	RESENTFUL			
	GENEROUS			
	DISGUST			
	ANGER			
	GUILT			
	ENTHUSIASTIC			
	SHY			

What elements are already contained within you for greater spiritual awareness?

Journal entry

Weekly Random Act of Kindness: ____________________

DATE	ENERGY: 1-10	WEATHER	AFFIRMATION Il know all plants and life of every form are this moment blessed by God's loving grace through me.
51			
52			

Use either the workbook question or journal entry to populate the COE on the opposite page

Haiku

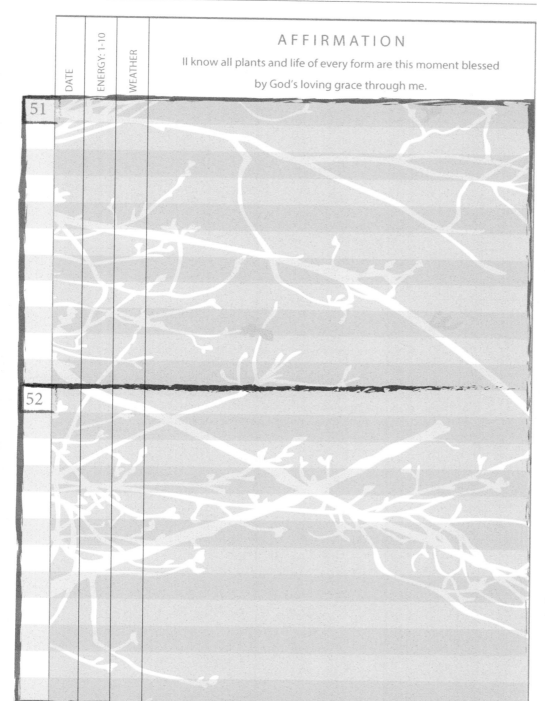

the first firefly...
but he got away
and i...
air in my fingers
-Issa

Hamsapaksa Mudra

Janu Sirsasana

Workbook questions

Chart of Emotions (COE)

ENTERED INTO THE MEI ___ JOURNAL ___ WORKBOOK ___

Scale 1 - 10	Question or Journal Entry 53 / Experienced Emotions	Past	Present	Future
	JOY			
	LOVE			
	HOPE			
	TRUST			
	ADMIRATION			
	FEAR			
	WORRIED			
	HAPPY			
	CALM			
	SAD			
	RESENTFUL			
	GENEROUS			
	DISGUST			
	ANGER			
	GUILT			
	ENTHUSIASTIC			
	SHY			

In what way has forgiveness played a role in your life? Give an example of having to forgive someone for something they did to you. How has that forgiveness set you free? What has that forgiveness done for them?

Chart of Emotions (COE)

ENTERED INTO THE MEI ___ JOURNAL ___ WORKBOOK ___

Scale 1 - 10	Question or Journal Entry 54 / Experienced Emotions	Past	Present	Future
	JOY			
	LOVE			
	HOPE			
	TRUST			
	ADMIRATION			
	FEAR			
	WORRIED			
	HAPPY			
	CALM			
	SAD			
	RESENTFUL			
	GENEROUS			
	DISGUST			
	ANGER			
	GUILT			
	ENTHUSIASTIC			
	SHY			

In a research study by Norman Cousins and UCLA, actors were called in to have their blood drawn. Immediately after, they were given an index card with a single emotion written on it. They then acted out that single emotion. After 20 minutes their blood was drawn for a second time. Research shows that negative emotions decreased the immune system while, positive emotions improved it. Please journal how you think out-of-balance emotions affect you:

Journal entry

Weekly Random Act of Kindness: ____________________

DATE	ENERGY: 1-10	WEATHER	AFFIRMATION All is good; there is no evil in God's loving eyes.
53			
54			

Haiku

with that new clothing
alas...spring
has been buried
in that wooden chest

–Saikaku

Kilaka Mudra

Marichyasana I

Use either the workbook question or journal entry to populate the COE on the opposite page

Workbook questions

Chart of Emotions (COE)

ENTERED INTO THE MEI ___ / JOURNAL ___ / WORKBOOK ___	Scale 1 - 10	Question or Journal Entry **55** / Experienced Emotions	Past	Present	Future
		JOY			
		LOVE			
		HOPE			
		TRUST			
		ADMIRATION			
		FEAR			
		WORRIED			
		HAPPY			
		CALM			
		SAD			
		RESENTFUL			
		GENEROUS			
		DISGUST			
		ANGER			
		GUILT			
		ENTHUSIASTIC			
		SHY			

Thoughts are subtle forms of energy. They are held and/or released into the ether at large. Is it possible that one person may pick up on the thoughts of another, and maybe even execute its very intention?
How do you release and let go of any negative thoughts in your life?

Chart of Emotions (COE)

ENTERED INTO THE MEI ___ / JOURNAL ___ / WORKBOOK ___	Scale 1 - 10	Question or Journal Entry **56** / Experienced Emotions	Past	Present	Future
		JOY			
		LOVE			
		HOPE			
		TRUST			
		ADMIRATION			
		FEAR			
		WORRIED			
		HAPPY			
		CALM			
		SAD			
		RESENTFUL			
		GENEROUS			
		DISGUST			
		ANGER			
		GUILT			
		ENTHUSIASTIC			
		SHY			

How mindfully aware are you in observing how other's habits and/or behaviors take root, even express themselves through you? Have you ever noticed another person's mannerism or peculiarity taking root or somehow expressing itself through you? Explain:

Journal entry

Weekly Random Act of Kindness: ______________________________

DATE	ENERGY: 1-10	WEATHER	AFFIRMATION You are beyond beginning and beyond end; you are the eternal life.
55			
56			

Use either the workbook question or journal entry to populate the COE on the opposite page

Haiku

an old tree was felled...
echoing,
dark echoing
thunder in the hills

–Meisetu

Bharmaram Mudra

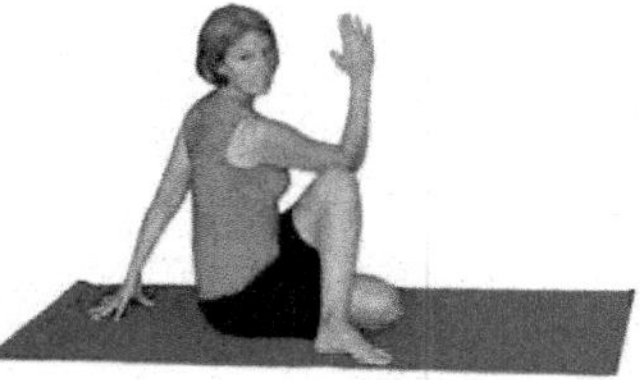

Marichyasana II Pose

Workbook questions

Chart of Emotions (COE)

Scale 1 - 10	Question or Journal Entry 57 / Experienced Emotions	Past	Present	Future
	JOY			
	LOVE			
	HOPE			
	TRUST			
	ADMIRATION			
	FEAR			
	WORRIED			
	HAPPY			
	CALM			
	SAD			
	RESENTFUL			
	GENEROUS			
	DISGUST			
	ANGER			
	GUILT			
	ENTHUSIASTIC			
	SHY			

ENTERED INTO THE MEI___ JOURNAL___ WORKBOOK___

If money were no issue at all in your life, how do you think you'd live your life differently? Please explain:

Chart of Emotions (COE)

Scale 1 - 10	Question or Journal Entry 58 / Experienced Emotions	Past	Present	Future
	JOY			
	LOVE			
	HOPE			
	TRUST			
	ADMIRATION			
	FEAR			
	WORRIED			
	HAPPY			
	CALM			
	SAD			
	RESENTFUL			
	GENEROUS			
	DISGUST			
	ANGER			
	GUILT			
	ENTHUSIASTIC			
	SHY			

ENTERED INTO THE MEI___ JOURNAL___ WORKBOOK___

How accepting do you think you'd be if you could foresee your death? What does that mean to you here and now?

Journal entry

Weekly Random Act of Kindness: ______________________________

DATE	ENERGY: 1-10	WEATHER	AFFIRMATION I am as weak as my weakest link, but I will never forget that I am as strong as my strongest.
57			
58			

Use either the workbook question or journal entry to populate the COE on the opposite page

Haiku

rainy afternoon...
little daughter
you will never
teach that cat to dance

-Issa

Katakamukha Mudra

Parivrtta Prasarita Podattonasana

4♣

Summer

Workbook questions

Chart of Emotions (COE)

ENTERED INTO THE MEI ___

JOURNAL ___

WORKBOOK ___

Scale 1 - 10	Question or Journal Entry **59** / Experienced Emotions	Past	Present	Future
	JOY			
	LOVE			
	HOPE			
	TRUST			
	ADMIRATION			
	FEAR			
	WORRIED			
	HAPPY			
	CALM			
	SAD			
	RESENTFUL			
	GENEROUS			
	DISGUST			
	ANGER			
	GUILT			
	ENTHUSIASTIC			
	SHY			

Please write and develop a mission statement as to what Life is to you:

Journal entry

Weekly Random Act of Kindness: ______________________

DATE	ENERGY: 1-10	WEATHER	AFFIRMATION Wherever there is God, there is beauty, and God is everywhere.
59			

Haiku

squads of frogs jumped in
when they heard the
plaunk-plash
of a single frog

–Wakyu

Ganesha Mudra

Gumakasana

Use either the workbook question or journal entry to populate the COE on the opposite page

Workbook questions

ENTERED INTO THE MEI ___ JOURNAL ___ WORKBOOK ___

Chart of Emotions (COE)

Scale 1 - 10	Question or Journal Entry 60 / Experienced Emotions	Past	Present	Future
	JOY			
	LOVE			
	HOPE			
	TRUST			
	ADMIRATION			
	FEAR			
	WORRIED			
	HAPPY			
	CALM			
	SAD			
	RESENTFUL			
	GENEROUS			
	DISGUST			
	ANGER			
	GUILT			
	ENTHUSIASTIC			
	SHY			

List five things that you absolutely love about your life. What have you recently done to support what it is that you love?

1-

2-

3-

4-

5-

ENTERED INTO THE MEI ___ JOURNAL ___ WORKBOOK ___

Chart of Emotions (COE)

Scale 1 - 10	Question or Journal Entry 61 / Experienced Emotions	Past	Present	Future
	JOY			
	LOVE			
	HOPE			
	TRUST			
	ADMIRATION			
	FEAR			
	WORRIED			
	HAPPY			
	CALM			
	SAD			
	RESENTFUL			
	GENEROUS			
	DISGUST			
	ANGER			
	GUILT			
	ENTHUSIASTIC			
	SHY			

If there were just one day that you could eliminate or erase from your life, which day would that be? In what way has that day benefited you?

Journal entry

Weekly Random Act of Kindness: ______________________________

DATE	ENERGY: 1-10	WEATHER	AFFIRMATION See beauty in seeming ugliness.
60			
61			

Use either the workbook question or journal entry to populate the COE on the opposite page

Haiku

moon-in-the-water
turned a white
sumersault...yes and
went floating off

–Ryota

Makara Mudra

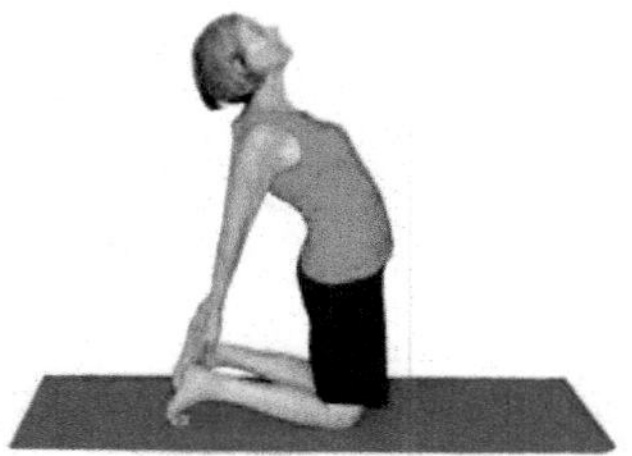

Ustrasana

Workbook questions

Chart of Emotions (COE)

ENTERED INTO THE MEI ___ JOURNAL ___ WORKBOOK ___

Scale 1 - 10	Question or Journal Entry **62** Experienced Emotions	Past	Present	Future
	JOY			
	LOVE			
	HOPE			
	TRUST			
	ADMIRATION			
	FEAR			
	WORRIED			
	HAPPY			
	CALM			
	SAD			
	RESENTFUL			
	GENEROUS			
	DISGUST			
	ANGER			
	GUILT			
	ENTHUSIASTIC			
	SHY			

At this part of my life, one of my greatest strengths can best be described as:

Chart of Emotions (COE)

ENTERED INTO THE MEI ___ JOURNAL ___ WORKBOOK ___

Scale 1 - 10	Question or Journal Entry **63** Experienced Emotions	Past	Present	Future
	JOY			
	LOVE			
	HOPE			
	TRUST			
	ADMIRATION			
	FEAR			
	WORRIED			
	HAPPY			
	CALM			
	SAD			
	RESENTFUL			
	GENEROUS			
	DISGUST			
	ANGER			
	GUILT			
	ENTHUSIASTIC			
	SHY			

What do you think you would learn about yourself were you suddenly transplanted to live in an entirely different culture?

Journal entry

Weekly Random Act of Kindness: ______________________

DATE	ENERGY: 1-10	WEATHER	AFFIRMATION God moves and has his/her being in every living creature.
62			
63			

Use either the workbook question or journal entry to populate the COE on the opposite page

Haiku

windy-web spider
what is your
silent speaking...
your unsung song

–Basho

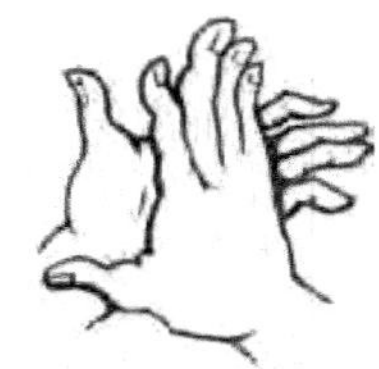

Cakra
Mudra

Eka Pada
Kapotasana

Workbook questions

Chart of Emotions (COE)

ENTERED INTO THE MEI ___ / JOURNAL ___ / WORKBOOK ___	Scale 1 - 10	Question or Journal Entry **64** Experienced Emotions	Past	Present	Future
		JOY			
		LOVE			
		HOPE			
		TRUST			
		ADMIRATION			
		FEAR			
		WORRIED			
		HAPPY			
		CALM			
		SAD			
		RESENTFUL			
		GENEROUS			
		DISGUST			
		ANGER			
		GUILT			
		ENTHUSIASTIC			
		SHY			

One hundred years from now, how do you think the world will have been changed or affected by your life?

Chart of Emotions (COE)

ENTERED INTO THE MEI ___ / JOURNAL ___ / WORKBOOK ___	Scale 1 - 10	Question or Journal Entry **65** Experienced Emotions	Past	Present	Future
		JOY			
		LOVE			
		HOPE			
		TRUST			
		ADMIRATION			
		FEAR			
		WORRIED			
		HAPPY			
		CALM			
		SAD			
		RESENTFUL			
		GENEROUS			
		DISGUST			
		ANGER			
		GUILT			
		ENTHUSIASTIC			
		SHY			

How can you learn to create new meaning in the otherwise everyday, mundane things you do? Please explain:

Journal entry

Weekly Random Act of Kindness: ______________________________

7♣

Summer 7♣

DATE	ENERGY: 1-10	WEATHER	AFFIRMATION You are as great as you think you are.
64			
65			

Use either the workbook question or journal entry to populate the COE on the opposite page

Haiku

experimenting ....
i hung the moon
on various
branches of the pine

–Hokushi

Nagabandha Mudra

Chaturanga Dandasana

Workbook questions

Chart of Emotions (COE)

ENTERED INTO THE MEI ___ / JOURNAL ___ / WORKBOOK ___	Scale 1 - 10	Question or Journal Entry **66** / Experienced Emotions	Past	Present	Future
		JOY			
		LOVE			
		HOPE			
		TRUST			
		ADMIRATION			
		FEAR			
		WORRIED			
		HAPPY			
		CALM			
		SAD			
		RESENTFUL			
		GENEROUS			
		DISGUST			
		ANGER			
		GUILT			
		ENTHUSIASTIC			
		SHY			

When your mind is clear, centered and focused, how would you describe the state of your emotions? What elements help create this mindset?

Chart of Emotions (COE)

ENTERED INTO THE MEI ___ / JOURNAL ___ / WORKBOOK ___	Scale 1 - 10	Question or Journal Entry **67** / Experienced Emotions	Past	Present	Future
		JOY			
		LOVE			
		HOPE			
		TRUST			
		ADMIRATION			
		FEAR			
		WORRIED			
		HAPPY			
		CALM			
		SAD			
		RESENTFUL			
		GENEROUS			
		DISGUST			
		ANGER			
		GUILT			
		ENTHUSIASTIC			
		SHY			

When your mind is NOT clear, centered and focused, how would you describe the state of your emotions? What elements help create this mind-set?

Journal entry

Weekly Random Act of Kindness: ______________________________

DATE	ENERGY: 1-10	WEATHER	AFFIRMATION God is the one and only that has the right to judge right or wrong. He and He alone can see the great plan.
66			
67			

Use either the workbook question or journal entry to populate the COE on the opposite page

Haiku

on his garden path
this sparrow
scatters pebbles...
man forgotten

-Shoha

Simhamukha Mudra

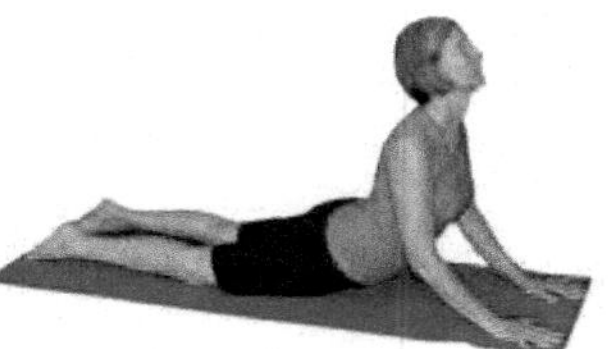

Urdvha Mukha Svanasana

Workbook questions

Chart of Emotions (COE)

ENTERED INTO THE MEI___ JOURNAL___ WORKBOOK___

Scale 1 - 10	Question or Journal Entry **68** / Experienced Emotions	Past	Present	Future
	JOY			
	LOVE			
	HOPE			
	TRUST			
	ADMIRATION			
	FEAR			
	WORRIED			
	HAPPY			
	CALM			
	SAD			
	RESENTFUL			
	GENEROUS			
	DISGUST			
	ANGER			
	GUILT			
	ENTHUSIASTIC			
	SHY			

Sit comfortably for 15 minutes and repeat this mantra 108 times: "Om Namha Shivaha." How did this practice make you feel? Please explain:

Chart of Emotions (COE)

ENTERED INTO THE MEI___ JOURNAL___ WORKBOOK___

Scale 1 - 10	Question or Journal Entry **69** / Experienced Emotions	Past	Present	Future
	JOY			
	LOVE			
	HOPE			
	TRUST			
	ADMIRATION			
	FEAR			
	WORRIED			
	HAPPY			
	CALM			
	SAD			
	RESENTFUL			
	GENEROUS			
	DISGUST			
	ANGER			
	GUILT			
	ENTHUSIASTIC			
	SHY			

Can feelings of being unconditionally loved and accepted be felt without ever having used (or heard) words to express it?

Journal entry

Weekly Random Act of Kindness: ______________________________

DATE	ENERGY: 1-10	WEATHER	AFFIRMATION May every creature great and small be free from pain, anguish, despair and death.
68			
69			

Use either the workbook question or journal entry to populate the COE on the opposite page

Haiku

sad twilight cricket...
yes, i have wasted
once again
those daylight hours

–Kikaku

Tripataka Mudra

Paripur na Navasana

Workbook questions

ENTERED INTO THE MEI ___ JOURNAL ___ WORKBOOK ___

Chart of Emotions (COE)

Scale 1 - 10	Question or Journal Entry 70 / Experienced Emotions	Past	Present	Future
	JOY			
	LOVE			
	HOPE			
	TRUST			
	ADMIRATION			
	FEAR			
	WORRIED			
	HAPPY			
	CALM			
	SAD			
	RESENTFUL			
	GENEROUS			
	DISGUST			
	ANGER			
	GUILT			
	ENTHUSIASTIC			
	SHY			

If you were able to create an internationally recognized holiday, what would it be and why would you want it to exist?

ENTERED INTO THE MEI ___ JOURNAL ___ WORKBOOK ___

Chart of Emotions (COE)

Scale 1 - 10	Question or Journal Entry 71 / Experienced Emotions	Past	Present	Future
	JOY			
	LOVE			
	HOPE			
	TRUST			
	ADMIRATION			
	FEAR			
	WORRIED			
	HAPPY			
	CALM			
	SAD			
	RESENTFUL			
	GENEROUS			
	DISGUST			
	ANGER			
	GUILT			
	ENTHUSIASTIC			
	SHY			

Have you ever been so deep into a yoga pose that you actually found a hidden mind-body connection?

Journal entry

Weekly Random Act of Kindness: ______________________________

DATE	ENERGY: 1-10	WEATHER	AFFIRMATION The only truly wise person is one who feels him- or herself one with Nature.
70			
71			

Use either the workbook question or journal entry to populate the COE on the opposite page

Haiku

the night was hot...
stripped to the waist
the snail
enjoyed the moonlight

-Issa

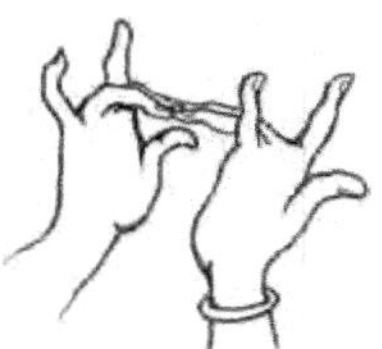

Khatva Mudra

Bharadvajasana

J♣

Summer

Workbook questions

Chart of Emotions (COE)

ENTERED INTO THE MEI___ / JOURNAL___ / WORKBOOK___	Scale 1 - 10	Question or Journal Entry **72** / Experienced Emotions	Past	Present	Future
		JOY			
		LOVE			
		HOPE			
		TRUST			
		ADMIRATION			
		FEAR			
		WORRIED			
		HAPPY			
		CALM			
		SAD			
		RESENTFUL			
		GENEROUS			
		DISGUST			
		ANGER			
		GUILT			
		ENTHUSIASTIC			
		SHY			

Please name one person with whom you have had a falling out, and have consequently severed that relationship. How might you respond differently to that or a similar situation today? Explain the falling out and what you've learned from it.

Chart of Emotions (COE)

ENTERED INTO THE MEI___ / JOURNAL___ / WORKBOOK___	Scale 1 - 10	Question or Journal Entry **73** / Experienced Emotions	Past	Present	Future
		JOY			
		LOVE			
		HOPE			
		TRUST			
		ADMIRATION			
		FEAR			
		WORRIED			
		HAPPY			
		CALM			
		SAD			
		RESENTFUL			
		GENEROUS			
		DISGUST			
		ANGER			
		GUILT			
		ENTHUSIASTIC			
		SHY			

In what ways might your deep-rooted beliefs be holding you back from advancing yourself forward in the world?

Journal entry

Weekly Random Act of Kindness: ______________________________

DATE	ENERGY: 1-10	WEATHER	AFFIRMATION Love is the joy of sharing others' joyous times, of taking half their burdens on your back and pushing with them until the last steep climb on the road of life is conquered.
72			
73			

Use either the workbook question or journal entry to populate the COE on the opposite page

Haiku

with the new clothes
remember... the
crow stays black
and the heron white

—Chora

Sakata Mudra

Yoga Mudra

Workbook questions

Summer

ENTERED INTO THE MEI___ JOURNAL___ WORKBOOK___

Chart of Emotions (COE)

Scale 1 - 10	Question or Journal Entry 74 / Experienced Emotions	Past	Present	Future
	JOY			
	LOVE			
	HOPE			
	TRUST			
	ADMIRATION			
	FEAR			
	WORRIED			
	HAPPY			
	CALM			
	SAD			
	RESENTFUL			
	GENEROUS			
	DISGUST			
	ANGER			
	GUILT			
	ENTHUSIASTIC			
	SHY			

The word fear is an acronym:
False. Experiences. Acting. Real.
In what way does fear play a role in your life?

ENTERED INTO THE MEI___ JOURNAL___ WORKBOOK___

Chart of Emotions (COE)

Scale 1 - 10	Question or Journal Entry 75 / Experienced Emotions	Past	Present	Future
	JOY			
	LOVE			
	HOPE			
	TRUST			
	ADMIRATION			
	FEAR			
	WORRIED			
	HAPPY			
	CALM			
	SAD			
	RESENTFUL			
	GENEROUS			
	DISGUST			
	ANGER			
	GUILT			
	ENTHUSIASTIC			
	SHY			

This is an exercise in what is called idiokinetic visualization. Sit comfortably, take five full minutes to visualize yourself doing a single yoga pose. Be as detailed as possible in you efforts. Please journal your experience.

Journal entry

Weekly Random Act of Kindness: ___

DATE	ENERGY: 1-10	WEATHER	AFFIRMATION Vibrations of nature are the very keystone of my heart-felt being
74			
75			

Haiku

a summer shower...
along all the
street, servants
slapping shut shutters

–Shiki

Puspaputa Mudra

Supta Matsyandrasana

Use either the workbook question or journal entry to populate the COE on the opposite page

K♣

Workbook questions

Summer

Chart of Emotions (COE)

ENTERED INTO THE MEI ___ JOURNAL ___ WORKBOOK ___

Scale 1 - 10	Question or Journal Entry / Experienced Emotions	Past	Present	Future
	JOY			
	LOVE			
	HOPE			
	TRUST			
	ADMIRATION			
	FEAR			
	WORRIED			
	HAPPY			
	CALM			
	SAD			
	RESENTFUL			
	GENEROUS			
	DISGUST			
	ANGER			
	GUILT			
	ENTHUSIASTIC			
	SHY			

If possible, get a photograph of yourself from between the ages of five to eight. Become very relaxed and look deep into the face of the photo. Imagine what you were like at that age. What are the common denominators of who you were then and who you are now? Does the same element of your soul speak to you? Is there a creative connection? Please spend an ample amount of time contemplating this exercise. Journal your results.

Journal entry

Weekly Random Act of Kindness:

DATE	ENERGY: 1-10	WEATHER	AFFIRMATION Don't stop the source of supply by hoarding and thoughts of greed.

76

Haiku

suddenly you light
and as suddenly
go dark...
fellow firefly

–Chine

Arala
Mudra

Dandayamana
Ardha Chandrasana

Use either the workbook question or journal entry to populate the COE on the opposite page

Workbook questions

Chart of Emotions (COE)

ENTERED INTO THE MEI ___ JOURNAL ___ WORKBOOK ___

Scale 1 - 10	Question or Journal Entry **77** / Experienced Emotions	Past	Present	Future
	JOY			
	LOVE			
	HOPE			
	TRUST			
	ADMIRATION			
	FEAR			
	WORRIED			
	HAPPY			
	CALM			
	SAD			
	RESENTFUL			
	GENEROUS			
	DISGUST			
	ANGER			
	GUILT			
	ENTHUSIASTIC			
	SHY			

In what areas of your life are you too confident or, conversely, not confident enough? Please explain:

Chart of Emotions (COE)

ENTERED INTO THE MEI ___ JOURNAL ___ WORKBOOK ___

Scale 1 - 10	Question or Journal Entry **78** / Experienced Emotions	Past	Present	Future
	JOY			
	LOVE			
	HOPE			
	TRUST			
	ADMIRATION			
	FEAR			
	WORRIED			
	HAPPY			
	CALM			
	SAD			
	RESENTFUL			
	GENEROUS			
	DISGUST			
	ANGER			
	GUILT			
	ENTHUSIASTIC			
	SHY			

The unconscious mind really has no concept of time. What do you think your life would be like if all the parts and pieces of who you are were randomly rearranged? What do you think the overall picture would look like?

Journal entry

Weekly Random Act of Kindness: ______________________________

DATE	ENERGY: 1-10	WEATHER	AFFIRMATION Self-deprecation is a path running fast downhill into the valley of failure and despair.
77			
78			

Haiku

again coolness comes...
silver undersides
of leaves
evening-breeze blown

–Shiki

Catura Mudra

Garhbasana

Use either the workbook question or journal entry to populate the COE on the opposite page

Workbook questions

ENTERED INTO THE MEI ___

JOURNAL ___

WORKBOOK ___

Chart of Emotions (COE)

Scale 1 - 10	Question or Journal Entry **79** / Experienced Emotions	Past	Present	Future
	JOY			
	LOVE			
	HOPE			
	TRUST			
	ADMIRATION			
	FEAR			
	WORRIED			
	HAPPY			
	CALM			
	SAD			
	RESENTFUL			
	GENEROUS			
	DISGUST			
	ANGER			
	GUILT			
	ENTHUSIASTIC			
	SHY			

Think about some conflict in your life right now. Through the process of journaling, how might you find more resolve?

ENTERED INTO THE MEI ___

JOURNAL ___

WORKBOOK ___

Chart of Emotions (COE)

Scale 1 - 10	Question or Journal Entry **80** / Experienced Emotions	Past	Present	Future
	JOY			
	LOVE			
	HOPE			
	TRUST			
	ADMIRATION			
	FEAR			
	WORRIED			
	HAPPY			
	CALM			
	SAD			
	RESENTFUL			
	GENEROUS			
	DISGUST			
	ANGER			
	GUILT			
	ENTHUSIASTIC			
	SHY			

When you are in the presence of children, how do you think they think and feel about you?

Journal entry

Weekly Random Act of Kindness: ____________________

DATE	ENERGY: 1-10	WEATHER	AFFIRMATION When the dawn of light floods our heart with its beauty, all else fades into nothingness.
79			
80			

Use either the workbook question or journal entry to populate the COE on the opposite page

Haiku

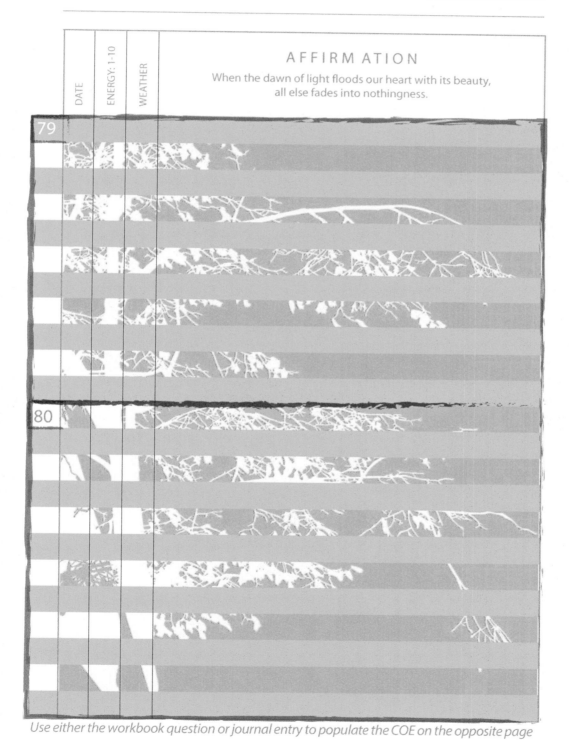

we stand still to hear
tinkle of far
temple bell...
willow-leaves fallen

–Basho

Sivalinga Mudra

Virasana

Workbook questions

ENTERED INTO THE MEI ___ JOURNAL ___ WORKBOOK ___

Chart of Emotions (COE)

Scale 1 - 10	Question or Journal Entry **81** / Experienced Emotions	Past	Present	Future
	JOY			
	LOVE			
	HOPE			
	TRUST			
	ADMIRATION			
	FEAR			
	WORRIED			
	HAPPY			
	CALM			
	SAD			
	RESENTFUL			
	GENEROUS			
	DISGUST			
	ANGER			
	GUILT			
	ENTHUSIASTIC			
	SHY			

What images run through your mind? Describe a common recurring thought (or thought process) that always seems to work through your mind:

ENTERED INTO THE MEI ___ JOURNAL ___ WORKBOOK ___

Chart of Emotions (COE)

Scale 1 - 10	Question or Journal Entry **82** / Experienced Emotions	Past	Present	Future
	JOY			
	LOVE			
	HOPE			
	TRUST			
	ADMIRATION			
	FEAR			
	WORRIED			
	HAPPY			
	CALM			
	SAD			
	RESENTFUL			
	GENEROUS			
	DISGUST			
	ANGER			
	GUILT			
	ENTHUSIASTIC			
	SHY			

In this moment when I close my eyes to center myself, the colors and feelings within me can best be described as having this kind of effect on me:

Journal entry

Weekly Random Act of Kindness: ______________________________

DATE	ENERGY: 1-10	WEATHER	AFFIRMATION You make the destiny which you fear.
81			
82			

Use either the workbook question or journal entry to populate the COE on the opposite page

Haiku

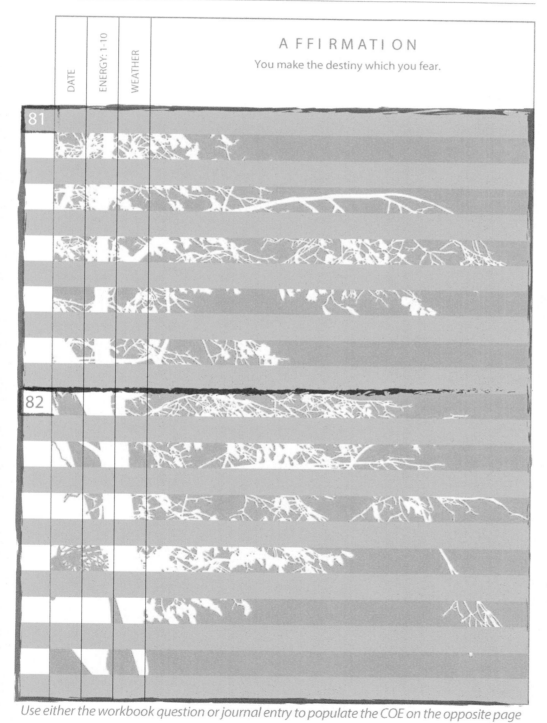

night long in the cold
that monkey sits
conjecturing
how to catch the moon

–Shiki

Sarpasirsa Mudra

Salambhasana

Workbook questions

Fall

Chart of Emotions (COE)

ENTERED INTO THE MEI___ JOURNAL___ WORKBOOK___

Scale 1 - 10	Question or Journal Entry 83 Experienced Emotions	Past	Present	Future
	JOY			
	LOVE			
	HOPE			
	TRUST			
	ADMIRATION			
	FEAR			
	WORRIED			
	HAPPY			
	CALM			
	SAD			
	RESENTFUL			
	GENEROUS			
	DISGUST			
	ANGER			
	GUILT			
	ENTHUSIASTIC			
	SHY			

If I were a tree, I would describe the roots of my existence as:

Chart of Emotions (COE)

ENTERED INTO THE MEI___ JOURNAL___ WORKBOOK___

Scale 1 - 10	Question or Journal Entry 84 Experienced Emotions	Past	Present	Future
	JOY			
	LOVE			
	HOPE			
	TRUST			
	ADMIRATION			
	FEAR			
	WORRIED			
	HAPPY			
	CALM			
	SAD			
	RESENTFUL			
	GENEROUS			
	DISGUST			
	ANGER			
	GUILT			
	ENTHUSIASTIC			
	SHY			

If I were a tree, I would like my trunk to consists of:

Journal entry

Weekly Random Act of Kindness: ______________________

DATE	ENERGY: 1-10	WEATHER	AFFIRMATION Know and feel the joy of living a consecrated life of giving as an open channel to God's gifts.
83			
84			

Use either the workbook question or journal entry to populate the COE on the opposite page

Haiku

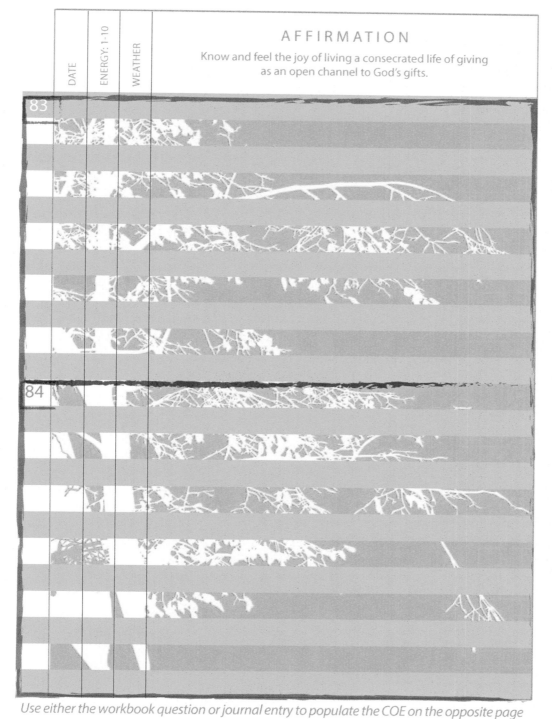

supper in autumn
flat light through
an open door
from a setting sun

—Chora

Kapitta
Mudra

Setu
Bhandasana

Workbook questions

Chart of Emotions (COE)

Scale 1 - 10	Question or Journal Entry 85 / Experienced Emotions	Past	Present	Future
	JOY			
	LOVE			
	HOPE			
	TRUST			
	ADMIRATION			
	FEAR			
	WORRIED			
	HAPPY			
	CALM			
	SAD			
	RESENTFUL			
	GENEROUS			
	DISGUST			
	ANGER			
	GUILT			
	ENTHUSIASTIC			
	SHY			

ENTERED INTO THE MEI ___ JOURNAL ___ WORKBOOK ___

If I were a tree, my limbs and branches would:

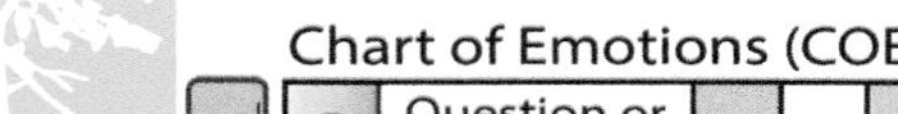

Chart of Emotions (COE)

Scale 1 - 10	Question or Journal Entry 86 / Experienced Emotions	Past	Present	Future
	JOY			
	LOVE			
	HOPE			
	TRUST			
	ADMIRATION			
	FEAR			
	WORRIED			
	HAPPY			
	CALM			
	SAD			
	RESENTFUL			
	GENEROUS			
	DISGUST			
	ANGER			
	GUILT			
	ENTHUSIASTIC			
	SHY			

ENTERED INTO THE MEI ___ JOURNAL ___ WORKBOOK ___

If I were a tree, the "fruit" I would bear could be described as tasting like and having this kind of effect on me and everyone else:

Journal entry

Weekly Random Act of Kindness: ______________________________

DATE	ENERGY: 1-10	WEATHER	AFFIRMATION See God in everything; then separateness falls off, leaving only light.
85			
86			

Haiku

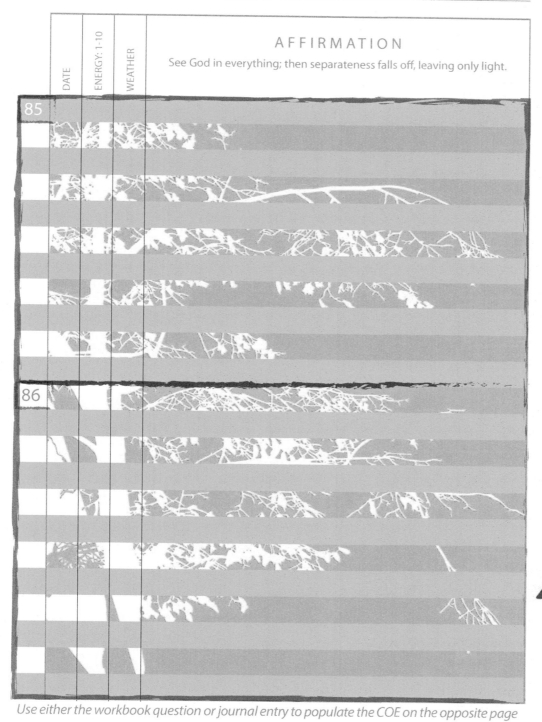

on a leafless bough
a crow is perched
the Autumn dusk

-Basho

Mahasir Mudra

Halasana

Use either the workbook question or journal entry to populate the COE on the opposite page

Workbook questions

Chart of Emotions (COE)

ENTERED INTO THE MEI ___ JOURNAL ___ WORKBOOK ___

Scale 1 - 10	Question or Journal Entry **87** / Experienced Emotions	Past	Present	Future
	JOY			
	LOVE			
	HOPE			
	TRUST			
	ADMIRATION			
	FEAR			
	WORRIED			
	HAPPY			
	CALM			
	SAD			
	RESENTFUL			
	GENEROUS			
	DISGUST			
	ANGER			
	GUILT			
	ENTHUSIASTIC			
	SHY			

You know that you have the ability to end any habit, but is there any one habit that seems almost impossible to get rid of? Please explain:

Chart of Emotions (COE)

ENTERED INTO THE MEI ___ JOURNAL ___ WORKBOOK ___

Scale 1 - 10	Question or Journal Entry **88** / Experienced Emotions	Past	Present	Future
	JOY			
	LOVE			
	HOPE			
	TRUST			
	ADMIRATION			
	FEAR			
	WORRIED			
	HAPPY			
	CALM			
	SAD			
	RESENTFUL			
	GENEROUS			
	DISGUST			
	ANGER			
	GUILT			
	ENTHUSIASTIC			
	SHY			

In life, we sometimes learn or find out things about other people we would never have otherwise believed. Is there anything about you that you think other people would never believe?

Journal entry

Weekly Random Act of Kindness: ____________________

DATE	ENERGY: 1-10	WEATHER	AFFIRMATION Fear is a monster killing all true godliness.
87			
88			

Haiku

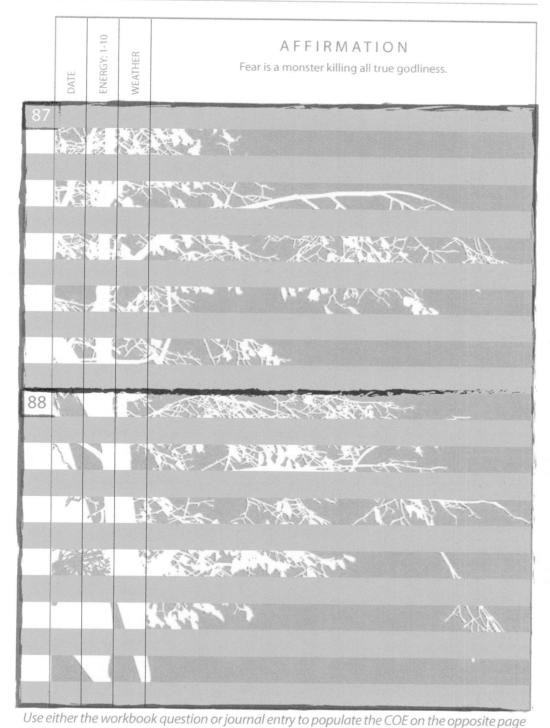

a windblown grass...
hovering mid-air
in vain
an autumn dragonfly

–Basho

Mukalam Mudra

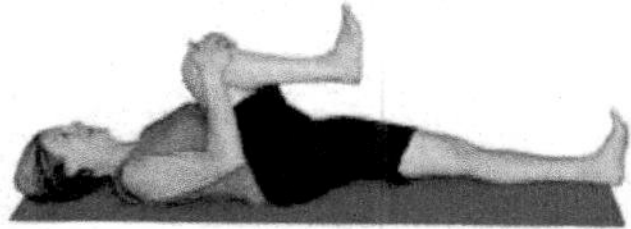

Pawan Muktasana

Use either the workbook question or journal entry to populate the COE on the opposite page

Workbook questions

Chart of Emotions (COE)

ENTERED INTO THE MEI ___ JOURNAL ___ WORKBOOK ___

Scale 1 - 10	Question or Journal Entry **89** / Experienced Emotions	Past	Present	Future
	JOY			
	LOVE			
	HOPE			
	TRUST			
	ADMIRATION			
	FEAR			
	WORRIED			
	HAPPY			
	CALM			
	SAD			
	RESENTFUL			
	GENEROUS			
	DISGUST			
	ANGER			
	GUILT			
	ENTHUSIASTIC			
	SHY			

Gather one raisin or one nut of some sort. Find a quiet and comfortable place to sit. Carefully examine the physical characteristics of the raisin or nut and then feel and observe the texture and temperature. Hold it in your left hand and feel the quantum vibration. Put it in your mouth and again feel its texture and temperature with your tongue and mouth. Take one bite and then stop. Repeat by taking one bite every 30 seconds or so until the nut or raisin has completely melted into liquid form. You should not have anything physical to swallow. The raisin or nut completely dissolves with the saliva of the mouth. Once dissolved, feel its pranic energy radiating throughout your body. What was this experience like for you?

Chart of Emotions (COE)

ENTERED INTO THE MEI ___ JOURNAL ___ WORKBOOK ___

Scale 1 - 10	Question or Journal Entry **90** / Experienced Emotions	Past	Present	Future
	JOY			
	LOVE			
	HOPE			
	TRUST			
	ADMIRATION			
	FEAR			
	WORRIED			
	HAPPY			
	CALM			
	SAD			
	RESENTFUL			
	GENEROUS			
	DISGUST			
	ANGER			
	GUILT			
	ENTHUSIASTIC			
	SHY			

In what way, if any, has your religion and/or nature helped to make you the beautiful person you are today?

Journal entry

Weekly Random Act of Kindness: ____________________

DATE	ENERGY: 1-10	WEATHER	AFFIRMATION Find God and you have found the source of all supply.
89			
90			

Haiku

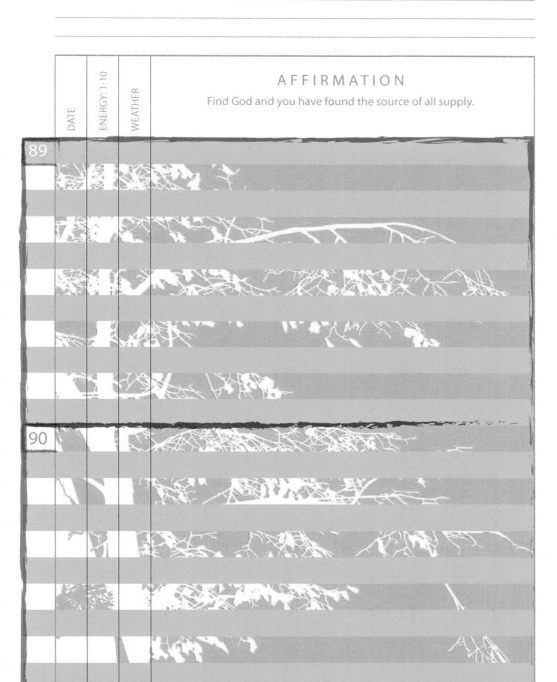

now the old scarecrow
looks just like
other people...
drenching autumn rain

–Seibi

Sukatunda Mudra

Viparita Karani

Use either the workbook question or journal entry to populate the COE on the opposite page

Workbook questions

ENTERED INTO THE MEI ___ JOURNAL ___ WORKBOOK ___

Chart of Emotions (COE)

Scale 1 - 10	Question or Journal Entry **91** / Experienced Emotions	Past	Present	Future
	JOY			
	LOVE			
	HOPE			
	TRUST			
	ADMIRATION			
	FEAR			
	WORRIED			
	HAPPY			
	CALM			
	SAD			
	RESENTFUL			
	GENEROUS			
	DISGUST			
	ANGER			
	GUILT			
	ENTHUSIASTIC			
	SHY			

If you could write a letter to one person with whom you have experienced conflict, but never worked it out who would that person be, and what would you say? (Please see the *Unsaid Things exercise on page 155).*

ENTERED INTO THE MEI ___ JOURNAL ___ WORKBOOK ___

Chart of Emotions (COE)

Scale 1 - 10	Question or Journal Entry **92** / Experienced Emotions	Past	Present	Future
	JOY			
	LOVE			
	HOPE			
	TRUST			
	ADMIRATION			
	FEAR			
	WORRIED			
	HAPPY			
	CALM			
	SAD			
	RESENTFUL			
	GENEROUS			
	DISGUST			
	ANGER			
	GUILT			
	ENTHUSIASTIC			
	SHY			

Sometimes our most painful experiences can yield unexpected benefits. One such experience can best be described as:

Journal entry

Weekly Random Act of Kindness: ____________________

DATE	ENERGY: 1-10	WEATHER	AFFIRMATION Oh, what joy to feel the vibrant pulsating life of God throbbing through the universe and through you in joyous ecstasy.
91			
92			

Haiku

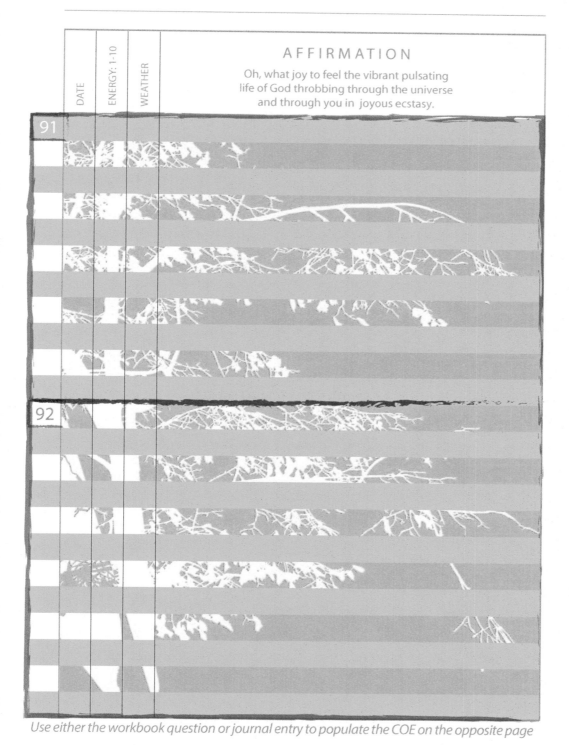

here is the dark tree
denuded now
of leafage...
but a million stars

—Seibi

Kurma Mudra

Sarvangasana

Use either the workbook question or journal entry to populate the COE on the opposite page

Workbook questions

Chart of Emotions (COE)

ENTERED INTO THE MEI ___ JOURNAL ___ WORKBOOK ___

Scale 1 - 10	Question or Journal Entry 93 / Experienced Emotions	Past	Present	Future
	JOY			
	LOVE			
	HOPE			
	TRUST			
	ADMIRATION			
	FEAR			
	WORRIED			
	HAPPY			
	CALM			
	SAD			
	RESENTFUL			
	GENEROUS			
	DISGUST			
	ANGER			
	GUILT			
	ENTHUSIASTIC			
	SHY			

When it comes to being confronted with conflict, this is how I see myself evolving:

Chart of Emotions (COE)

ENTERED INTO THE MEI ___ JOURNAL ___ WORKBOOK ___

Scale 1 - 10	Question or Journal Entry 94 / Experienced Emotions	Past	Present	Future
	JOY			
	LOVE			
	HOPE			
	TRUST			
	ADMIRATION			
	FEAR			
	WORRIED			
	HAPPY			
	CALM			
	SAD			
	RESENTFUL			
	GENEROUS			
	DISGUST			
	ANGER			
	GUILT			
	ENTHUSIASTIC			
	SHY			

Of the many gifts in your life, which do you hold in high esteem? Please explain:

Journal entry

Weekly Random Act of Kindness: ______________________________

DATE	ENERGY: 1-10	WEATHER	AFFIRMATION In the power of the tongue lies life and death.
93			
94			

Use either the workbook question or journal entry to populate the COE on the opposite page

Haiku

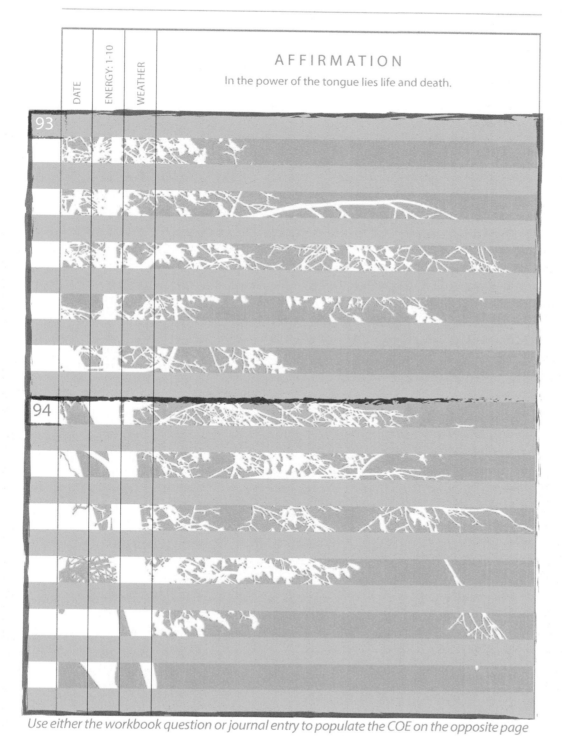

white chrysanthemums
making all else
about them
reflected riches

—Chora

Samputa Mudra

Vashistasana

Workbook questions

Chart of Emotions (COE)

ENTERED INTO THE MEI ___ JOURNAL ___ WORKBOOK ___

Scale 1 - 10	Question or Journal Entry **95** / Experienced Emotions	Past	Present	Future
	JOY			
	LOVE			
	HOPE			
	TRUST			
	ADMIRATION			
	FEAR			
	WORRIED			
	HAPPY			
	CALM			
	SAD			
	RESENTFUL			
	GENEROUS			
	DISGUST			
	ANGER			
	GUILT			
	ENTHUSIASTIC			
	SHY			

If it is true that we attract thoughts, people and animals into our lives, how have these attractions impacted your life? Please explain.

Chart of Emotions (COE)

ENTERED INTO THE MEI ___ JOURNAL ___ WORKBOOK ___

Scale 1 - 10	Question or Journal Entry **96** / Experienced Emotions	Past	Present	Future
	JOY			
	LOVE			
	HOPE			
	TRUST			
	ADMIRATION			
	FEAR			
	WORRIED			
	HAPPY			
	CALM			
	SAD			
	RESENTFUL			
	GENEROUS			
	DISGUST			
	ANGER			
	GUILT			
	ENTHUSIASTIC			
	SHY			

Many of the things we perceive in life are nothing more than our own projections. One example of this might be:

Journal entry

Weekly Random Act of Kindness: ______________________________

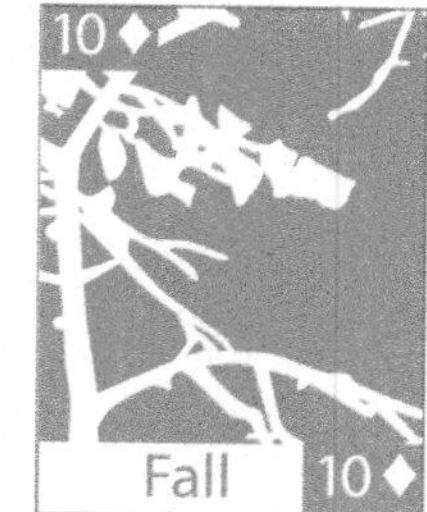

DATE	ENERGY: 1-10	WEATHER	AFFIRMATION Opulence is God's will for humans. Have faith in God's abundant supply.
95			
96			

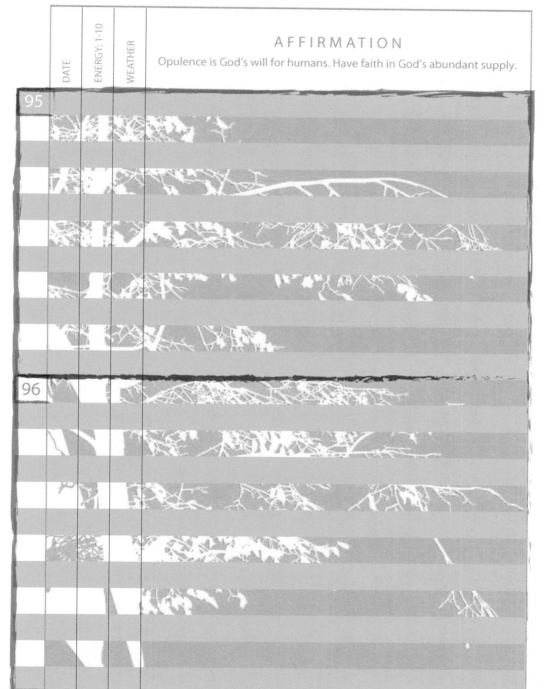

Use either the workbook question or journal entry to populate the COE on the opposite page

Haiku

from the temple steps
i lift to the
autumn moon
my veritable face
–Basho

Mayura Mudra

Urdvha Dhanurasana

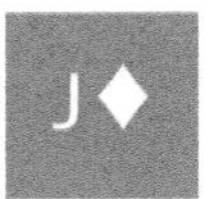

Fall

Workbook questions

Chart of Emotions (COE)

ENTERED INTO THE MEI ___ JOURNAL ___ WORKBOOK ___	Scale 1 - 10	Question or Journal Entry 97 / Experienced Emotions	Past	Present	Future
		JOY			
		LOVE			
		HOPE			
		TRUST			
		ADMIRATION			
		FEAR			
		WORRIED			
		HAPPY			
		CALM			
		SAD			
		RESENTFUL			
		GENEROUS			
		DISGUST			
		ANGER			
		GUILT			
		ENTHUSIASTIC			
		SHY			

What kinds of behaviors provoke you and leave you with the feeling of guilt? Where do you think this strong emotion comes from?

Chart of Emotions (COE)

ENTERED INTO THE MEI ___ JOURNAL ___ WORKBOOK ___	Scale 1 - 10	Question or Journal Entry 98 / Experienced Emotions	Past	Present	Future
		JOY			
		LOVE			
		HOPE			
		TRUST			
		ADMIRATION			
		FEAR			
		WORRIED			
		HAPPY			
		CALM			
		SAD			
		RESENTFUL			
		GENEROUS			
		DISGUST			
		ANGER			
		GUILT			
		ENTHUSIASTIC			
		SHY			

Three advantages of allowing myself to be open and vulnerable to others might include:

Journal entry

Weekly Random Act of Kindness: ____________________

DATE	ENERGY: 1-10	WEATHER	AFFIRMATION God does not choose those who shall be favored with Her gifts. God puts blessings on all alike. Some are wise and gather in the crops; others leave the fruit of life to wither on the vine.
97			
98			

Haiku

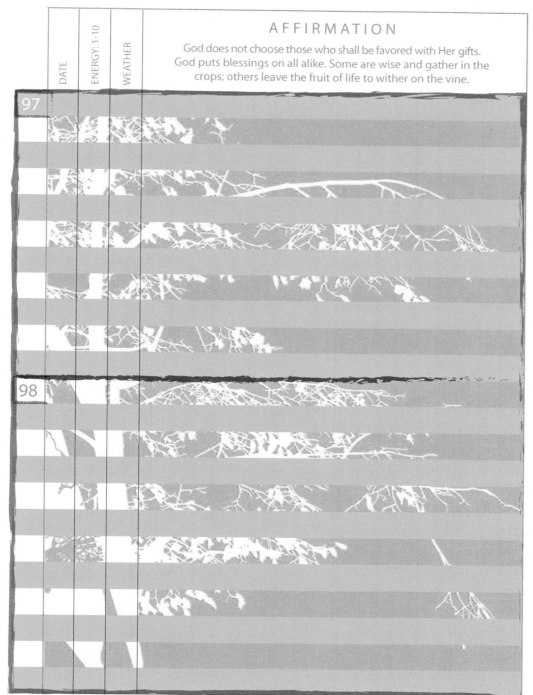

nights are getting cold...
not a single insect
now attacks
the candle

–Shiki

Samkha Mudra

Adho Mukha Vrksasana

Use either the workbook question or journal entry to populate the COE on the opposite page

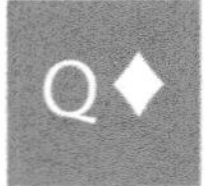

Workbook questions

Chart of Emotions (COE)

ENTERED INTO THE MEI ___ JOURNAL ___ WORKBOOK ___

Scale 1 - 10	Question or Journal Entry **99** / Experienced Emotions	Past	Present	Future
	JOY			
	LOVE			
	HOPE			
	TRUST			
	ADMIRATION			
	FEAR			
	WORRIED			
	HAPPY			
	CALM			
	SAD			
	RESENTFUL			
	GENEROUS			
	DISGUST			
	ANGER			
	GUILT			
	ENTHUSIASTIC			
	SHY			

List three things that you hold to be true about money. What are your strengths and perceived issues with money?

Chart of Emotions (COE)

ENTERED INTO THE MEI ___ JOURNAL ___ WORKBOOK ___

Scale 1 - 10	Question or Journal Entry **100** / Experienced Emotions	Past	Present	Future
	JOY			
	LOVE			
	HOPE			
	TRUST			
	ADMIRATION			
	FEAR			
	WORRIED			
	HAPPY			
	CALM			
	SAD			
	RESENTFUL			
	GENEROUS			
	DISGUST			
	ANGER			
	GUILT			
	ENTHUSIASTIC			
	SHY			

For whom, if anyone, are you (or would like to be) a role model? What three important values or traits would you like to impart? Who was one of your role models as a child?

Journal entry

Weekly Random Act of Kindness: ______________________

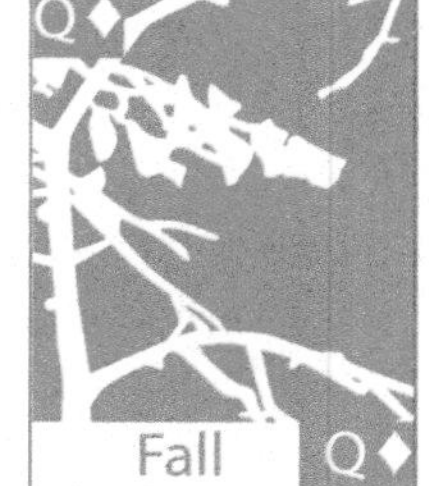

DATE	ENERGY: 1-10	WEATHER	AFFIRMATION Love God and God alone.
99			
100			

Use either the workbook question or journal entry to populate the COE on the opposite page

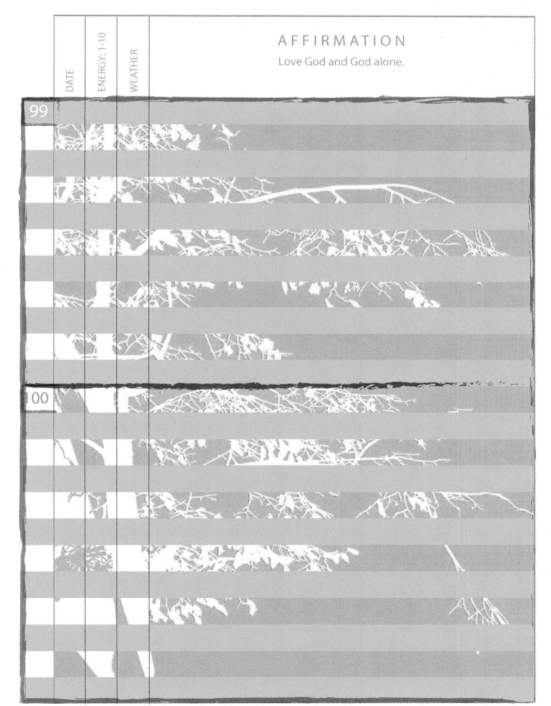

Haiku

swallows flying south...
my house too
of sticks and paper
only a stopping-place

–Kyorai

Kartarisvastika Mudra

Salamba Sirsasana

Fall

Workbook questions

Chart of Emotions (COE)

Scale 1 - 10	Question or Journal Entry **101** / Experienced Emotions	Past	Present	Future
	JOY			
	LOVE			
	HOPE			
	TRUST			
	ADMIRATION			
	FEAR			
	WORRIED			
	HAPPY			
	CALM			
	SAD			
	RESENTFUL			
	GENEROUS			
	DISGUST			
	ANGER			
	GUILT			
	ENTHUSIASTIC			
	SHY			

ENTERED INTO THE MEI ___ JOURNAL ___ WORKBOOK ___

Our minds are like a filmstrip, sometimes being played over and over again. If, in that nonstop filmstrip, you could insert three motivating words that would remind you to just *bring yourself back to your home base,* what would those words be and why?

Chart of Emotions (COE)

Scale 1 - 10	Question or Journal Entry **102** / Experienced Emotions	Past	Present	Future
	JOY			
	LOVE			
	HOPE			
	TRUST			
	ADMIRATION			
	FEAR			
	WORRIED			
	HAPPY			
	CALM			
	SAD			
	RESENTFUL			
	GENEROUS			
	DISGUST			
	ANGER			
	GUILT			
	ENTHUSIASTIC			
	SHY			

ENTERED INTO THE MEI ___ JOURNAL ___ WORKBOOK ___

How, if at all, are the objects of your senses a universe unto themselves? What role do you play in the unfolding journey of the universe?

Journal entry

Weekly Random Act of Kindness: ______________________________

DATE	ENERGY: 1-10	WEATHER	AFFIRMATION Open the windows of your soul and perceive God in all his/her glory.
101			
102			

Haiku

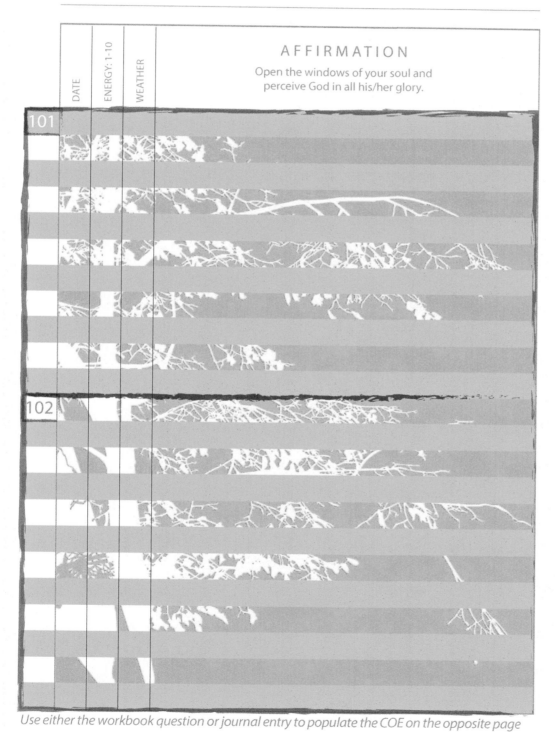

autumn breezes shake
the scarlet flowers
my poor child
could not wait to pick

—Issa

Alapadma Mudra

Shavasana

Use either the workbook question or journal entry to populate the COE on the opposite page

Chapter 3

Wired to the Strange Universe of Thought, Form and Art

"I have come to accept the feeling of not knowing where I am going. And I have trained myself to love it. Because it is only when we are suspended in mid-air with no landing in sight, that we force our wings to unravel and alas begin our flight. And as we fly, we still may not know where we are going to. But the miracle is in the unfolding of the wings. You may not know where you're going, but you know that so long as you spread your wings, the winds will carry you."
- C. JoyBell C.

As Hermes Trismegistus once said: "That which is below is like that which is above and that which is above is like that which is below to do the miracles of one only thing." This is a beautiful reminder that man by himself is incomplete. Man looks outside himself for greater meaning. He eventually understands that everything in the universe (including himself) is nothing more than a mirrored image wherefore one object represents and has meaning through the other. In our modern age, we all know that we construct our own reality. No two people share the same. They are simply representatives to the universe at large. So when we work with our nervous system rather it be from the mudras, pranayamas, bandhas, chakras or just the poses themselves, please know that your effort to become more whole is much greater than it may appear to be. One of the reasons I chose to incorporate the mudras and meridians of the hand of this book was because, based on the principles of the Homunculus, there are so many more nerve pathways leading from hand to the brain: More than any other single part of the body. Most all acupuncturists, neurologists and physicists will tell you— energy takes the path of least resistance. Thus, where there is congestion or an energetic blockage, there is a disruption of balance and equanimity.

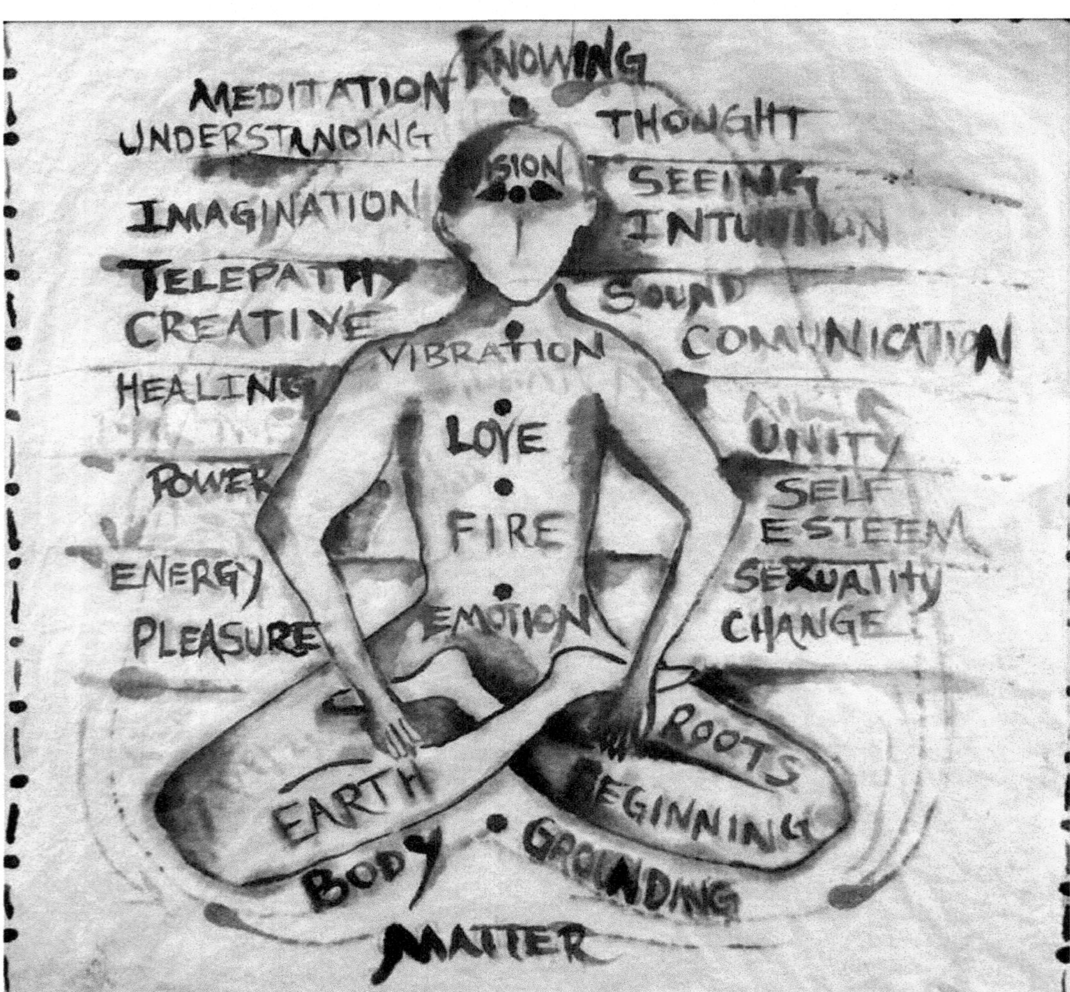

Homunculus

The "Little Man"

Neurologists can map which parts of the brain control various parts of the body. Stimulating the sensory or motor cortex with a weak electric current does the mapping. The stimulation often produces tingling or movement in part of the body. Humans put great emphasis on speech and manipulation of objects by the hands, so humans have large amounts of cortex devoted to mouth, tongue, and hands. Different species have different patterns. Rats get a lot of information from their whiskers, so they have large amounts of sensory cortex devoted to their whiskers. The following diagram on the left represents a slice of cortex near the fissure of Rolando, running from the top of the head on downwards toward the ear. The diagram indicates the location and amount of cortex devoted to each part of the body. At location #22, for example (just above the lateral fissure by the ear), stimulation produces a swallowing reflex. At location #3, at the top of the head, stimulation results in toe movement. Altogether, the map of brain connections to the body in this particular strip of cortex looks like this, with the amount of cortical tissue represented by the size of the body part in the diagram.

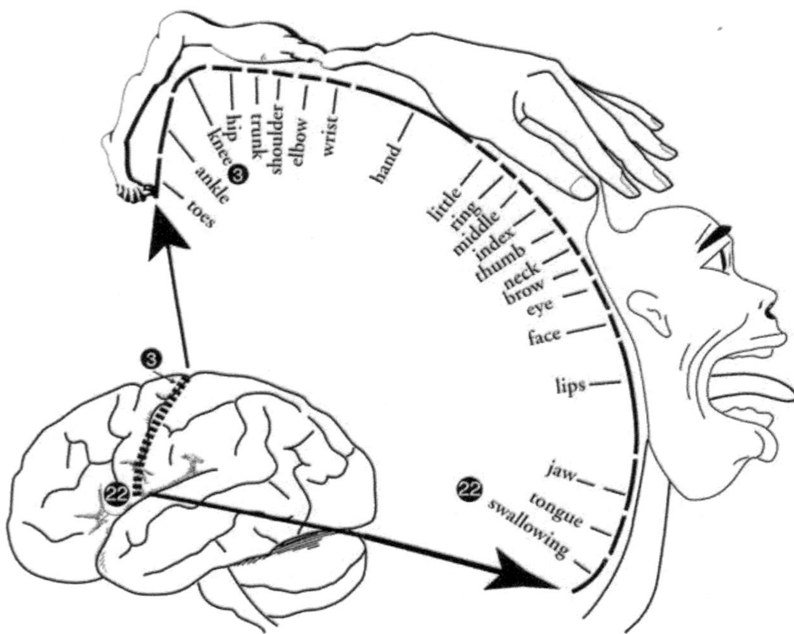

The diagram looks a bit like a grotesque little man, so it is called the homunculus (ho-MUN-que-lus) which, means "little man" in Latin. The first homunculus diagram was drawn by Wilder Penfield in the 1940s and looks similar to the one above. Notice that the hands, lips, and tongue are large because of the large areas of cortex devoted to these areas of the body in humans. What sort of humorous references to the homunculus are common?

The homunculus is a textbook diagram, certainly not a self or center of consciousness in the brain. However, humorous references to the homunculus as a little person in the head are common among psychologists alike.common among psychologists alike. One psychologist might say to another, "But how exactly is this mental activity carried out? Does the homunculus do it?" This is a way of saying, "You have not given us an adequate explanation!"

What is evidence that cortical mapping can change with experience? Actually there are many homunculi in the brain, if the word refers to an area of cortex where body surfaces are mapped. Such maps can change with experience. People who read Braille (which is done with an index finger) develop large areas responsive to stimulation from the index finger. A homunculus mapped on the motor cortex of such a person would have a huge index finger. This flexibility in the brain inspired some therapies for brain-damaged patients. In one study, people who suffered partial paralysis of an arm after a stroke were able to regain full use of the arm by having the other (good) arm immobilized (prevented from moving). This encouraged development of the cortex that controlled the "bad" arm, resulting in partial recovery of the patient's ability to move that arm.

With kind permission from Dr. Dewey at psywww@gmail.com.

What Are Yoga Mudras?

Subtle zones and mappings of the hand

Mudra dates back more than 5000 years.The word mudra is derived from two Sanskrit root words – Mud, which means 'delight' and Rati that means to bring forth. In an ancient yoga book called *Gheranda Samhita*, the reference of mudras is made note of in Sutra 100. It is believed that there were originally 108 basic mudras. Each must have represented what in Jotishi (the science of light) is called the 108 lunar mansions or vedas. Traditionally, mudras have been used during meditation, while doing yoga poses and even in dance. Holding mudras helps produce an altered state of mind. Using mudras is nothing more than learning how to concentrate and allow for a more efficient "flow" of electrons via the meridians and biorhythms of the body and mind. Historically, people have used mudras as symbols to communicate and transmit their different experiences, to share an infinite number of anthropological expressions of their spiritual and material worlds.

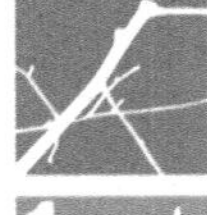
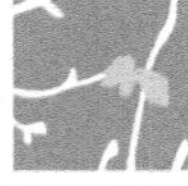

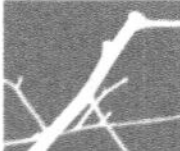
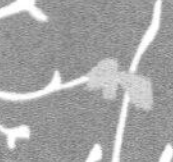

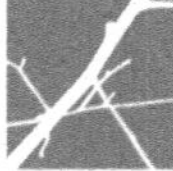

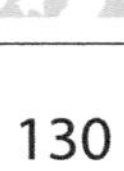

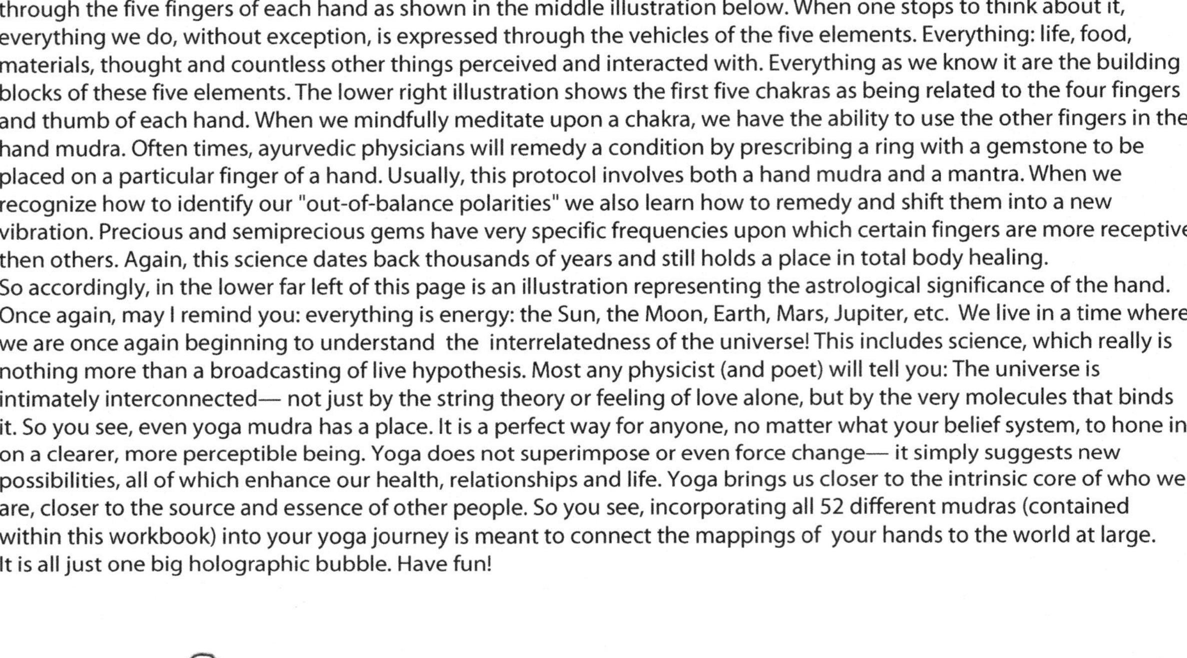

In ayurvedic healing, there exists five elements, all of which nourish and bind the universe. Each element is represented through the five fingers of each hand as shown in the middle illustration below. When one stops to think about it, everything we do, without exception, is expressed through the vehicles of the five elements. Everything: life, food, materials, thought and countless other things perceived and interacted with. Everything as we know it are the building blocks of these five elements. The lower right illustration shows the first five chakras as being related to the four fingers and thumb of each hand. When we mindfully meditate upon a chakra, we have the ability to use the other fingers in the hand mudra. Often times, ayurvedic physicians will remedy a condition by prescribing a ring with a gemstone to be placed on a particular finger of a hand. Usually, this protocol involves both a hand mudra and a mantra. When we recognize how to identify our "out-of-balance polarities" we also learn how to remedy and shift them into a new vibration. Precious and semiprecious gems have very specific frequencies upon which certain fingers are more receptive then others. Again, this science dates back thousands of years and still holds a place in total body healing.

So accordingly, in the lower far left of this page is an illustration representing the astrological significance of the hand. Once again, may I remind you: everything is energy: the Sun, the Moon, Earth, Mars, Jupiter, etc. We live in a time where we are once again beginning to understand the interrelatedness of the universe! This includes science, which really is nothing more than a broadcasting of live hypothesis. Most any physicist (and poet) will tell you: The universe is intimately interconnected— not just by the string theory or feeling of love alone, but by the very molecules that binds it. So you see, even yoga mudra has a place. It is a perfect way for anyone, no matter what your belief system, to hone in on a clearer, more perceptible being. Yoga does not superimpose or even force change— it simply suggests new possibilities, all of which enhance our health, relationships and life. Yoga brings us closer to the intrinsic core of who we are, closer to the source and essence of other people. So you see, incorporating all 52 different mudras (contained within this workbook) into your yoga journey is meant to connect the mappings of your hands to the world at large. It is all just one big holographic bubble. Have fun!

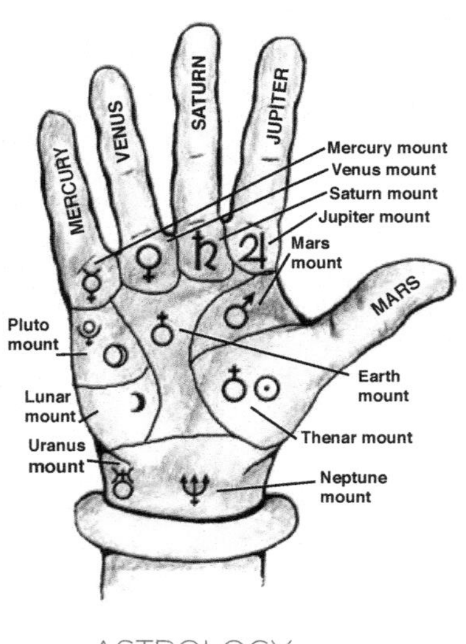

ASTROLOGY

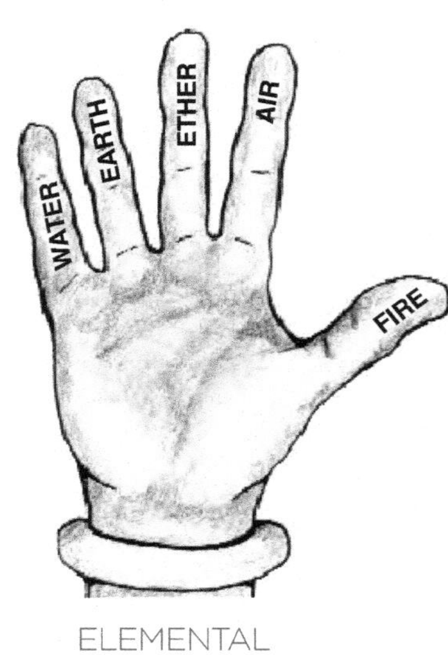

ELEMENTAL

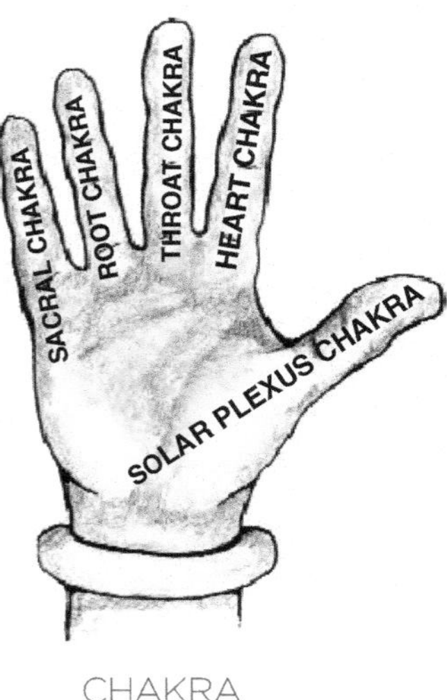

CHAKRA

Mudras & Meridians

Things to know when practicing

The central nervous system consists of the spinal cord and the brain. The peripheral nervous system originates from the spinal cord and provides innervations to inner organs and other somatic parts, such as the skin, connective tissue, muscles, etc. At the very endings of the peripheral nervous system, one will find the proprioreceptors. They are located throughout the skin, muscles, connective tissues and various other places as well. Proprioreceptors respond to touch, pressure, temperature, vibration and various other forms of stimulation both: physical, subtle and mental.

Therefore, the body is a gateway and map into the inner workings of our deepest consciousness and health pathways. By lengthening, retracting, bending, curling, crossing-over, stretching, and touching the fingers, palms, wrists, arms, torso, legs and feet to each other, we can, in effect, communicate to the many different subtle components of our physical and even less physical parts of the body. Hand mudras can be held anywhere from seconds to minutes, or even hours at a time. Just as with yoga poses, mudras can a help to alleviate many imbalances of the body and mind. Mudras and yoga poses alike help to bring about more awareness to the many forms of thinking and expressions of feeling.

When holding mudras, the appropriate level of pressure (or tension) exerted from pressing one part of the hand, especially the fingers to another, should be as subtle as the pressure of a light pinecone being held in the palm of your hand— although there are subtle variances that go far beyond the scope of this book. Nonetheless, the process of holding mudra's helps to re balance the body and mind. Many mudras facilitate healing in an individual, as quickly as 10 seconds, while for others it may be a longer process such as days, weeks or even months at a time. As we have already seen in the illustrations below, different parts of the hand correlate to specific areas of the body and brain. Mudra's help balance and calm emotions. They help curb strong behaviors. In the beginning, while working with mudra's, much of the healing that occurs may seem to be visually imagined, but with time become felt on a physiological level. In a way, one of the main benefits of using mudra's is that they help us focus and concentrate our mental energy. Many clinicians claim hand mudras mirror foot reflexology. Hand mudras are nothing more than applied-pressure treatments. Their concentrated pressure acts upon the different junctures (nadis) of the hands, fingers and palms. Each hand comprises the wrist, palm, fingers and thumb—it is a mechanically complex and highly sensitive structure. Each hand consists of 27 bones and a complexity of muscles and tendons. The three main nerves that travel to the hand transmit electrical impulses to and from the brain. This helps to enable the hand to perform highly intricate functions including the ability to feel the most delicate sensations. It is important to note that the ability of proprioceptors to respond to touch is limited, especially when the tips of the fingers are pressing too strongly, those proprioceptors will almost totally stop to propagate sensory impulses. This phenomenon of losing sensitivity is called "proprioceptors' level of adaptation."

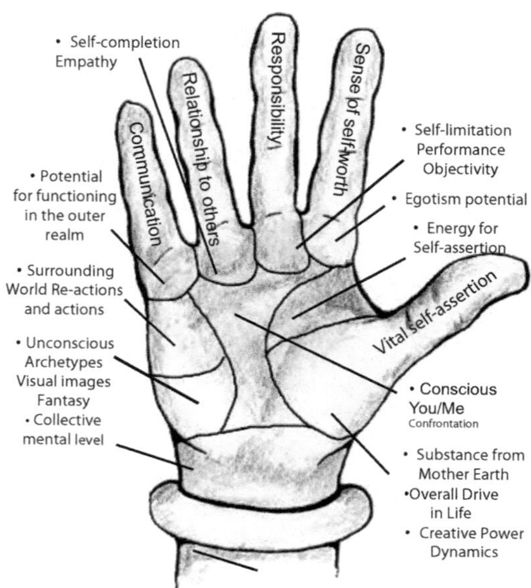

The Science of Meridians

(Zones and workings of the hand)

MERIDIANS I

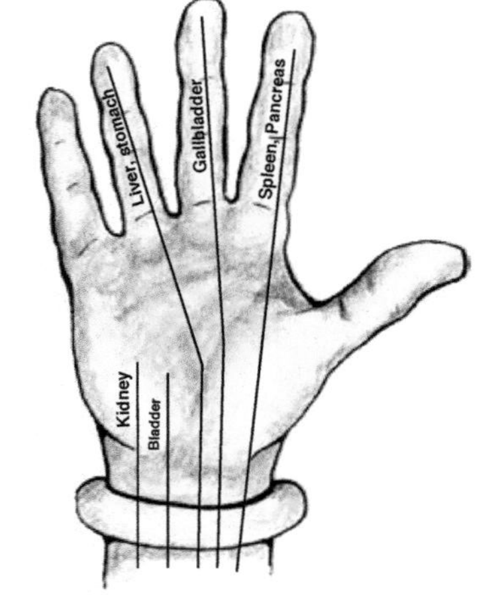

MERIDIANS II

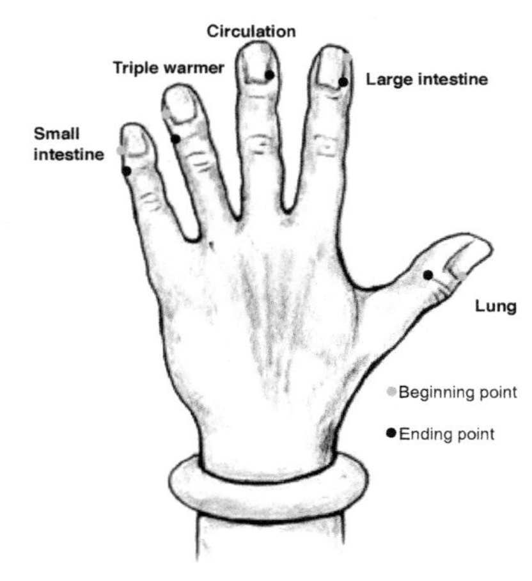

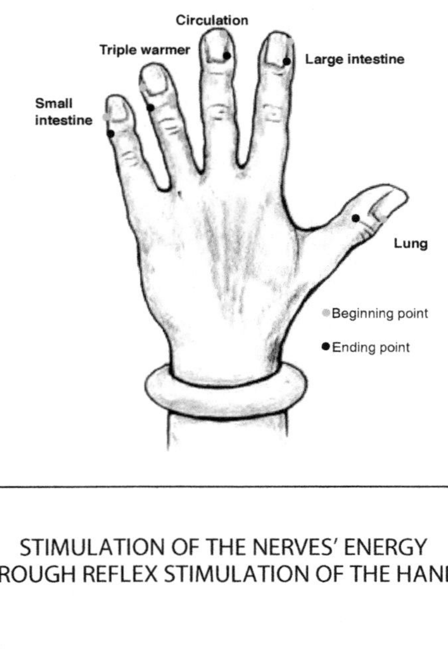

LEFT PALM ZONES I

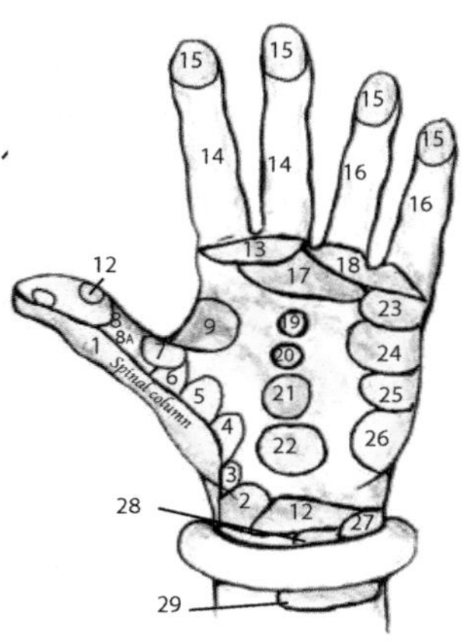

RIGHT PALM ZONES II

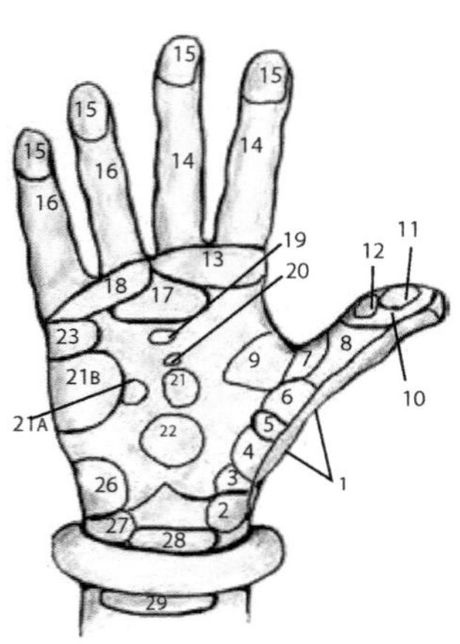

1) Spinal column
2) Uterus / Prostrate
3) Lumbar region
4) Bladder
5) Pancreas
6) Thyroid / Parathyroid
7) Throat
8) Head
8a) Neck
9) Stomach
10) Brain
11) Pineal gland
12) Pituitary gland
13) Eyes
14) Eyes
15) Frontal and maxillary sinuses
16) Ear
17) Chest, lung, and bronchial tubes
18) Ears
19) Solar plexus
20) Adrenal gland
21) Kidneys
21a) Gallbladder
22) Intestines
23) Arm and shoulder
24) Liver
25) Ball Bladder
26) Hips and thighs
27) Ovaries / testes
28) Lymph
29) Sciatic nerve

STIMULATION OF THE NERVES' ENERGY THROUGH REFLEX STIMULATION OF THE HANDS.

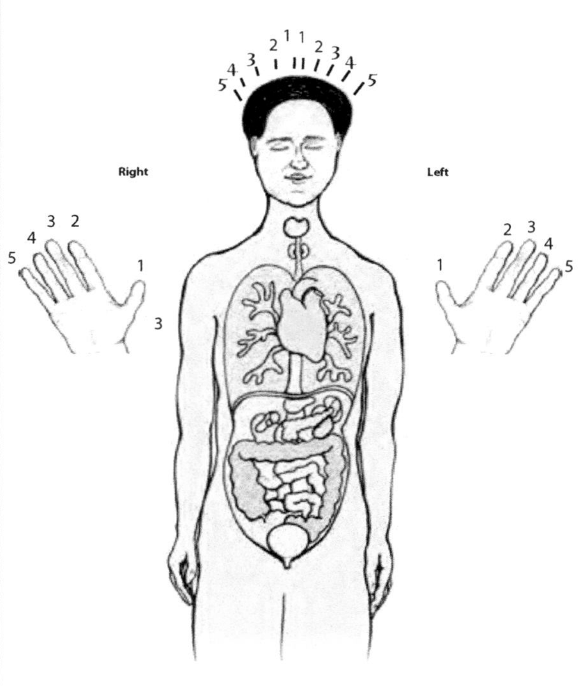

Introduction to Pranayama

(Five Healthy Breathing Techniques)

Pranayama = breath control
Prana = the fundamental life force/energy Ayama = to stretch, extension, prolongation. To channel and control pranayama is the conscious use of breathing as a tool to cultivate pranic energy inside the body. Breathing techniques have always been an integral part of yoga and mindfulness meditation. Therefore, when we first learn and hear about "pranayama," we must realize that it's a subcomponent of the larger system of the eight limbs of yoga more properly called Ashtanga, which in English translates to "Eight Limbs." Pranayama is the fourth of eight limbs of the science of yoga.

Regardless of which door one enters into the discipline of yoga, it is imperative to know that all eight branches are intimately connected and therefore work in tandem. That is to say, the body and mind are bridged and strengthened with greater control when incorporating more than one of the eight limbs of yoga into their daily life. The focus and end goal of pranayama is to learn how to channel and transport very subtle forms of pranic energy. There are purported to be well over 72,000 nadis (acupuncture junctions) in the body. All these nadis revolve around the three different parts of breathing as outlined below:

- Purak: Inhalation of breath
- Rechaka: Exhalation of breath
- Kumbhaka: Retention of breath

Pranayama is described in the Yoga Sutras of Patanjali. It is much more than just a mechanical respiratory exercise: It helps to obliterate and/or minimize daily stress and other psychological and neurotic conditions. When properly learning how to incorporate the many different pranayama techniques into one's daily life, it is only then that we come to learn how to master the mechanics and underpinnings of the mind or what is more commonly called chitta. Learning how to consciously change the biorhythms of the body and mind is unlike anything else. More often than not, we are learning how to rewire the circuitry and biochemistry of the brain. Pranayama helps us to change the alpha, beta, theta and delta wave lengths of the brain. It allows us to masterfully channel the subtle energy waves from one power substation to another. In many ways, the science of prana works hand in hand with what Rosicrucian philosophy calls the "Etheric Envelope." Basically, the Etheric Envelope consists of four different grades or parts. Simplistically speaking, it is the notion of what we commonly call the invisible force ether. Its four parts consist of the first being "Chemical" ether, the second is "Life" ether, the third is "Light" ether and the fourth "Reflecting" ether. As you may have guessed, ether is not what is physical to the eye; however, neither are feelings. I think the important thing to understand is that everything in the universe has its opposite polarity, or set of complementary charges such as the charges of positive and negative poles in electricity.

So with these principles in mind, pranayama leads us into the second half of the Eight Limbs of Yoga (Pratyahara, Dharana, Dhyana and Samadhi). It helps escalate our experience by inducing the body and mind to higher states of subtle consciousness. Of the already mentioned 72,000 nadis, 40 are considered to be secondary and 7 are the major chakras of the body (see page 138). It is through the gate of pranayama that we learn to experience the sublime effects of the healing chakras.

It is pranayama itself that helps to move and transport the very subtle forms of energy from within and around the body. You see, once we learn to introduce and redefine the patterns and ratios of the breath, it is unlike anything you may have ever experienced. Pranayama helps to build and maintain the body's nervous system. Its uncanny powers allow for multiple immediate feedback loops, which ultimately help to bridge and strengthen the neurological components of the mind, body and spirit.

As Swami Rama once pointed out, there was once a Sufi scholar quoted to say "the subject of breath is the deepest of all the subjects with which mysticism or philosophy is concerned, because breath is the most important thing in life." The first breath begins at life once outside the womb. The beginning of respiration transforms the dynamics of the circulatory and neurological systems.

Introduction and Notes on Pranayama

(Five Breathing Techniques— (View videos online at www.alightfromwithwithin.net)

Here are some general guidelines to consider in the practice and instruction of pranayama:

1. Begin by clearing the nasal passages of any blockage by blowing the nose or using the neti pot (kriya technique).
2. As in asana practice, pranayama is best performed on an empty stomach.
3. Pranayamas such as Dirgha or Ujjai are most easily introduced to beginners in a reclining or supported reclining position. Bhramari should not be taught in a reclining position.
4. Initially, simply observe the dynamics of the breath without attempting to control it. Then begin to regulate gradually, leading over time into full pranayamas.
5. In seated pranayamas, it is essential that the practitioner is supported by bolsters, blankets, and any other props as necessary to achieve a straight, extended spine, so that the spinal nerves can draw prana, or energy, from the breath, rather than causing strain to the nervous system.
6. Be sure that the exhalation is smooth and even; if there is any choppiness or strain, stop the practice and return to the natural rhythm of breath.

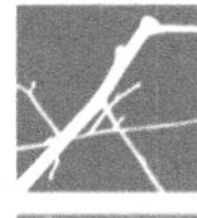

Definition

Pranayama is the conscious use of breathing as a tool to cultivate and move pranic energy inside and around the body. Prana is the essence of life in its most subtle form. Prana is found in all things, but humankind's ability to control this flow provides an immeasurable tool for transcendence. "Prana" means the fundamental life force and "yama," means to channel or control. The various pranayama techniques are used to channel subtle energy into the body or one might also say to bring energy into the subtle channels of the body. Yama in Vedic literature and iconography, is also the god of death, so if prana is the essence of life, the experience of breathing is the mid ground between life and death as we know it. Another explanation from the Sanskrit is that "ayama" (which means to expand) following "prana" suggests that the goal is to expand the body with vital force.

General Pranayama guidelines

1. As in asana practices, pranayama is best performed with little abdominal congestion due to meals or drinks.

2. Choose a reclining position initially for pranayama practice.

3. Do not force the breath to move or stop moving initially; simply watch what happens.

4. In seated pranayama practices, keep the spine extended.

Benefits

The movement of the diaphragm places increased pressure on the internal organs. This has the following effects:

1. Acts to increase digestive homeostasis by facilitating peristalsis (normally incited by parasympathetic nervous system control), which is the wavelike movement of contractions of the intestines. Peristalsis works like a gentle pump for vascularizing the abdominal organs. It impacts the liver and helps with the removal of waste products. Also it acts on the kidneys by creating a massaging effect with the diaphragm. One role that the kidneys play is in controlling blood pressure.

2. The spleen, which is involved in the immune system function, is massaged and better able to perform its job of filtering blood, and storing lymphatic tissue and white blood cells.

3. The movement of the diaphragm supports the movement of lymphatic fluid from the lower body to the thorax where it is reabsorbed into the circulatory system. This aids in the production of immune system agents.

4. Pranayama regulates the flow of blood to the brain, which can stimulate both hemispheres of the brain creating balance between the sympathetic and parasympathetic nervous systems. Additionally, pranayama stimulates the olfactory bulb, which rests near the emotional center of the brain, and can have a quieting effect. Pranayama is effective for clearing the mind and concentrating attention mentally.

5. The full use of the lungs can prevent toxic buildup of waste materials in the bloodstream. Pranayama techniques affect the heart rate. Slow, even breathing can reduce the heart rate.... and in some cases canslow heart rate. This effect reduces the workload on the heart and makes its actions more efficient.

6. Many pranayama techniques can increase the flow of blood to the base of the lungs to remove fluids that build up there. The base of the lungs— where more alveoli are found due to gravity— do not naturally absorb as much oxygen because the gas more easily is drawn into the upper portion of the bronchial tract. Further, pranayama can increase the amount of oxygen transferred into the alveoli by extending the length of breath into the lower lobe of the lungs.

7. Pranayama affects the residual amount (functional residual capacity) of oxygen, which remains in the lungs more often than not making room for more air uptake by the alveoli.

The Five ALFW Pranayamas:

- Dirgha
- Ujjayi
- Kapalabhati
- Nadi Shodhana
- Bhramari

1- Dirgha Pranayama (4 variations)
In Sanskrit, Dirgha means "to lengthen," but it is also commonly called yogic breath or three-part breath. This technique is commonly introduced as one type of yogic breathing but may also include other forms of breath lengthening that have subtly different impacts on the physical body and nervous system.

Learning Points

The basis of three-part or breath-lengthening pranayama is the smooth movement of the lower abdomen, thoracic (lateral muscles or intercostal), and the clavicles or chest. Based on intentions, and the direction of the breath, these three areas can be used to create a subtle stimulating or relaxing experience.

1) Abdomen soft; breathe from the abdomen upwards toward the clavicles. Exhale from the upper lungs (clavicles) downward to the abdomen.

This is the most relaxing of the techniques. Helpful with stress, hypertension, and heart disease, it increases the downward flow of energy and is helpful for digestion, elimination, and conditions like constipation. It slows the breathing process down, which increases the amount of carbon dioxide in the bloodstream. This may seem counterintuitive but this supports the cells functioning at maximum capacity with more efficient use of the oxygen within the bloodstream. In the same way that we can now produce cars that work with less fuel, pranayama uses the least amount of fuel optimally and efficiently.

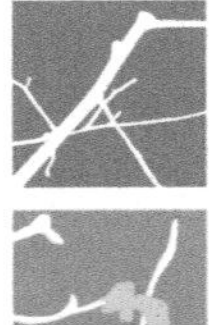

2) Abdomen firm, breathe from the abdomen upwards toward the clavicle. Exhale from the upper lungs (clavicle) downward to the abdomen. This version of Dirgha creates a wave that can be felt at the back of the lung and kidney spaces. By holding the abdomen slightly firm and bringing the navel backwards to the spine, space is created in the back of the body. This strengthens the abdominal muscles. Because the diaphragm must work harder to descend downward, it brings awareness to this movement—tones the lower abdominal organs, lengthens the lower back muscles, and works to bring the pelvis and low back into balance. It is generally more invigorating than the first version, and thus could be used for conditions such as weight loss or to increase energy levels. This variation would be contraindicated in cases where tight and contracted breath was noted in students with abdominal injuries/surgeries, etc. When the intention is stress reduction, this version might have a destabilizing impact.

3) Abdomen soft, breathe from clavicles downward to the abdomen. Exhale from the lower abdomen upward towards the chest.

4) Abdomen firm, breath from the clavicles downward to the abdomen. Exhale from the lower abdomen upward towards the chest.

These variations move breath energy upward and are slightly more stimulating than bottom up breathing. They might be used to take energy from the lower abdomen in conditions such as diarrhea or dysmenorrhea. The variations increase the heat in the upper body especially and may be useful for conditions such as emphysema, asthma, and other respiratory ailments. This can be helpful for drawing up emotional material for processing. This breath format would be contra-indicated for those with heart conditions, hypertension, headaches, or tendency towards emotional instability.

2- Ujjayi Pranayama

As is the case with many Sanskrit expressions, the ujjayi pranayama has multiple considerations as to its meaning. Commonly referred to as the victorious breath (ujji means victory) but also possibly based on the concept of raising up which means greeting or the characteristic hissing sound generated when this breath is utilized. In the beginning of learning the pranayama, you may suggest that students imagine whispering to create the right constriction at the back of the throat. Then exhale eccentrically and softly whisper "ahhh." Traditional texts suggest the emphasis of the breath be directed from the nose to the center of the chest. The characteristic sound of this pranayama is a mindful reminder that the flow of the breath should be found in the beginning, middle, and end of all asanas. Practice of Ujayii with force can dry out the nose and throat and cause hoarseness, it is recommended to keep the ocean sound (as it is often called) so soft that only you and another standing immediately next to you could hear the sound.

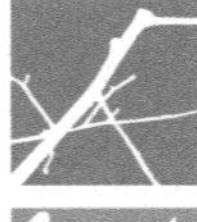

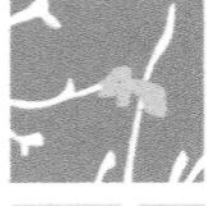

Contraindications:
Heart conditions, High blood pressure, migraines, chronic sinusitis.

3- Kapalabhati Pranayama
Kapal = skull
Bhati = to make lustrous or to shine

Kapalabhati, while sometimes not considered a classical pranayama so much as a kriya technique, is in either case a tool for cleansing the upper respiratory tract. The basic technique is to focus on the exhaling breath and quickly expel air through the nostrils in sets of 15 or 30 rounds. The inhalation phase of the breath is allowed to be completely relaxed and passive. Extending the tongue out of the mouth and panting like a dog on a hot summer day can achieve the technique. Then simply close the mouth and push the air out on the exhale only, through the nose. The rhythm of the expulsions should be kept even and smooth. Do not force the breath to do more rounds or repetitions than are comfortably within range. As your ability to do more builds with time, add additional repetitions and more rounds of Kapalabhati.

Contraindications:
This pranayama is not recommended for pregnant women, during menstruation, for those with unmedicated high blood pressure, or recent abdominal surgery.

4- Nadi Shodnah
Nadi = channel
Shodnah = to cleanse

Place the right hand in Vishnu Mudra (forefinger and middle finger bent toward the palm; thumb, ring, and pinkie in the air.) To do one round: close off right nostril with the thumb and inhale into the left nostril; close left nostril with ring and pinkie fingers, open the right nostril and exhale through the right, then inhale into the right nostril; close the right nostril, open the left, and exhale through the left nostril. Continue, doing 5-20 rounds. This pranayama is considered balancing for both brain hemispheres, it calms the mind and generally soothes. It is sometimes also called the sweet breath, because of its soothing nature.

5- Bhramari

Brahamari is the Sanskrit word for the black bee. The name follows the characteristic sound that is generated with this pranayama is engaged. The adjective bhramarin can also mean "sweet as honey" or "that which produces ecstasy" in Sanskrit. While there are multiple versions of each pranayama, beginning-level students should be able to perform the following technique. Inhale normally while closing off the ears by cupping the hands over them. Focus gaze and awareness to the space of the center of the forehead and back behind the nose bone, 4-6 inches. As you exhale, hum and lift the resonating sound upward into the ceiling of the soft palate. Focus on the sound as you exhale eccentrically. Perform nine rounds of the pranayama, then switch to a normalized breathing pattern, keeping attention focused inwardly. The humming sound should be smooth, even and continuous for the duration of the exhalation. The sound should be soft and mellow, making the front of the skull reverberate. This pranayama is classically used for those with high blood pressure. The vibratory nature of the pranayama is used to stimulate the primary endocrine glands and the brain itself. It is believed that this stimulation reduces the blood pressure, relieves anxiety, and increases the natural painkillers the brain produces. Do not perform this pranayama while in the supine position. People suffering from severe ear infections should not practice this pranayama until the infection has cleared up. Also, do not practice if you have unmedicated high blood pressure or a heart condition. Additionally, it is advised that emotionally distressed people not practice bhramari.

The Chakras

Seven Centers of Spiritual Energy of the Body

There are two kinds of time, Man's time and Nature's time. So there are also two kinds of thought: empirical and intuitive. Ultimately, these two different ways of being and thinking help us to feel safe, more organized, and make better sense of the world from within and around us. There are many different vibrations of energy that bind the elements of everything we know and experience. So we must ask ourselves this one question: What exactly is it that we hope to achieve when exploring and working with chakras? What tools do we need to begin our work? None. Everything you need is within you right now. Here is a point of comparison: When on Earth and looking up at the Moon, we assume there is nothing that physically connects us to it, except of course our thoughts and perhaps the air in between. Well, to me, that is exactly what the nature of chakras is all about! Chakras are the very space and energy in between the two orbits. Call it gravity or call it the Higgs field, it really does not matter. But one thing is for certain: Chakras exist and can be worked upon to create greater harmony from one to the other.

So we all know that in order for energy to be energy, it must have a way of expressing itself. The problem is there is many different ways to measure and observation it. But sometimes we get so caught up in wanting to figure the end result that we loose contact with the origin. This is called *Finger pointing to the moon*. I believe that when working with the chakras we can intuitively balance the psycho-emotional components of our well-being. We can more consciously bring to surface the powerful components residing within the complex of our being. Remember, chakras are nothing, but electrical substations aligned along "the grid." Therefore, we must insist on learning how to transmute the ill-regulated frequencies of all seven chakras. Healing and rebalancing our chakras help to unearth our inherent potential. They liberate the "buried treasure" from within. Sometimes in the process of life, we create an opportunity to reclaim our forgotten self. Ultimately, the facets and the nature of this hidden *self* are presented by way of contemplation. Yes, it is through contemplation and meditation that we come to realize many of the things that have come to define us were never really meant to be ours— or at least not for so long. So, we let go and move on to the next chapter of our life-- all in full awareness! Remember in the preface of this book we talked a little bit about the subject of tapta marga? Well, tapta marga is a way of burning away the three psychic knots of the wheel of chakras called Granthi. These knots, which act as barriers to the free flow of prana (frequency), represent three levels of psychophysical life. The first knot is below the navel and is called brahma-granthi. It is related to the senses and perhaps how it dominates the clarity of the mind. The second knot is below the heart and is called vishnu-granthi. It is related to our emotional life. The third knot is below the eyebrows and is called rudra-granthi. This is the area of our intellectual activity and discernment.

When we learn to identify and examine our old and outdated beliefs and behaviors, we can more easily let go of them. When this happens we discover many new seeds from within the essence, power and fabric of our being. Upon discovery of these seeds, we must always ask ourselves, "Are the conditions within me right for the fertilization of these new seeds?" A brilliant scientist by the name Dr. Konstantin G. Korotkov, who is based in St. Petersburg, Russia, invented what is called the Gas Discharge Visualization, or GDV. GDV is a technique by which the energy fields emanating from humans (and other biologically based life alike) may be viewed in real time. I am truly fascinated by his research and strongly encourage you to check out his website at http://www.korotkov.eu. With his GDV, he has scientifically quantified the existence of chakras by way of the fingertips of each hand. Here is a quote from his work: "So, by measuring the fingers, and images or light coming from the fingers, we recreate in the computer the model of the energy field around the body. And it was tested in many, many experiments. We have a lot of people in the world who can see energy, can see auras, so we correlated our measurement with their vision, and it was proven that there are really very high correlations. When we have some holes in the energy field, those holes may be some weak functional activity of the organ system. So the difference between our instrument, our approach, and an ultrasound, or tomography (MRI), we don't look to the structure of the organ, we look to its functional activity. If you eat appropriate food, you're absolutely in good condition; if you eat wrong food then it creates a lot of negative emotions, a lot of negative feelings." And so you see, it's never too late to own sprout a new seed from within your divine being! While in the vehicle of life, metaphorically speaking, we become gardeners in our right! In life we must remain intellectually curious. We must continue our efforts forward in always maintaining the thirst and thrust for life. In the end, we really do create or own reality— this is the blessing and ebb and flow of all that just is.

The First Chakra

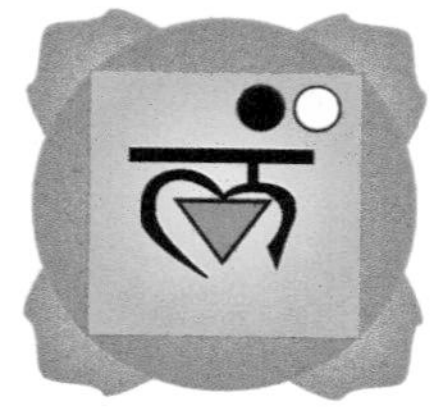

Root › 1st Chakra
Muladhara [Sanskrit Name]
Sense: Nose and smell

The 1st Chakra

FEATURES	Red	Petals: 4	Element: Earth
ENERGETIC LOCATION	Perineum		
PHYSICAL ASSOCIATION	Sacrum; external orifices of excretion		
ASSOCIATED GLAND	adrenal glands (Adrenaline), gonads (men)		
NERVOUS SYSTEM	Coccyxial nerve plexus		
AFFIRMATION	All is one I am safe	Sound: Lam	Musical note/Freq.: C/256HZ
FREEDOM RIGHT	To be here and have autonomy		
INNER STATE	Stillness, security and stability		
SHADOW	Fear		
EVOLUTION	The will to live. Jungle mentality—animal instincts for surviving in the physical body and being aware of environmental threats		
YOGIC LIFESTYLE	Being well grounded in physical reality allows for the capability of caring for oneself on this Earth. This is also the seat of kundalini, the creative energy that activates each of the chakras as it is released upward		
BREATH	Kapalabhati (Shining Skull) Pranayama.		
ASANAS	Groin openers such as Baddha Konasana (Bound Angle), Mandukasana (Frog), Prasarita Padottanasana (Expanded Leg Intense Stretch) Grounding poses such as Tadasana (Mountain Pose) or Vrksasana (Tree pose)		
SUMMARY	The need to survive and protect the physical body often evokes the fight or flight response. Fear of being powerful or creative pulls us back to this base chakra if we do not feel well grounded and safe.		

References
Brennan, B.A. (1988). Hands of Light.
Bruyere, R.L. (1994). Wheels of Light.
Fritz, S. (1995). Mosby's Fundamentals of Therapeutic Massage.
Gach, M.R. (1981). Acu-Yoga.
Judith, A. (1999). Wheels of Life.
Leadbeater, C.W. (1997). The Chakras.
Paulson, G.L. (1998). Kundalini and the Chakras. White, R. (1998). Chakras: A New Approach to Healing.

The Second Chakra

Naval ❯ 2nd Chakra
Svadhisthana [Sanskrit Name]
Sense: Tongue and taste

FEATURES	Orange	Petals: 6	Element: Water
ENERGETIC LOCATION	Lower abdomen ("Hara" of martial arts)		
PHYSICAL ASSOCIATION	Reproductive organs; intestines; lumbar region		
ASSOCIATED GLAND	Gonads—testes and ovaries		
NERVOUS SYSTEM	Lumbosacral and prostatic plexus		
AFFIRMATION	Honor each other	Sound: Vam	Musical note/Freq.: D/ 283Hz
FREEDOM RIGHT	To feel and have pleasure		
INNER STATE	Feelings and emotions		
SHADOW	Guilt		
EVOLUTION	Sensual emotion and sexuality		
YOGIC LIFESTYLE	Conscious eating, safe sex and healthy entertainment		
BREATH	Kapalabhati (Shining Skull) Pranayama		
ASANAS	Asanas: Sarvangasana (shoulder stand), halasana (plow), and backbends such as Ustrasana (camel), Bhujangasana (cobra), and Navasana (boat)		
SUMMARY	Appreciation of the physical and material sensations of this life may be easily abused in our society, which is based on money and consumerism. Most advertising appeals to the desires of the 2nd chakra.		

The Third Chakra

Personal Power › 3rd Chakra
Manipura [Sanskrit Name]
Sense: Eyes and sight

FEATURES	Yellow	Petals: 10	Element: Fire
ENERGETIC LOCATION	Solar plexus		
PHYSICAL ASSOCIATION	Stomach, pancreas, liver, gallbladder, spleen		
ASSOCIATED GLAND	Adrenal glands (corticosteroids), pancreas		
NERVOUS SYSTEM	Solar plexus		
AFFIRMATION	Respect yourself	Sound: Ram	Musical note/Freq.: E/ 320
FREEDOM RIGHT	To be an individual		
INNER STATE	Joy or anger (anger is an expression of powerlessness)		
SHADOW	Ego/victim consciousness		
EVOLUTION	Community; hierarchies of power		
YOGIC LIFESTYLE	Taking control over one's life and responsibility for one's health		
BREATH	Ujjayi		
ASANAS	Setu Bandhasana (bridge) Matsyendrasana (spinal twist)		
SUMMARY	Center of reasoning and logic as well as "gut level" emotions of personal interest. The seat of Freud's Ego driven by the desire for personal security and comfort.		

The Fourth Chakra

Heart Center › 4th Chakra
Anahata [Sanskrit Name]
Sense: Skin and touch

FEATURES	Green	Petals: 12	Element: Air
ENERGETIC LOCATION	Under the sternum (breastbone)		
PHYSICAL ASSOCIATION	Heart, lungs, breasts, circulatory system		
ASSOCIATED GLAND	Thymus (immune system)		
NERVOUS SYSTEM	Electrical system of the heart, cardiac plexus		
AFFIRMATION	Love is divine power	Sound: Yam	Musical note/Freq.: F/ 341 Hz
FREEDOM RIGHT	To feel and have pleasure		
INNER STATE	Compassion, nurturance and love		
SHADOW	Depression and grief (loss)		
EVOLUTION	Integration of the "lower" (Chakras 1-3) and "higher" (Chakras 5-6) aspects of the consciousness. Self-preservation, ego and power integrate with the capacity for transcendence.		
YOGIC LIFESTYLE	The ability to express love of self and others		
BREATH	Dirgha pranayama		
ASANAS	Chest openers		
SUMMARY	Development of social consciousness, empathy, tolerance and the capacity to forgive oneself as well as others.		

The Fifth Chakra

Creative ❯ 5th Chakra
Vishuddhi [Sanskrit Name]
Sense: Ears and hearing

FEATURES	Blue	Petals:16	Element: Ether
ENERGETIC LOCATION	Throat		
PHYSICAL ASSOCIATION	Mouth, vocal cords, trachea, cervical vertebrae		
ASSOCIATED GLAND	Thyroid and parathyroid glands (general metabolism)		
NERVOUS SYSTEM	Parasympathetic system especially the valgus nerve		
AFFIRMATION	Thy will be done.	Sound Ham	Musical note/Freq.: G 384 Hz
EXPRESS YOURSELF	Recognize your own needs		
FREEDOM RIGHT	To speak and hear the truth		
INNER STATE	Synthesis of ideas into symbols		
SHADOW	Lies/ fear of expressing oneself		
EVOLUTION	Using the strong base of the first two chakras, the power and passion of the 3rd chakra and the love and compassion of the heart chakra to bring about nonattachment in the creative state.		
YOGIC LIFESTYLE	Mental concentration and focus		
BREATH	Bhramari		
ASANAS	Sarvangasana (shoulder stand) and Halasana (plow) increase circulation to the thyroid gland		
SUMMARY	Communication. Processing information through language—reading, hearing, speaking and thinking—constitutes a major portion of our education. Consciousness at this chakra brings understanding of symbols, archetypes and myths.		

The Sixth Chakra

Third Eye ❯ 6th Chakra
Ajna [Sanskrit Name]
Sense: Mind

FEATURES	Indigo Petals: 2 Elements: All combined/Light
ENERGETIC LOCATION	Above midpoint of eyebrows
PHYSICAL ASSOCIATION	Base of the brain just behind the bridge of the nose
ASSOCIATED GLAND	Pituitary (master gland)
NERVOUS SYSTEM	Brain: medulla plexus
AFFIRMATION	Seek truth. Do not harm. Sound: AUM Musical note/Freq.: A 448Hz
FREEDOM RIGHT	The right to see
INNER STATE	Clairvoyance and intuition
SHADOW	Illusion
EVOLUTION	Basic fears from the first chakra may surface as you follow your intuition, which are more you than your logical mind.
YOGIC LIFESTYLE	Light stimulating the pineal gland, which some consider being the Third Eye.
BREATH	Nadi shodna pranayama
ASANAS	Symmetrical and balanced postures. Right and left brain working together (ida and pingala).
SUMMARY	True intelligence is seated here. The truth is realized, seeing clearly to the essence of things, beyond the constraints of space and time.

The Seventh Chakra

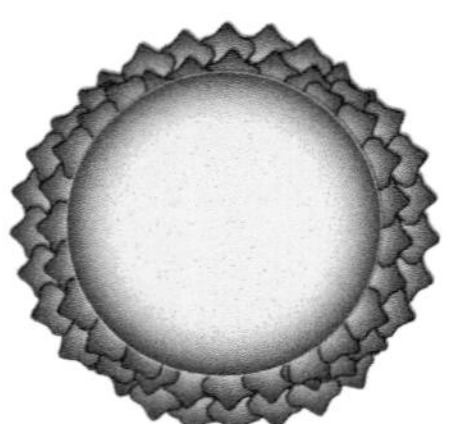

Crown › 7th Chakra
Sahasrara [Sanskrit Name]
Sense: Mind

FEATURES	Violet	Petals:1000	Element: All combined
ENERGETIC LOCATION	Top of the head		
PHYSICAL ASSOCIATION	Beyond the body		
ASSOCIATED GLAND	Brain (epithalamus)		
NERVOUS SYSTEM	Endocrine clock and an endocrine calendar		
AFFIRMATION	Be in the present	Sound: Ah	Musical note/Freq.: B 480 Hz
FREEDOM RIGHT	The right to know and to learn		
INNER STATE	Understanding		
SHADOW	Attachment		
EVOLUTION	Connection to the infinite, the spiritual quest		
YOGIC LIFESTYLE	Meditation		
BREATH	Dhirga		
ASANAS	Savasana (corpse pose)		
SUMMARY	1st and 2nd chakras are energy bases. 3rd chakra provides courage. 4th chakra demonstrates faith and trust in love. 5th chakra opens to experience in the moment. 6th chakra realizes that intuition is more you than your mind. 7th chakra is union with the divine, the highest states of consciousness.		

Symbol of Your Soul Exercise

Yantra exercise

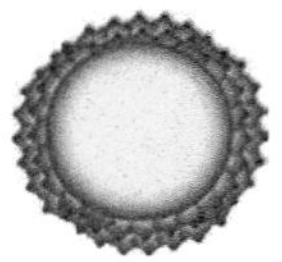

FOR THIS INSPIRING EXERCISE, it is important that you hone in on your heart center or heart chakra. When you hear the words heart chakra or heart center what is its meaning to you? What experience comes to mind?

Creating the stage: Lie down or sit comfortably in sukhasana, half lotus or any other comfortable position that suits you well.

Focus on your breath to calm your thinking, intuitive and feeling body.

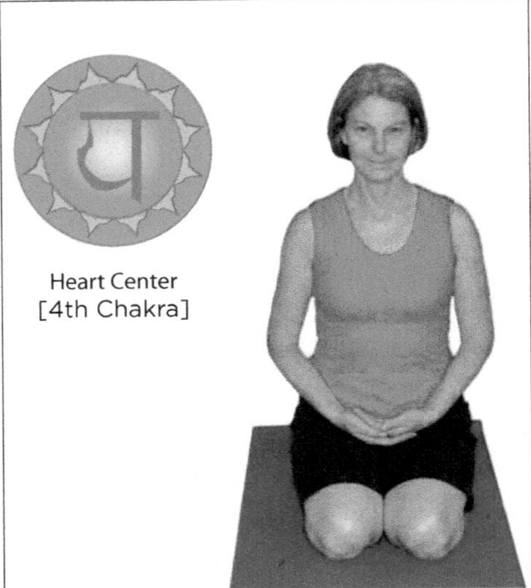
Heart Center
[4th Chakra]

Now begin to imagine that your heart center is so much more than just a place for the physical muscle of the heart. Maybe refer back to the heart chakra on page #142. Refamiliarize yourself with all its attributes.

Explore the possibility that your heart center is an energetic entity that resembles a luminous nebulous cloud. One that extends throughout your entire body. It is an expression that by the process of awareness, one can tune into the source related to their soul purpose.

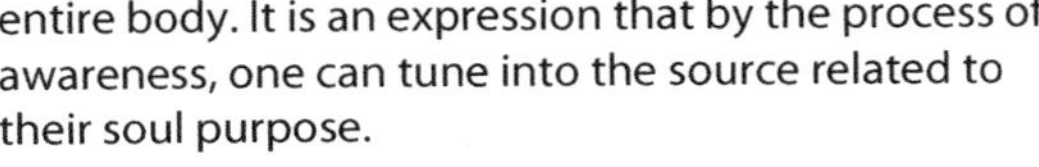

Once you've grounded yourself, are fully relaxed and in a meditative-like state, open the communication channels and ask your heart center to search deep within to present you with a symbol that represents your soul's purpose.

Once this symbol surfaces, explore its characteristics; i.e., what colors are there? What is the surface or appearance of your symbol? Are there lines, curves, open or closed loops? Are there triangles, squares or other geometrical forms? Are there any layers? Is there an imagined odor? How can its texture best be described and incorporated?

Once you are comfortable and have a good mental representation of your soul symbol, begin to draw a picture or representation of it by using crayons, pencils, scissors, glue and glitter (or whatever else you may need or want to create and render your symbol. There will be a list of questions for you to answer upon the completion of your final soul symbol.

Your soul symbol should be configured and drawn out on the next page. Please do your work in a quiet, soft neutral setting.

Please note: There are no words or instructions on the opposite page. This is because words have a tendency to bring one into a more logical mind-set, thereby restricting the creative process. You may also place a blank piece of paper over this page. Feel free to practice on as many blank sheets of paper.

Before you begin your soul exercise, here are a few items that we think you should have available:

- Crayons
- Pencils/Pens
- Paint/Glitter
- Scissors
- Any other supplies you see fit to use

Note: Remember to have fun with this creative exercise. It is critically important to keep your feeling heart open. My recommendation would be to read the instructions on this page over and over again, so that on any given day, when the time is right, you may begin the process of your soul symbol.

Symbol of Your Soul Exercise

What do you feel and think this symbol means to you?

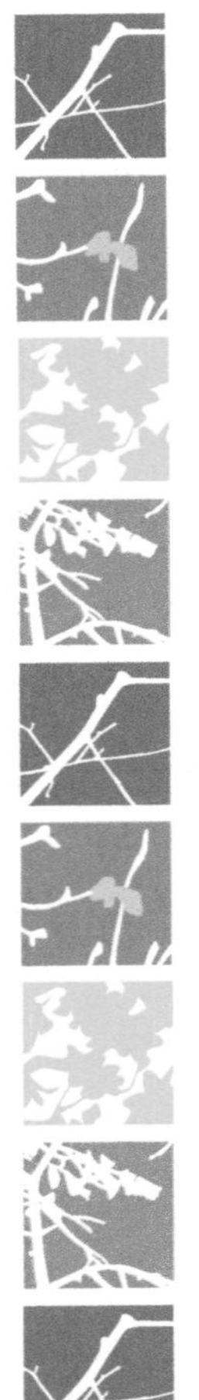

Does your symbol relate to harmony or conflict?

Do you think that your soul is trying to tell you something through this symbol?

What do you think the colors mean? Can they be explained by some of the threads in your life?

If your symbol could speak to you with words, what do you think it might be trying to tell you?

Is your soul symbol something that represents your past, present or future, or perhaps all three? Explain.

Creating Resolve Exercise

Identifying the Inner Source(s) of Conflict in Your Life

CLOSE YOUR EYES and contemplate any unresolved inner conflict or issues. Then, as rapidly as possible, finish the following stem sentences without mentally editing any of your responses.

This is how I would best describe the following conflict...

When it comes to this conflict, I should...

When it comes to this conflict, I should not...

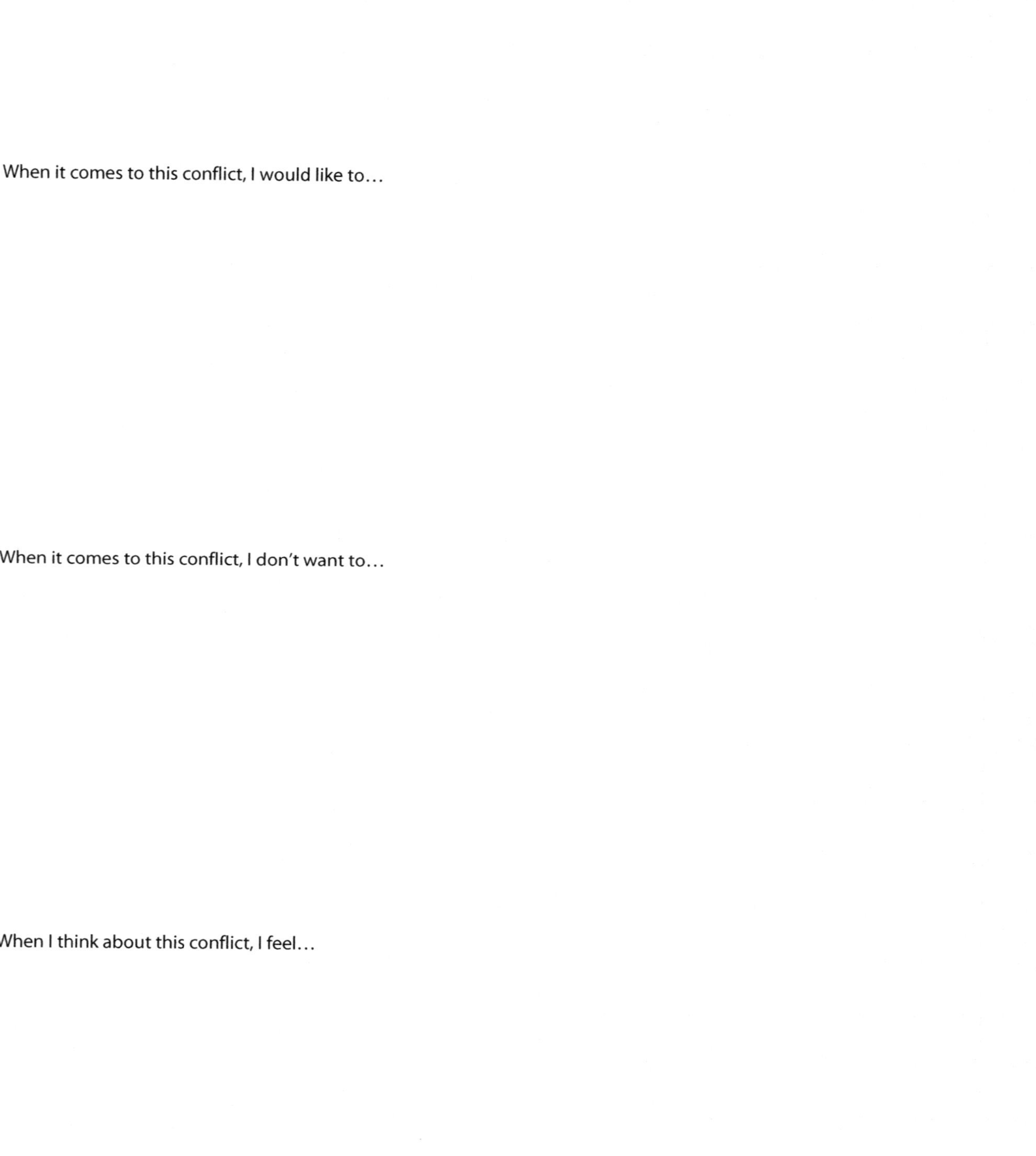

When it comes to this conflict, I would like to...

When it comes to this conflict, I don't want to...

When I think about this conflict, I feel...

Creating Resolve Exercise (cont.)

Identifying the Inner Source(s) of Conflict in Your Life

Every time this conflict comes up, I'm convinced other people think I'm…

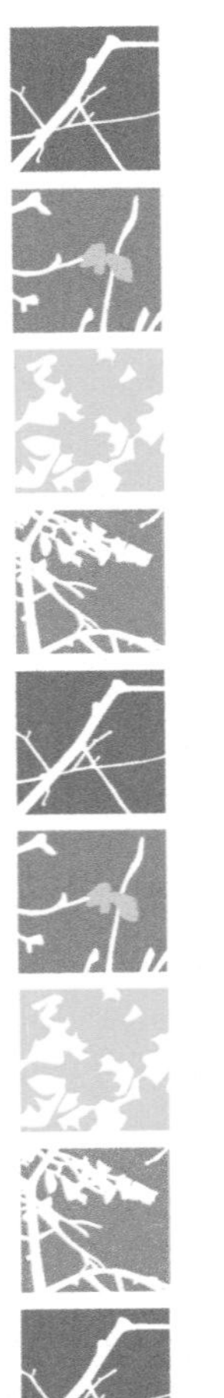

What I really want to happen with this conflict is…

If I was honest with others as to how I really feel about this conflict, they would think that…

If I had my way with this conflict, I would…

If I were really honest with myself as to how I feel about this conflict, I would know that…

The best solution I can think of when it comes to this conflict is that…

One Year From Now Exercise:

A one-year reminder of your intention

This is my goal: Write myself a letter with the intention of reading or receiving it a year from now i.e. "My name is Kim, this is my journal, and I want to remind myself, that one year from now, I..."

|MO |DAY |YR

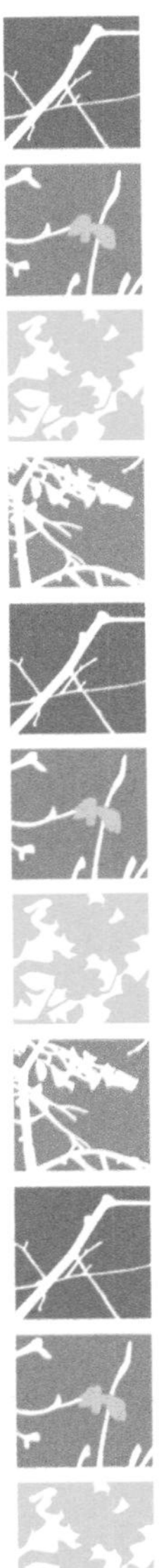

Unsaid Things...

Quotes and Releasing Unsaid

Call, write or contact someone you know or have not talked to in some years, tell them whatever it is that you've always wanted to express to them (but for some reason did not). Regardless of the circumstances, this exercise is designed to free you up on an energetic level. Sometimes, we create scenarios in our heads, and more often than not, there is no real basis for them. Is there a living relative, adversary or long-lost friend you've always wanted to tell something to but didn't? Call them and do so. If it is a person who is deceased, imagine contacting them. Communicate the things you've always wanted to say to them. Please journal your experience.

Chapter 4
Theory, Physics and Elements of Your Practice

The Eight Limbs of Yoga

1.YAMA (discipline)

The first limb of yoga covers five moral disciplines or obligations to the self and others!

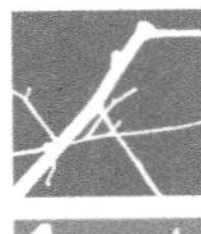

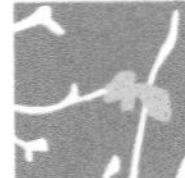

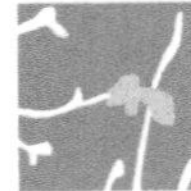

a. ahimsa (nonharming)
b. satya (truthfulness)
c. asteya (nonstealing)
d. brahmacharya (chastity)
e. aparigraha (greedlessness)

These directives help destroy negative human characteristics or conditions.

The first directive, ahimsa, is nonviolence in thought and action. Most of the world's religions emphasize this idea. Violence seems to be an integral part of human nature. It does not always take the form of physical assault, but sometimes as fear, hostility, and disapproval.

Satya is translated as real, genuine, or honest, and this is usually taken to mean one should tell the truth. It is mentioned many times in yogic literature.

Nonstealing, or asteya, is closely related to ahimsa, since stealing violates the person from whom things are taken.

Chastity, or brahmacharya, is addressed by most spiritual traditions. Generally speaking, sexual stimulation is thought to interrupt the impulse toward enlightenment by indulging the desire for sensory experience and by draining energy.

Greedlessness, or aparigraha, is defined as the nonacceptance of gifts. We are encouraged to cultivate voluntary simplicity, since possessions lead to attachment and fear of loss.

2. NIYAMA (restraint)

As the yama are concerned with our outer actions, so the niyama are concerned with our inner life. The five practices are:
a. shauca (purity)
b. samtosha (contentment)
c. tapas (austerity)
d. svadhyaya (self-study)
e. ishvara-pranidhana (devotion to god)

Shauca, or purity, is different from cleanliness. It is inner or mental purity brought about by meditation and concentration. The goal is to "mirror the light of the transcendental self with out distortion."

Contentment, or samtosha, means not coveting more than what is at hand. It is the voluntary sacrifice of what is transient anyway. Sages around the world speak of this virtue, as it equalizes pleasure and sorrow.

Austerity, or tapas, includes such practices as fasting; prolonged immobilized standing or sitting; the bearing of hunger, thirst, cold, and heat; and formal silence. These practices raise energy that is then used to achieve higher awareness. Tapas is not self-torture, however. Svadhyaya, or self-study, is not intellectual learning, but rather "the meditative pondering of truths revealed by seers and sages who have traversed those remote regions where the mind cannot follow and only the heart receives and is changed." It is one's own exploration of the hidden meanings of the scriptures.

The final part of niyama is devotion to god, or ishvara-pranidhana. The god referred to here is free of illusion, forever aware of truth.

3. ASANA (yoga posture)

The first two limbs, yama and niyama, concern the mind. Asana, or posture, expands this to involve the physical body. This is what many Westerners think of when they consider yoga practice. At first, posture was essentially immobilization of the body. Later in yoga's history, it came to mean what we recognize today, the collection of poses for therapeutic purposes. The focus at this level is on making the physical body a stable platform for the deepening of the journey toward meditative unfolding.

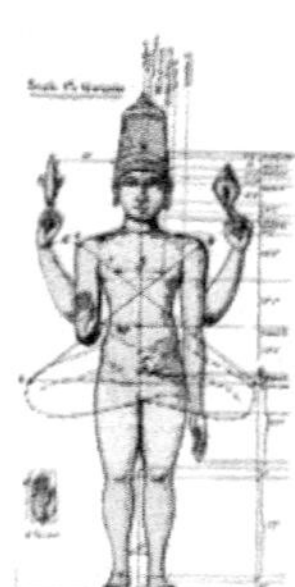

The Eight Limbs of Yoga (Cont'd)

4. PRANAYAMA (breath control)

When yogins have become aware of their inner climate and have gained control of their muscular tensions and physical state, they become more attuned to the life force as it circulates in the body. The next step is to support awareness of energy systems and emotional states through the practice of pranayama (literally "extension of prana," or life force. The idea of this life force is familiar to man cultures: the Chinese call it chi, the Polynesians mana, the Native Americans orenda. Modern scientists refer to bioplasma.

Through regulation of the breath, along with concentration, prana can be stimulated and directed, usually toward the head. As prana rises, attention follows and leads to more and more subtle experiences. Finally, pranic energy reaches the crown, and consciousness may be changed radically, leading to ecstasy (samadhi).

5. PRATYAHARA (sense withdrawal)

The practice of posture and breath control leads to the shutting out of external stimuli. When consciousness is sealed off from the environment, this is the state of sensory internalization, or pratyahara. Sanskrit texts compare this process to "a tortoise contracting its limbs." The mind grows very active when removed from sensory input. This allows for the deepest concentration.

6. DHARANA (concentration)

Concentration is the focusing of attention to a given locus (desha) which may be a particular part of the body, such as a chakra or an external object such as the image of a deity. This is a highly intensified form of the concentration we experience every day. The difference is that dharana is "a whole-body experience free from muscular and other tension, and therefore with an extraordinary dimension of psychic depth, in which the creative inner work can unfold." This is both difficult and sometimes dangerous work. Yogic concentration is a high-energy state, and it is easy to see how this psychic energy could go awry.

7. DHYANA (meditation)

Deep concentration leads naturally to a state of meditative contemplation, or dhayana. All thoughts regard the object of concentration and accompany a state of peaceful, calm disposition. Alertness is intensified rather than dulled, although there is little or no awareness of the external environment.

8. SAMADHI (ecstasy)

The final limb is elusive and difficult to define fully. Samadhi occurs when "all the fluctuations (vritti of ordinary waking consciousness are entirely stilled through meditation. Psychologists and practitioners have differently interpreted it.

While many texts and teachers refer to the hierarchy of the eight limbs, the vast number of Western students begin formally with the third limb of practice (asana). The first five techniques are often called the outer limbs of practice, while the remaining three more subtle aspects are called the inner limbs. The linear progression through these practices is only one way of conceptualizing them. Because each limb has as its ultimate goal the realization of "ultimate truth", one could start from any lace and cultivate practice from that point. It is useful to consider the eight limbs a circular progression rather than a tree with higher and lower branches. One can also focus practice on only one limb while maintaining awareness of the underlying unity between all the limbs.

McAfee, John. The Secret of the Yamas: A Spiritual Guide to Yoga. Woodland Publications, 2001. pp. 19-21.

Feuerstein, Georg. The Yoga Tradition. Hohm Press, AZ, 1998.

Introduction to the Eight Limbs Infinity Loop™

Pratyahara Dharana Dhyana Samadhi

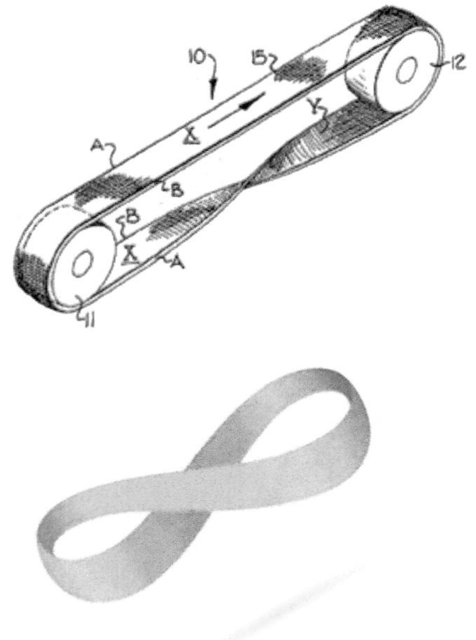

Welcome to the Eight Limbs Infinity Loop™ exercise. Whether you're aware of it or not, you probably see the Infinity loop (below) tens, if not a hundreds of times a day. It is everywhere! On every soda can, glass bottle, plastics and paper. It is the recycling symbol of our modern times. The interesting thing about the infinity loop is that there are no two continuous sides to it— at least not in the conventional sense of the word. That said, the infinity loop is really just a one-sided loop coming back onto itself through a half twist. Again, there are no delineations of having more then one side such as in a regular flat strip of paper. In the old days of conveyor belts, there was but one side used, and until it was worn it had to be replaced. And then, in 1949, Owen H. Harris came up with the brilliant idea of half turning one side of the belt (180 degrees) onto the other end to form a mobius strip (or loop). The same belt now lasts much longer than the one-sided belt. Why? Well, because instead of the belt revolving over the rollers again and again (from one side only, now the infinity belt (loop spins around (to move merchandise from both sides of the belt, thereby minimizing the wear and tear of the otherwise, one-sided belt. One of the reasons I chose to incorporate the Infinity Loop exercise into this yoga book is because the eight limbs (branches) of yoga are no different. As a matter of fact, it is a bit ironic that the infinity loop looks like and has the same meaning as the number 8.

Therefore, imagine that as illustrated above, there were the first three or four limbs of yoga printed on the closest side of the strip. And then, on the farthest side of the strip were the other four or five limbs of yoga. As mentioned earlier in the book, the first three or four limbs of yoga are considered to be the outer limbs while the second set of four or five are considered to be the inner limbs. Truth be told, all eight limbs of yoga work in conjunction to each other. More to the point, the eight limbs of yoga may be interdependent and one can enter into the "path" from any order. For example, some people enter yoga by practicing Asana, Pranayama, Meditation, Sense withdraw and even Samadhi.

One of the main ideas of this book is to impart the notion that, through the awareness of yoga, one, invariably passes through all the eight limbs of yoga-- it's just a matter of time before it becomes apparent. To the left edge of this page you will see printed the last four limbs of yoga. Now on the other side of this same page you will see the first four limbs of yoga. Together, both sides of this page contain all eight limbs. And when you take the time to cut it out (along the dashed lines), they will then have a thin strip of paper with the eight limbs. Now, if you follow the directions on the next page you will see that when one end of the strip of paper is turned 180° and attached to the opposite end of the strip, you will have created your very first Eight Limbs Infinity Loop or mobius strip. Again, it goes something like this: let's say you have a strip of paper and that on the one side (we'll call that side A) you glue a bread crumb onto the center of it. And then you set or place an ant or some other bug on the other side (we'll call this side B). Now, if the ant could only travel from one long end of the other (without crossing over the sides) to get the crumb, it would have no choice but to cross over the side edge to get it. But with an infinity loop, the ant just travels along the same long edge, finally reaching its crumb; no crossover necessary.

On another note, the infinity loop is nothing more than a feedback loop. There are two kinds of feedback loops: positive and negative. Each serves a very specific function. However, it is indeed the negative feedback loop that mimics an infinity loop. Infinity loops are in fact negative feedback loops. They create stability. The principles of the caduceus are also an infinity loop. Yes, it creates and maintains balance biologically, electrically, mechanically and spiritually. Many of the things in life are regulated by nature's ways; "That which is above is from that which is below, and that which is below is from that which is above, working the miracles of one."

Directions for making the Eight Limbs Infinity Loop™

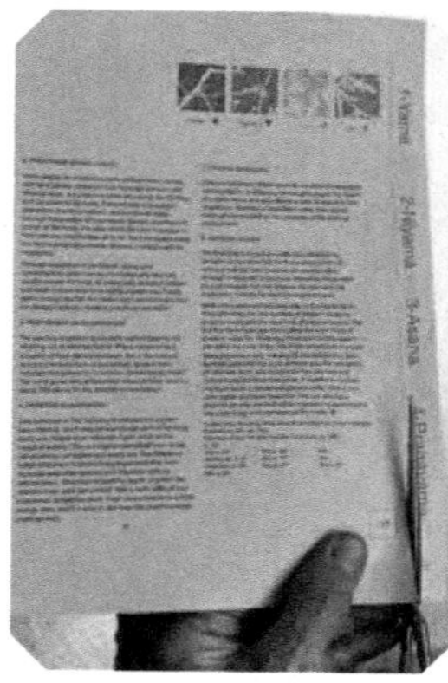

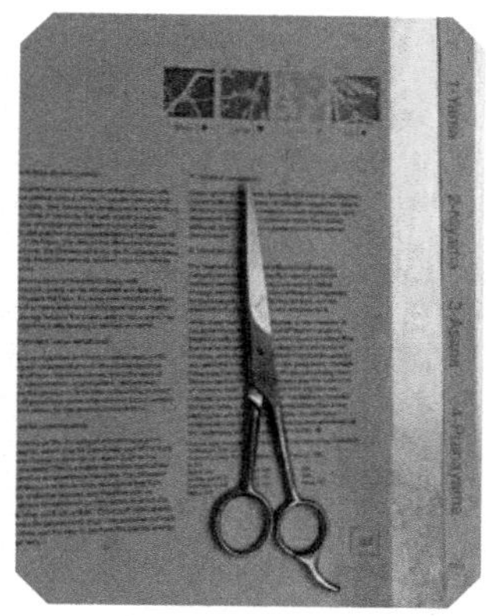

In the top row of this page you will see three images. The one in the middle best represents what an Eight Limbs Infinity Loop™ is all about. The picture on the top left shows how that on page 157 the infinity or mobius strip is being cut out (with scissors) from that page.

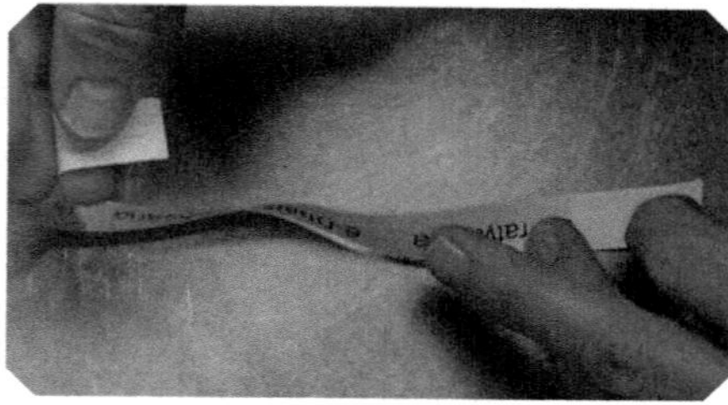

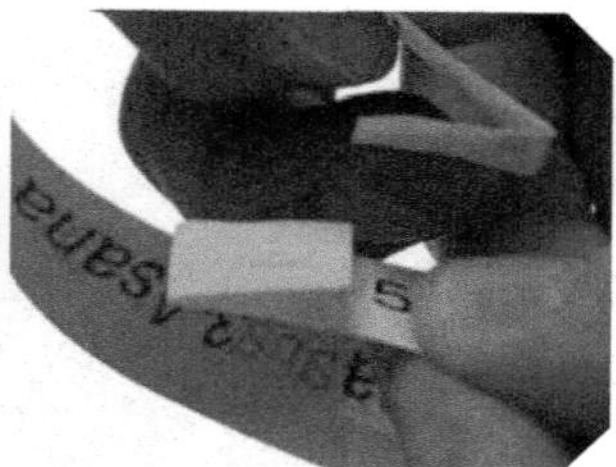

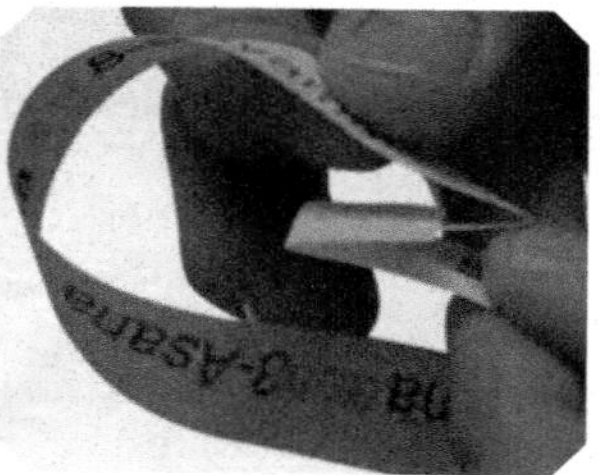

The left most picture (middle row) shows the cut infinity loop strip. As is pictured, when the strip lay flat to the surface of a table it has two fold marks at either end of the strip. Simply fold each end at the dotted line and then take just one end and put a half twist in the strip-- in other words turn one end over 180°. Once the ends have been folded with the half twist, simply interlock the two folds.

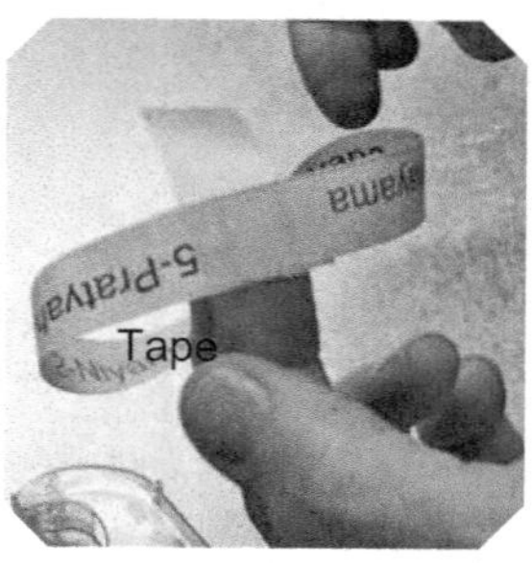

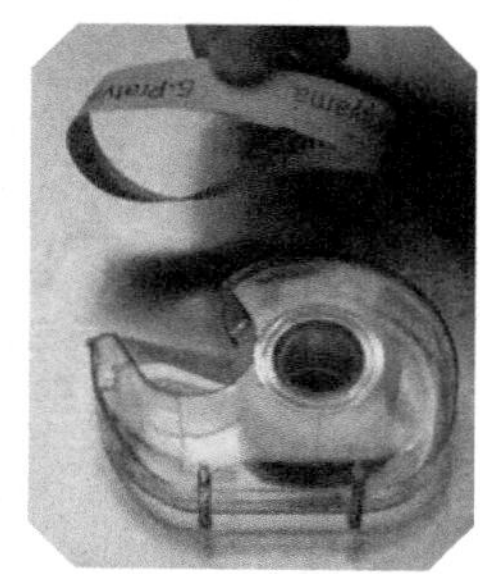

While holding the two folded ends of the newly formed infinity loop simply tape the folds in place as is shown in the lower left picture. Tape should be about 1 1/4" long. When finished, it should look like the Eight Limbs Infinity Loop™ as is pictured on the far lower right. Now spin loop through your fingers to visualize how it is that all the eight limbs of yoga work their magic through the vehicle of your own life!

Positions and Planes of the Body[1]

ANATOMICAL POSITION

Begin by standing erect, feet and palms facing forward.

PLANES

1. Median (midsagittal) – front to back in the midline, parallel to the long axis
2. Sagittal – front to back, parallel to the long axis
3. Frontal (coronal) – side to side, parallel to the long axis
4. Transverse (horizontal) – front to back
5. Perpendicular to the long axis

DIRECTIONS

1. Anterior (ventral) / Posterior (dorsal) – front / back
2. Superior (cephelad) / Inferior (caudad) – up / down
3. Medial / Lateral / Median – toward midline / away from midline / in the midline
4. Proximal / Distal – nearer to / farther from a reference point (often but not always the midline)
5. External / Internal – outside / inside
6. Ipsilateral / Contralateral –
7. Same side / Supine / Prone – lying on back/ stomach
8. Valgus – angles lateral from point of reference (i.e. genu valgus)
9. Varus – angles medial from point of reference (i.e. genu varus)

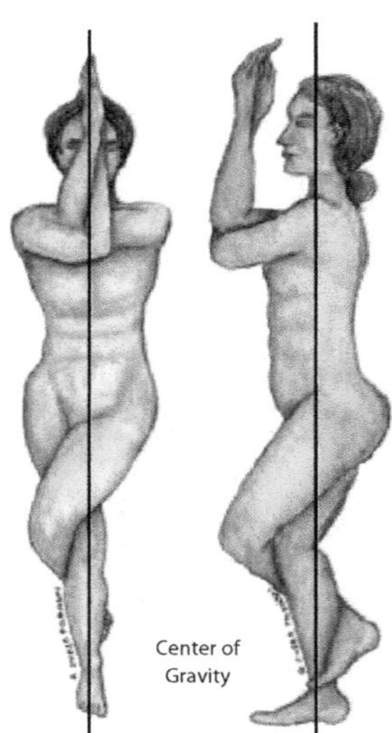

An erect human body strives to maintain its plumb line of gravity perpendicular to the gravitational field of the earth. Centers of gravity, judged three-dimensionally, a re an important focus for yoga practice.

MOVEMENTS

1. Flexion / Extension – decrease/increase angle between 2 structures (usually in sagittal plane)
2. Abduction/Adduction – away from /toward midline (nonmidline structures only) (usually in coronal plane)
3. Lateral flexion – bend sideways (midline structures only)
4. Rotation – medial (internal) / lateral (external)
5. Circumduction – combination of 1 and 2 and sometimes 3
6. Protraction/Retraction – push out/pull in
7. Elevation/Depression – lift up/pull down
8. Dorsiflexion / Plantar Flexion – (foot) toestoward chin / point toes
9. Inversion / Eversion – (foot) sole medial/lateral
   a) Supination/pronation
      Forearm – palm forward (up)/backward (down)
   b) Foot – inversion/eversion
10. Opposition – tip of thumb toward tips of other finger

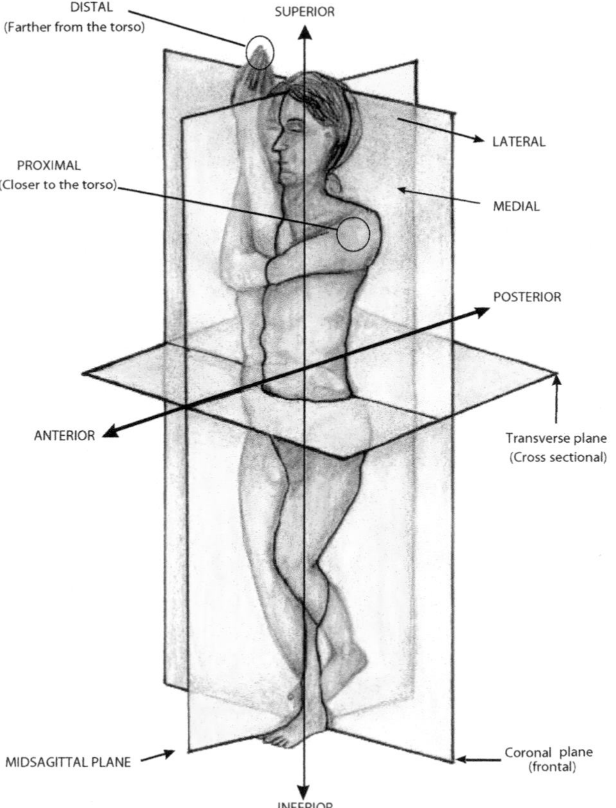

PLANES OF THE BODY (Garudasana)

[1] Adapted from "Joint Motion," American Academy of Orthopaedic Surgeons, 1965.

Principles of Alignment

FIRST, SECOND AND THIRD CLASS LEVERS

All levers use the principle of opposing two forces about a fixed pivot or fulcrum. The fulcrum pits an effort force (EF) against a resistance force (RF), and its placement can greatly ease the task of moving an object or working through a pose. The distance from an EF to a given fulcrum is called the force arm (FA) while the distance from the same fulcrum to a Resistance Force is the system's resistance arm (RA). The body uses three classes of levers for yoga.

FIRST CLASS LEVER can be compared to a seesaw. A fulcrum rests at the center of gravity in such a system; an EF and an RF balance each other on either side of the fulcrum.

A prime example of first class lever in the human body is the neck joint. The atlas, the uppermost vertebra of the cervical (neckspine is a fulcrum that bears the weight of the head. The head's center of gravity is slightly above and to the fore of the atlas, but this first class lever system allows counterbalance and movement with minimal muscular effort. Other examples of first class levers are the pelvis, which balances on the heads of the legs' femurs, and even each femur itself balances on the tibia below it. Poor posture or muscular dysfunction can seriously fatigue and even disrupt lever function and lead to serious, painful consequences.

SECOND CLASS LEVERS

The principle of opposing two forces about a fixed pivot or fulcrum finds a different arrangement in the second class lever. Here, the RF is between the EF and the fulcrum. The length of the effort arm is much longer than the length of the resistance arm. In lever systems, the placement as well as the distance between the pivot and the forces in play can significantly increase or decrease the work of the muscles involved. Pushing the body up on one's toes exemplifies use of a second class lever system. The EF exerted by powerful calf muscles through the Achilles tendon uses the ball of the foot as a fulcrum. Dancers and construction workers alike can testify that this is an exhausting effort.

THIRD CLASS LEVERS

Third class levers depend not just upon an Effort Force opposing a RF about a fulcrum, but the importance of placement and distance between these components. Where the human body uses third class levers, it favors mobility and agility over efficiency and power. Third class levers operate like a construction crane: EF is applied close to a fulcrum and often distant from the RF.

With FIRST CLASS LEVERS, two forces are exerted on either side of an axis, much as with a seesaw. A natural lever arrangement of hard bone allows muscles to work and fine-tune activity with efficient ease.

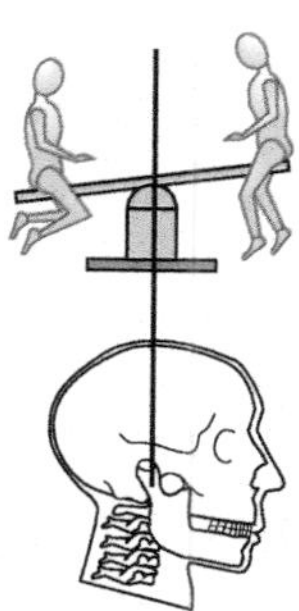

As a SECOND CLASS LEVER, the foot pushes the body off the ground as the Achilles tendon is drawn upward by the calf muscles. The ball of the foot functions as a fulcrum. This is much like pulling the handles of a wheelbarrow up and forward. Here, the wheel is a fulcrum.

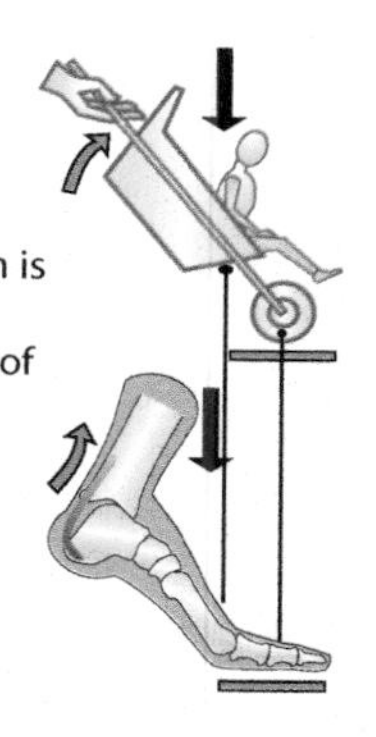

The THIRD CLASS LEVER is essentially a crane. The EF is close to the fulcrum, and the distance to the RF makes a considerable difference in the power required to accomplish work.

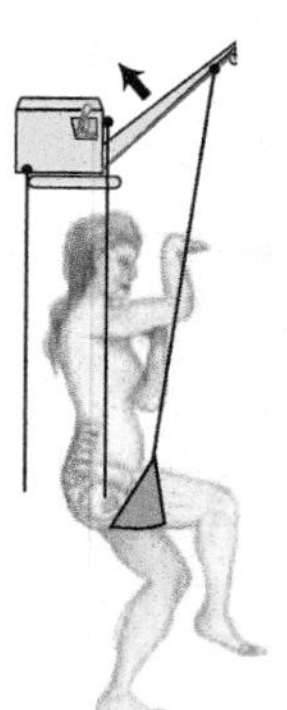

Alignment and Form

Motion of the Arm and the Shoulder

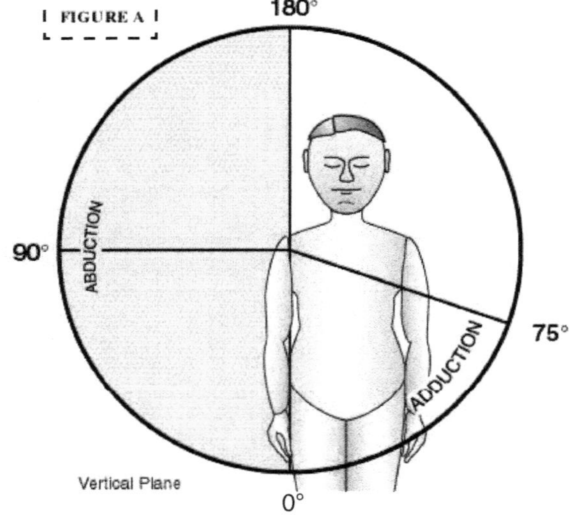

GENERAL OBSERVATIONS ABOUT DESCRIBING ARM-AT-SHOULDER MOTION

At its shoulder joint, the arm has a nearly full range of global motion. Useful, meaningful descriptions of the position of an arm relative to the shoulder require reference to both the vertical and horizontal planes in which they operate. For all too long, medical and therapeutic literature has applied terms such as "forward flexion," "abduction," and "backward extension," which focus on the vertical or upward movement of the arm. A consistent and universally recognized terminology for defining horizontal motion is only being developed in recent years. And it is still best to describe arm-at-shoulder motions by first illustrating them and then immediately clarifying the terms used in any given text.

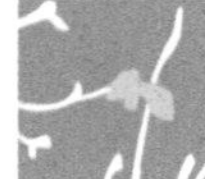

DISTINGUISHING MODES OF ARM-AT-SHOULDER MOTION

In moving the arm at the shoulder, two modes of motion come into play: true glenohumeral motion (shoulder and arm, and scapulothoracic motion shoulder blade and trunk movement).

True glenohumeral motion is a smooth, rhythmical upward rising of the arm at the shoulder from 0° to a full 180°. such an act however also brings into play scapulothoracic motion, an upward and forward rotation of the scapula on the chest wall.

The shoulder is capable of a nearly 360° range of global rotation and arm-at-shoulder motion is best examined and described by having a person stand while performing arm rotations. A subject who is lying down is restricted to only 180°.

I. Vertical (Upward Motion of the shoulder

Figure A | Abduction and Adduction

Abduction is the raising of the extended arm up and away from the side of the body (in its coronal plane). The angle of the arm can range from 0° through 180° in this plane. Adduction refers to the opposite motion of the arm, that is, toward the torso's midline or beyond it, in an upward plane.

Figure B | Forward Flexion (Forward Elevation) and Backward Extension

If the arm is raised forward and upward out to where the hand is in front of the body (in the anterior sagittal plane), this is termed "Forward Flexion." It can range in this motion from 0° to 180°. A motion opposite to this act is called "depression" of the arm.

"Backward extension" requires moving the arm backward and upward, behind the body (in the posterior sagittal plane). The nature of this joint restricts such motion within a range from 0° to about 60°.

II. Horizontal (Sideway) Motion Of The Shoulder

Figure C | Horizontal Flexion

"Horizontal Flexion" refers to motion within a level plane in front of the body and level with the arm and shoulder joint (that is, motion in the horizontal plane anterior to the coronal plane across the body.)

"Horizontal Extension" is a counter-motion, movement in the horizontal plane posterior to the coronal plane across the body.

Alignment and Form (cont.)

Motion of the Arm and the Shoulder

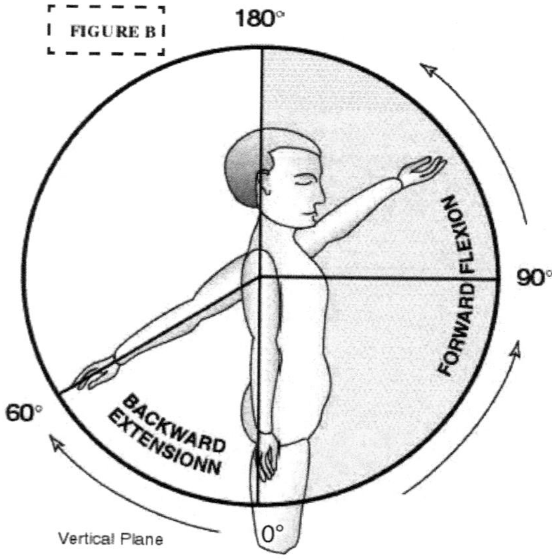

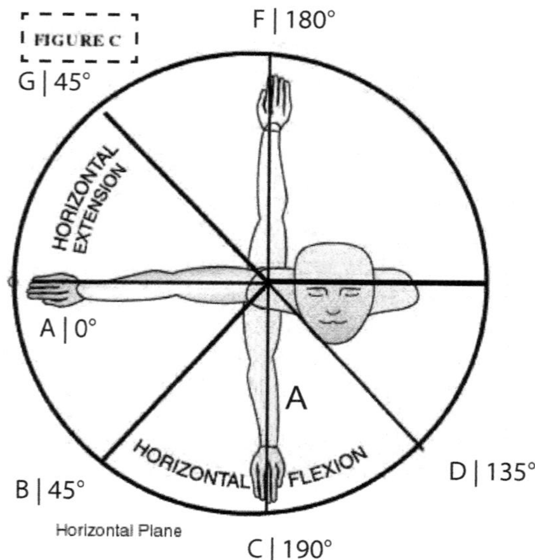

Please note: Similar movements apply to the legs. However, normal range of motion of the legs is completely different from the arms.

DESCRIPTIONS OF THE UPWARD MOTIONS OF THE ARM IN VARIOUS HORIZONTAL POSITIONS

A) Neutral Abduction

The motion of the arm up and away from the side of the body in a range from 0° to 180°. This motion, "neutral abduction," can extend from position G to position C.

B) Abduction at 45° of Horizontal Flexion

The motion of the arm up and away from the side of the body while maintaining 45° of horizontal flexion. when, for example, the horizontal flexion remains 45° and the upward motion is 90°, the proper description is "90° of abduction at 45° of horizontal flexion." Note that this describes the position of the arm in two planes: the abduction is the vertical, and the flexion is horizontal.

C) Forward Flexion

If the arm is moved upward, or vertically, directly in front of the body and within a range of 0° to 180°, this motion is referred to as "forward flexion."

D) Abduction in 135° of Horizontal Flexion

If the arm is moved upward, as in position D (left) this adduction of the arm is described as "adduction in 135° of horizontal flexion."

E) Neutral Adduction of the Arm

The arm hangs parallel to the side of the body.

F) Backward Extension

The arm is moved upward, vertically, directly behind the body as shown above.

G) Abduction of the Arm at 45° of Horizontal Extension

The arm is moved upward, vertically, at an angle of 45° relative to the body as shown above.

Yoga Pose Classification[1]

THE EIGHT DIFFERENT CLASSIFICATIONS OF YOGA POSES

STANDING ASANAS

Standing postures have the unique capability of allowing us to feel connected to the earth through our feet, while allowing us to feel that we can rise up to infinite possibilities. In other words, they teach us how to keep a strong, steady base even as we extend ourselves from around our center of mass. Although generally, they are not classified as pure balancing poses, they all contain an element of balance in their execution. From a physical standpoint, standing poses allow us to fairly easily activate the muscles and joints.

Standing poses can be classified as symmetrical or asymmetrical. Symmetrical poses have both sides of the body doing the same thing. Some examples include Tadasana and Utkatasana. Asymmetrical poses have each side of the body doing something different. Poses such as Utthita Trikonasana and Virabhadrasana I and II are examples of asymmetrical poses.

In general, for each asymmetrical pose done on one side, it should be practiced on the other side as well.

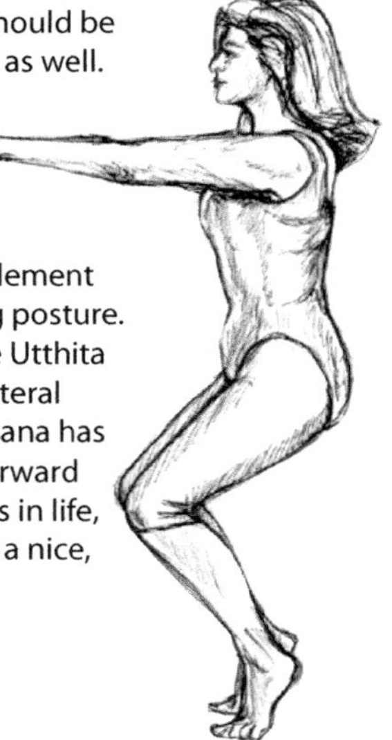

Standing poses can also include characteristics of other types of postures. Already mentioned is the element of balance in each standing posture. Another example would be Utthita Trikonasana, which has a lateral bend element to it. Utkatasana has some characteristics of a forward bend. Thus, like most things in life, asanas don't always fit into a nice, clean box.

LATERAL BENDS

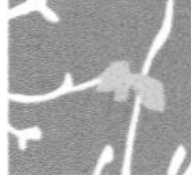

In our daily activities, pure lateral bending is uncommon. Typically, if we reach for something to our left side, we will displace the hips backward and to the left, while the chest and shoulders move forward and to the left. This type of movement decreases the amount of lateral bend in any given movement. In contrast, in lateral bend asanas, to get the most benefit from the posture, we want to maximize the lateral flexion and extension of the torso by limiting the rotation of the hips, chest and shoulders.

Lateral bend asanas have many benefit. They build strength and stability in the musculature of the pelvis, spine, rib cage, and shoulders. They aid in maintaining the elasticity of the rib cage, which in turn, increases breathing capacity. Also, by alternately compressing and stretching the kidneys, intestines, liver, and other abdominal organs, lateral bends stimulate the function of these organs.

In all lateral bend asanas, it is important to lengthen the spine with each inhalation, which creates more space between the vertebrae. In that way, you can maximize the potential for lateral flexion without compressing the intervertebral discs. Further, by extending the arm on the side that is being stretched, and keeping it in line with the shoulder and torso, you can maximize the stretch of the muscles and connective tissue of the rib cage and torso.

1 Adapted from Jane Alenier, Ryt Yoga Pose Classification, 2005.

Yoga Pose Classification (cont.)

THE EIGHT DIFFERENT CLASSIFICATIONS OF YOGA POSES

BALANCING ASANAS

Usually, when we think of balancing postures, we think of postures where we are standing on one leg, even though all standing poses have some element of balance in them. This section will cover those standing postes where balance is the primary element.

In general, balancing postures strengthen the body and improve mental concentration. However, once you possess a threshold level of strength, concentration is probably more important than strength for maintaining balance—if concentration is lacking, no amount of strength will keep you from falling. Try to maintain Vrkshasana (tree pose) while thinking about what the yoga student next to you is doing. You will probably fall out of the pose!

Balancing postures can teach us many life lessons. Using Vrkshasana again as an example, in order to stay upright, your standing leg has to continually make adjustments. These adjustments are so great that they can typically be seen with the naked eye. What can we learn from this visual lesson, and thus teach our students? In order to be grounded, you must be willing to adapt. But the reverse is true as well. If we adapt too much, we will lose our balance in the pose, as well as in our lives.

FORWARD BEND ASANAS

In our daily lives, we perform forward bending much more than we do back bending. For example, it is quite common to reach forward to grab something by forward bending. In addition, many of us spend hours forward bending by sitting in chairs at the office, home or elsewhere. However, unless we make a conscious effort to do otherwise, much of the forward bending we do throughout the day is done with a rounded back and the hips thrust forward, which can put excessive strain on the lower back.

Forward bends can be classified as symmetrical, e.g., Uttanasana, or asymmetrical, e.g. Parsvottanasana. Generally, asymmetrical forward bends isolate and deepen the stretching effects on one side of the body, while symmetrical bends work both sides of the body equally. Also, many postures have elements of forward bending in them, but may be classified in another way. For example, Adho Mukha Svanasana could be considered a forward bend, but it also has an inversion character to it.

Forward bends can be performed in a supine position, e.g., Apanasana, seated, e.g., Pascimatanasana, kneeling, e.g., Garbhasana, or standing, e.g., Uttanasana. Generally, supine and kneeling forward bends are simpler and safer than the other types of forward bends and thus are appropriate for beginners. Standing bends, by the use of gravity, allow for the greatest range of motion.

Seated postures are typically the most restrictive, and while they can allow for deep stretching, they have the greatest risk for causing injury due to the tendency to bend from the lower back while seated, rather than from the hip.

Depending on the particular posture, forward bend asanas have many benefits. Forward bends stretch and strengthen the spine, the entire length of the erector spinae muscles, and other posterior muscles and ligaments that stabilize the vertebrae. They also strengthen the abdominal muscles and massage the intestines, kidneys and adrenal glands, stimulating the working of these organs. Forward bends enhance hip flexibility and thus help prepare us to be able to sit comfortably for meditation. Forward bends also have great mental benefit. They generally are soothing to the nervous system, thus creating a feeling of calm, reduced stress, and lowered levels of anxiety.

Yoga Pose Classification [1]

EIGHT DIFFERENT CLASSIFICATIONS OF YOGA ASANA

TWIST ASANAS

Twist asanas offer many benefits. They build strength and flexibility in the abdominal muscles, and maintain the elasticity of the intervertebral discs and ligaments. By alternately compressing and stretching the chest and abdominal areas, twists stimulate respiratory function and the functioning of the abdominal organs.

Twisting can also correct the body's bilateral asymmetry. During our daily activities, if we habitually twist more to one side, this will distort the body's symmetry, eventually creating structural problems. This problem is more common than you may think. Always holding the groceries on the same side, shoveling snow from one side, favoring one side when sleeping, or any number of other activities that incorporate twists create a situation where one side is favored over the other. Since twisting, by its nature, is asymmetrical, a conscious twisting practice as part of an overall yoga routine offers the opportunity to correct imbalances in the body's symmetry.

There are certain precautions that should be taken when twisting. By their very character, twists compress the intervertebral discs. If there are preexisting conditions that make the spine already compressed e.g., hyperkyphosis, hyperlordosis, or scoliosis, it is especially important to avoid too much force in the twist when using the arms or legs as levers, and to make sure to lengthen the spine on the inhalation. In all twists, the rotation should be generated from the abdomen by contracting the abdominal muscles on the exhalation, rather than forcing the rotation with arm or leg leverage.

SEATED ASANAS

Seated asanas often have characteristics of other types of postures. For example, Paschimotasana is a seated posture, however the primary focus is forward bending. In this section, we will cover two of the seated poses that don't easily fit into other categories: Dandasana and Baddha Konasana.

Dandasana is the seated equivalent of Tadasana. It teaches us the proper way to sit and is the foundation for all the other seated poses. It can look deceptively simple, yet it has numerous benefits. When great attention is paid to alignment, Dandasana opens and lifts the chest, strengthens the abdominal muscles, and improves muscular stamina of the lumbar spine and legs. Also, since many people can easily hold it for extended periods, Dandasana provides a wonderful opportunity to explore the subtlety of movement in a calm and conscious manner. Emotionally, Dandasana helps focus the mind and reduces stress.

Baddha Konasana extends the spine, flexes the hips, and promotes good urinary and reproductive health. Ideally, the lumbar spine in Baddha Konasana is in exactly the same position as that of Dandasana. However, having the soles of the feet together and close to the perineum prevents forward rotation of the pelvis. This, in turn, makes it difficult to fully extend the spine and can create a rounding of the back. If you find our back curving as you bring your feet closer to the perineum, move the feet farther forward.

Baddha Konasana also has a forward bend element to it. As you begin to bend forward in Baddha Konasana, bringing the head toward the feet, practice humility. The head is symbolic of the ego, and the feet are symbols of humility and peace. Joining the head and feet together can help create a more humble and reflective personality.

Yoga Pose Classification (cont.)

EIGHT DIFFERENT CLASSIFICATIONS OF YOGA ASANA

BACKBEND ASANAS

In ordinary activities through out the day, we may typically spend a lot of time hunched forward, whether due to sitting for prolonged periods at our desks or other activities. Backbends counteract the effects of constantly hunching over, and thus can help improve our posture. They can stretch and strengthen many muscles of the body, including the illiopsoas muscles, an important link between the spine and the legs. Backbends also gently massage the abdominal organs, stimulating their function. Generally, they are energizing and can help relieve depression and provide greater focus.

Backbends can stretch and strengthen different muscle groups depending on the type of backbend that is being practiced. For example, in prone backbends, such as Bhujangasana or Ardha Shalabasana, you are lifting your body up against gravity and returning to the starting position with the help of gravity. Thus, in these types of postures, you are primarily strengthening the posterior musculature of the back and hips.

In contrast, other types of backbends, such as Ustrasana, work the opposite way; gravity assists the movements into the posture, but you are going against gravity to come out of it. These types of backbends tend to facilitate a deep stretching of the iliopsoas muscles as well as provide anterior stretching of the chest and abdominal areas.

Probably the most difficult aspect of back bending is lengthening the entire spine so that the effort can be spread over a greater area of the back. A common error is to put too much effort into the lumbar region, which can cause unnecessary compression in that area of the spine.

INVERSION ASANAS

Inversion asanas have many benefits. These benefits are collectively known as "viparita karani" or "active reversal." Through their effect of turning the body upside down, inversions tone many organs in the body, stimulate the adrenal glands, and strengthen the muscles, ligaments, and connective tissues. In addition, inversions help improve posture, digestion, circulation, and respiration. Emotionally, they can lift your spirits. They also promote balance and efficiency in the entire body. However, in order to realize the "active reversal" effect, it is important to stay in the posture without stressing the body in any way whatsoever.

Any posture where the head is below the waist, or the legs are raised above the head, has some inversion quality to it and thus provides at least some of the benefits of inversions. However, this section mainly includes those postures where the inversion is the primary effect.

The most common risk while performing inversions such as Halasana and Sarvangasana is injury to the neck. This risk can be cumulative, and may manifest years later. Thus, it is critical to honor any input that tells you to go slowly or not at all. Proper sequencing and keen attention to alignment will help minimize the risk of injury.

1 Adapted from Jane Alenier, Ryt Yoga Pose Classification, 2005.

21 Yoga Warm-ups for the Body

Warm-up Sequences from Head to Toes

Instructions › Background

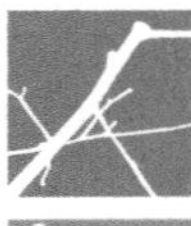
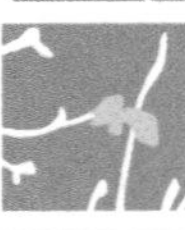

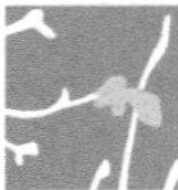

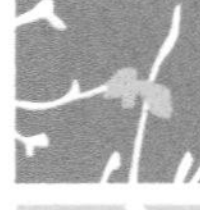

DEFINITION

Warm-ups are gentle yoga movements. They are usually done in repetition, on each side, and should not stress the body.

The purpose of the warm-up is twofold: (1) to gently provide a stretch that will increase warmth and blood flow to the area, and lubricate joints; and (2target muscle and joint groups for later postures in a class.

Warm-ups can be postures that have been broken down to their essential actions on the body structure.

BENEFITS

1. Increases body temperature, blood flow and breathing, and lubricate connective tissues so that they become pliable for greater range of motion. Increase neuronal signals between muscles and nervous system.
2. Provides greater somatic awareness of the body. Increase the flow of subtle energy, or prana, that connects body parts as a whole.
3. Provide an opportunity for safe exploration of range of motion so that unconscious efforts to accomplish a pose do not lead to strained tissues, muscle pulls, or bone misalignments.

GENERAL GUIDELINES

1. Link flowing breath with the movements for an ideal work-breath duration.
2. Flow from one gentle movement into the next.
3. Slow movements are the basis and foundation of warm-ups.
4. Warm-ups can be held in full extension of a pose after several movements in and out of a sequence.
5. Be creative and spontaneous, but give some thought to possible warm-ups.

LEADING TIPS

1. Start slowly. Deepen respiration, and release any natural sounds that may be held inside the body. Pause briefly between each warm-up sequence to feel the results on an experiential level.
2. Keep the focus simple on the sensations in the area engaged in the warm-up and then on surrounding areas. Consider doing a feeling study: comparing an area warmed up with an area that has not yet been attended to.
3. In case of dizziness breathe, and slow the warm-up sequence down. Rest momentarily. There are many possible reasons for dizziness. The increase in oxygen to the system can override the brain's ability to function. Come to a squatting position, or rest in child's pose.
4. Facilitate the flow of breath with warm-ups for pranayama experiences later in a sequence. Using deep breathing and exhaling through the mouth with sounds to relax the body serves to create gentle vibrations inside, increase prana flow, and decrease toxin levels.

Head, Neck & Shoulders › Supine

HEAD ROTATIONS #1

- Inhale and lengthen tailbone from spine to crown of head.
- Exhale and rotate head to look over right shoulder.
- Inhale, back to center. Repeat to left.
- Repeat above, and after head rotates, drop the chin to the right shoulder gently pressing the left shoulder to ground.
- Repeat to left.

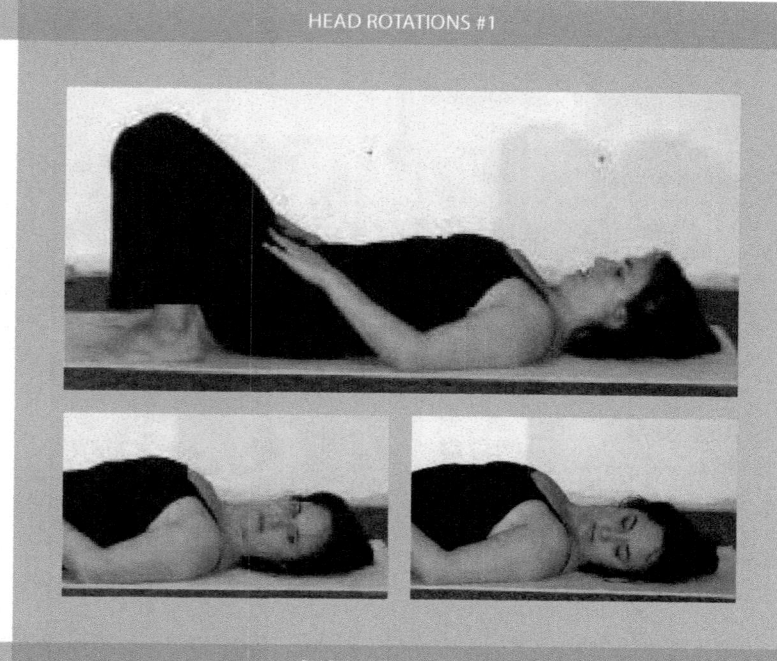

SHOULDER ROCKS #2

- Clasp elbows, making arms perpendicular to body.
- Exhale and move elbows to the right, keeping lower arms perpendicular to spine.
- Inhale to center and exhale to left.
- Repeat above, turning head in direction of arm movement.

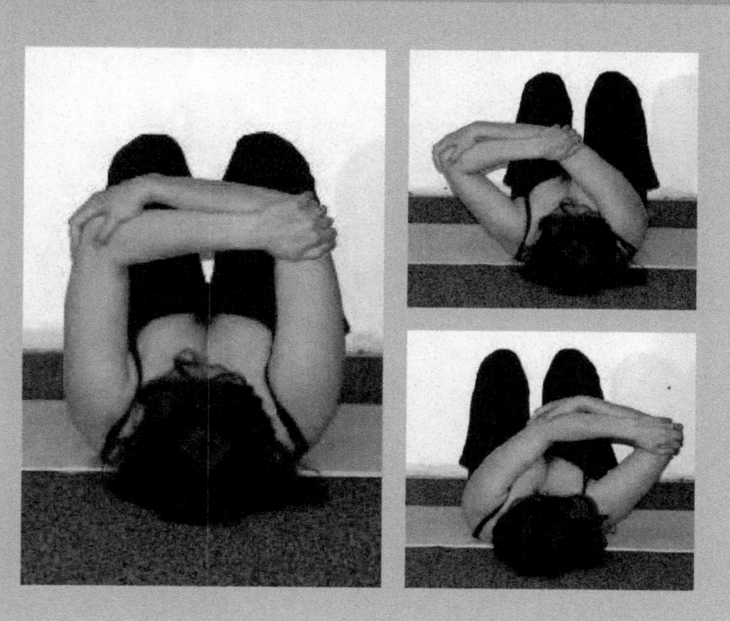

Head, Neck & Shoulders › Seated or Standing

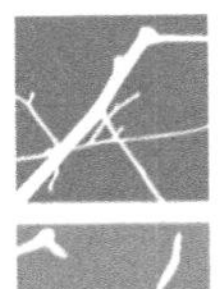
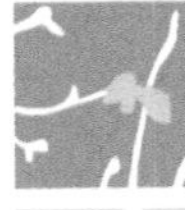

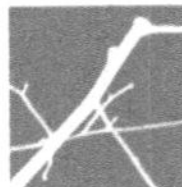

NECK STRETCH #3

- Inhale and lengthen spine. Exhale and drop chin to chest, keeping chest open and shoulder blades working down and back. Exhale, and move right ear to right shoulder. Inhale to center. Exhale to left. Inhale to center.
- Exhale and move right ear to diagonal between sternum and right shoulder, Inhale to center. Exhale and look over right shoulder. Inhale lengthen spine. Exhale and drop chin to shoulder. Inhale to center. Repeat on left side.
- Exhale and drop chin to diagonal between sternum and right shoulder. Inhale to center. Repeat to left.

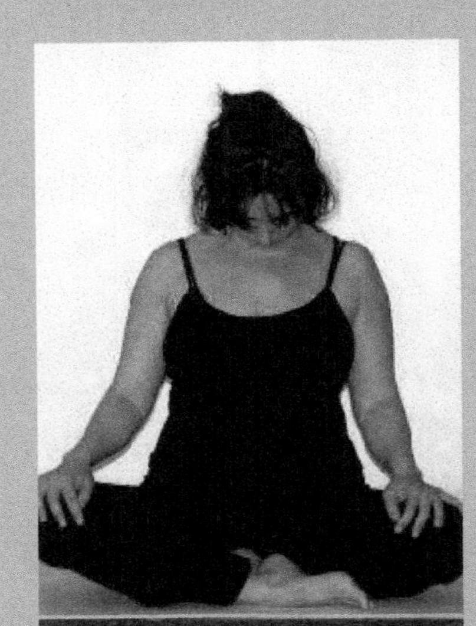

1/2 NECK CIRLCES #4

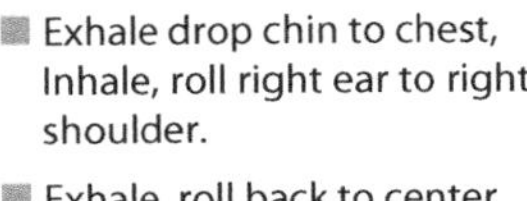

- Exhale drop chin to chest, Inhale, roll right ear to right shoulder.
- Exhale, roll back to center. Inhale, roll left ear to left shoulder.
- Move back and forth, making gentle half circles.
- NOTE: Never drop the head backwards into circles, as this can stress the central cervical vertebrae.

Head, Neck & Shoulders > Seated or Standing

NECK STRETCH WITH SHOULDER ROLLS #5

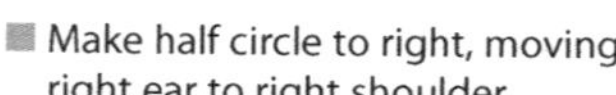

- Make half circle to right, moving right ear to right shoulder.
- Rotate left shoulder forward in slow, gentle circles.
- Reverse direction of shoulder roll to left side.

SHOULDER ROLLS #6

- Inhale and bring shoulders up toward the ears and circle them back, opening the chest and drawing the shoulder blades together.
- Continue the rotation, exhaling as the shoulders move down and forward.
- Repeat as much as you like and then reverse directions.

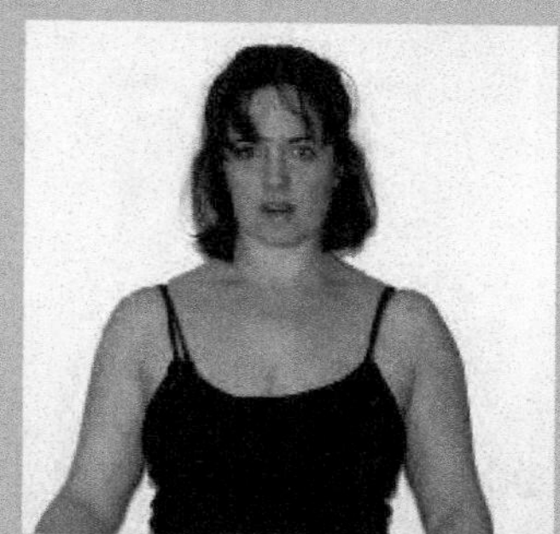

ELBOW CIRCLES #7

- Place hands on shoulders. Make full circles with the elbows, breathing as directed in the above exercise.
- Keep shoulders relaxed and down away from the ears.
- Reverse directions.

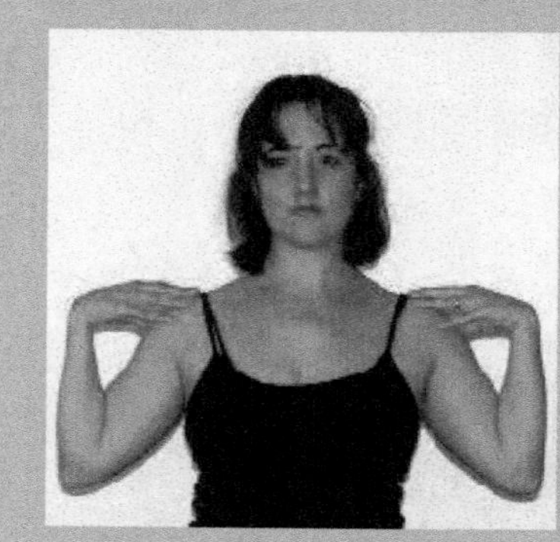

Neck & Spine › Supine

PELVIC ROCK #8

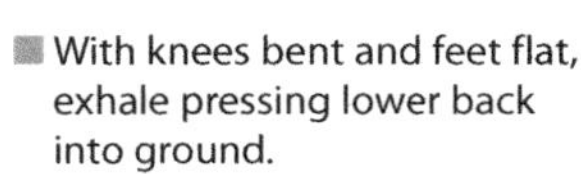

- With knees bent and feet flat, exhale pressing lower back into ground.
- Inhale and release.

SPINE ROLL #9

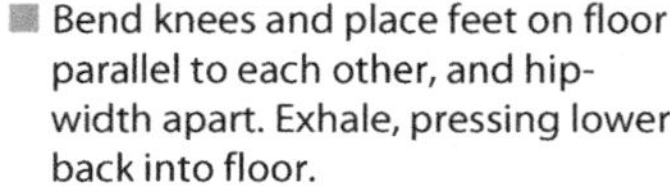

- Bend knees and place feet on floor parallel to each other, and hip-width apart. Exhale, pressing lower back into floor.
- Inhale and lift hips to ceiling, rolling up one vertebrae at a time, up to the shoulder blades.
- Exhale and roll down one vertebrae at a time.

ELBOW CIRCLES #10

- Draw knees to chest. Holding both shins, rock gently from side to side.

Neck & Spine > Table Pose

CAT (BIDILASANA) #11

- Inhale and lengthen spine.
- Exhale and drop tailbone and crown of head to floor.
- Inhale and lift tailbone and crown of head to ceiling.
- Move back and forth with the breath as much as necessary.

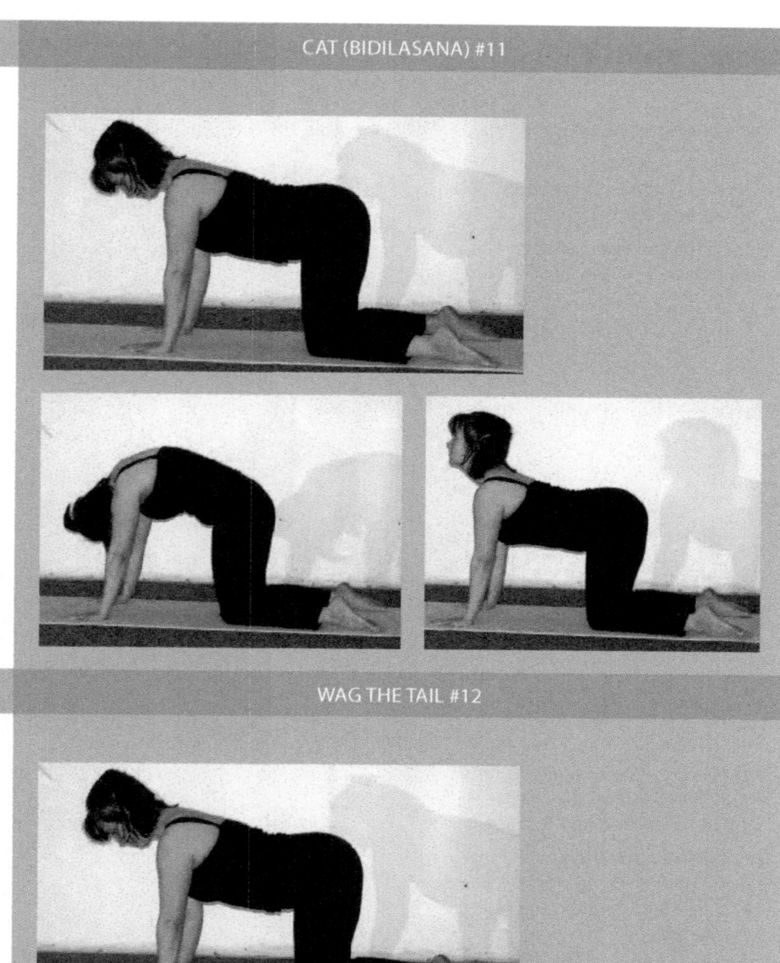

WAG THE TAIL #12

- Inhale, lengthen spine.
- Exhale, move the right hip to the right and the right ear toward the right hip.
- Inhale, come back to center.
- Repeat on the left side.
- Move back and forth with the breath.

Arm, Shoulders, Spine & HIPS > Table Pose

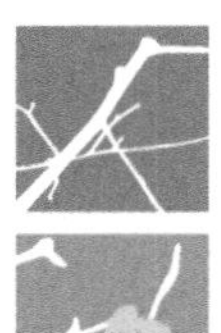

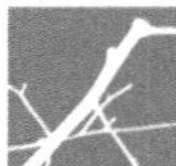
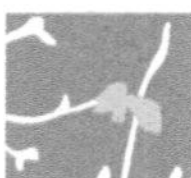

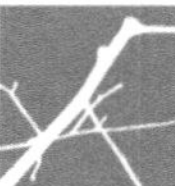
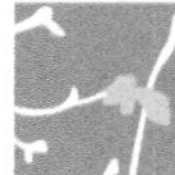

HIP CIRCLES #13

- Inhale and lengthen spine.
- Move the hips in a circular fashion to the right, then forward, around to the left, and back.
- Repeat a few times. Reverse the directions on the opposite side.

THREADING THE NEEDLE #14

- Inhale and extend the right arm, reaching the fingertips to the ceiling and opening the chest.
- Exhale and thread the right arm under the left, keeping the hips centered and rotating the rib cage to the left.
- When stable, start pressing the right shoulder blade to the floor.
- With every inhalation, lengthen the left arm along the floor, extending it over the head.

Hips & Knees > Seated

KNEE DROP #15

- Sit with knees bent, feet flat on floor, with hands behind for support.
- Exhale and allow the knees to gently fall to the right.
- Inhale and bring the knees back up to center, and then allow them to gently fall to the left while exhaling.
- Repeat as needed.

HIP ROCK & CIRCLES #16

- Hip Rocks:
  Left leg is extended or comfortably bent for support. Bend right knee and hold the right foot for support (and/or shin or calf).
- Gently rock the leg from side to side. Be conscious to allow all movement to stem from the hips.
- Hip Circles:
  Repeat the above directions, but rotate foot in circles parallel to the floor, moving gently from the ankle.

Legs, Feet & Toes › Seated or Supine

TOE CURLS #17

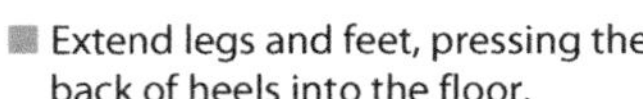

- Extend legs and feet, pressing the back of heels into the floor.
- Inhale, curling all the toes back toward the face while opening the toes away from each other (spreading).
- Exhale and curl all the toes away from the face. Keep the soles of the feet open and resilient.

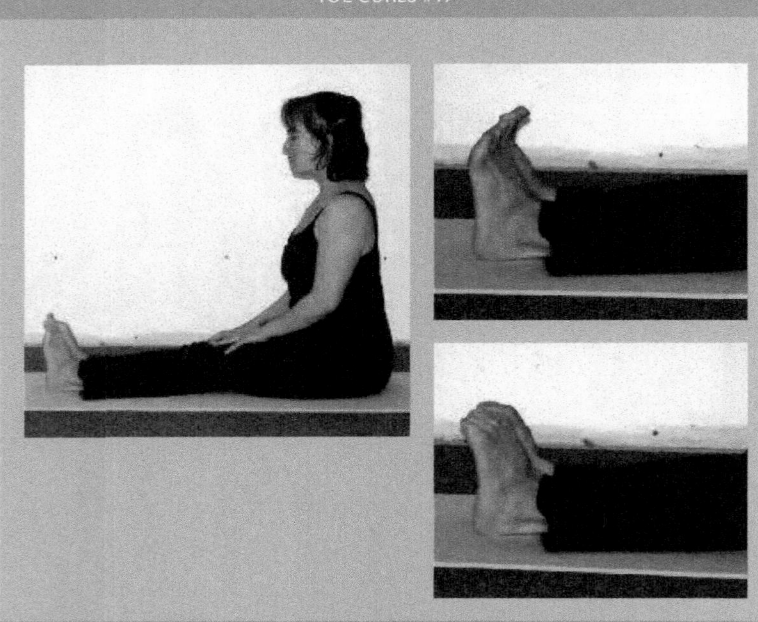

FEET STRETCHES #18

- Flex/Extend:
  Exhale and extend tops of feet down away from the body and point toes down towards floor. Inhale and extend bottoms of feet (heels) while moving toes back toward the face (flex feet).
- Side to Side:
  Extend tops of feet, relax toes, move outer edges of feet outwards away from each other, and then move inner edges of feet toward each other.
- Circles:
  Slowly move feet in a circular fashion. Circle feet inward, and then when finished with inner circle, switch and work feet in the opposite direction.

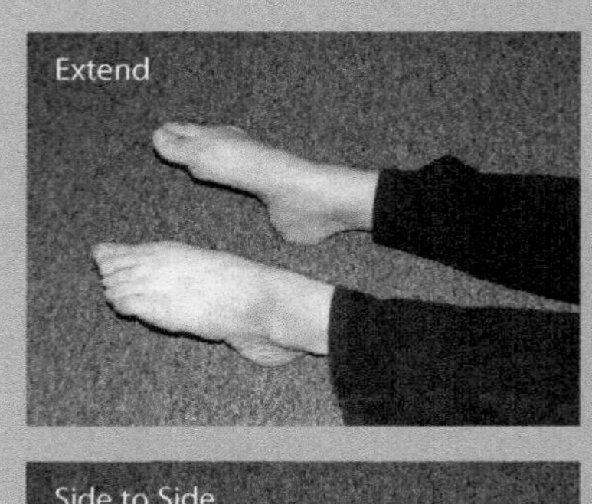

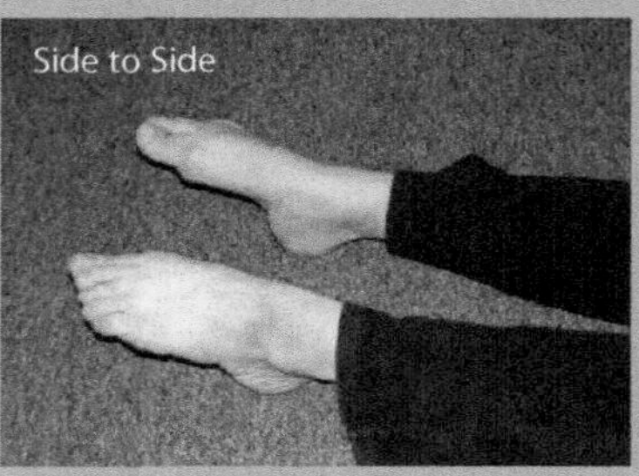

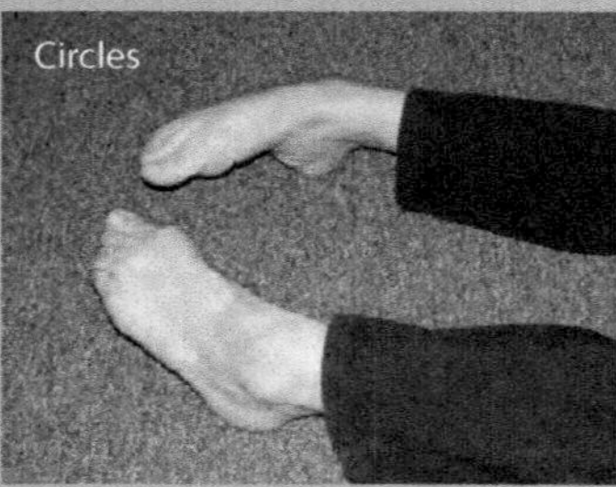

Arms, Wrists & Hands › Seated, Supine or Standing

FINGERS #19

- ONE:
  Extend arms in front of body. Inhale and open fingers away from each other. Exhale, close fingers to palm, one at a time.

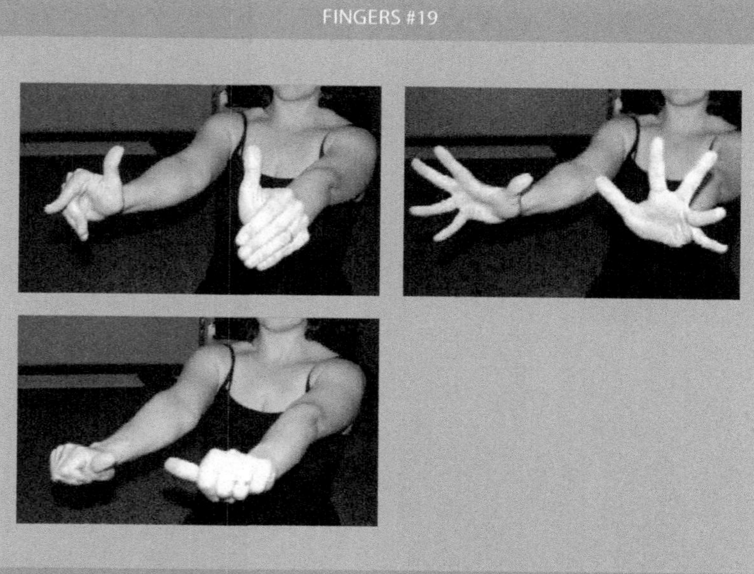

WRISTS #20

- TWO:
  Inhale and open hands spreading fingers. Move fingers back toward face, flexing top of wrist. Exhale, and keep hands open, flex inner wrist, pointing fingers toward the floor.

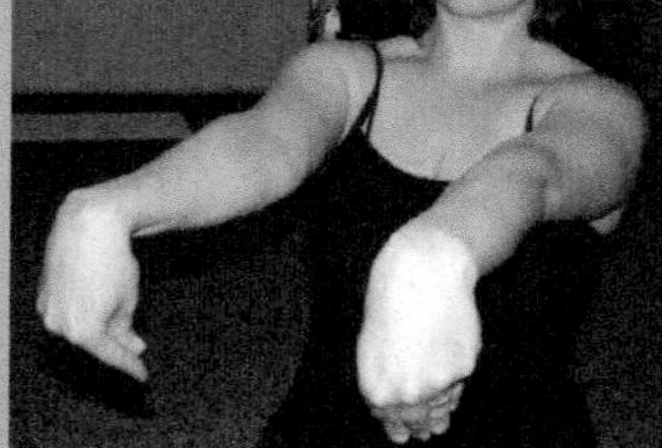

WRIST CIRCLES #21

- THREE:
  Extend fingers in line with wrists, keeping tops of hands facing up. Move thumb side of hand to inner wrist, then move pinky side of hand to outer wrist.
- Make circles with wrists.
- Repeat above directions with both hands held in a fist.

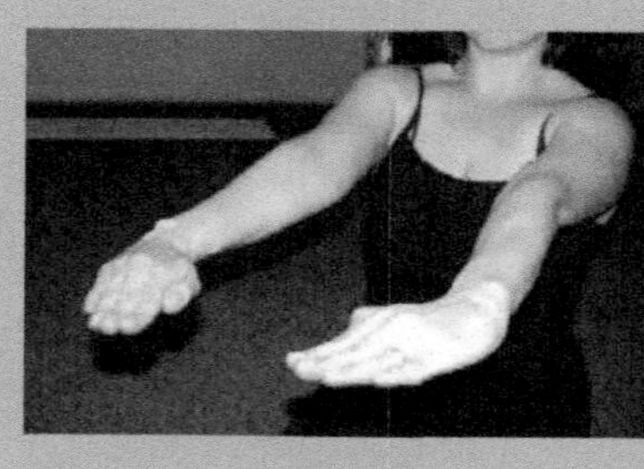

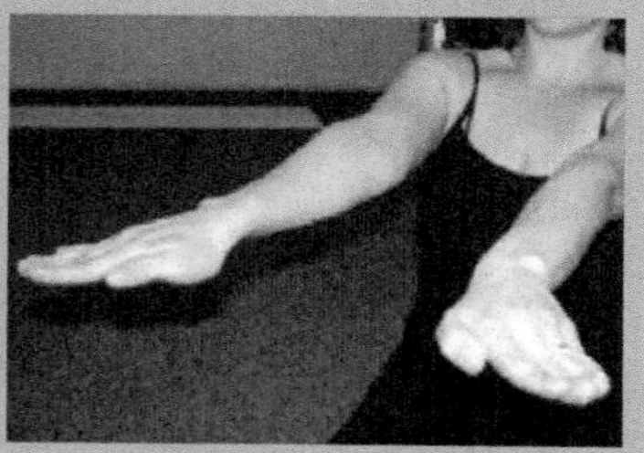

Part Two— Chapter 5
A Guide to Your Physical Yoga Practice

A word about stretching, bandhas and the yoga pose itself

There are a few important things to keep in mind when doing your physical yoga practice— either while at home, the office or even at a yoga studio. First, never ever practice in pain You can potentially hurt yourself and/or create chronic issues for yourself later on. Now on the other side of that same equation, get really close to your edge—just shy of any extreme discomfort or pain. What exactly do I mean by " close to your edge"? Well, because our physical and emotional bodies express themselves so very differently, it is important to stay tuned in to all of the various sensations when working through our physical practice. You see, some people have higher thresholds to physical stress and tension.

As a matter of fact, pain is a very subjective thing to experience. A gentle encounter with a needle to the tip of a finger may feel like a lot of pain to one person, while to another person that same sharp needle may need to pierce the skin in order for that person to actually experience any pain! When working close to your edge, foundation, form and awareness mean everything! If you think that your practice is not in good form and that you're forcing your body to do something it cannot or shouldn't do... you've already gone too far into the pose. Simply put: you're either reinforcing or creating unhealthy neuromuscular habitual patterns.

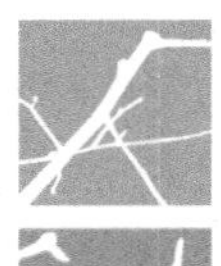

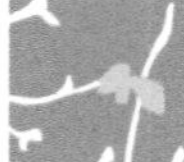

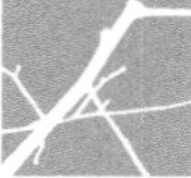
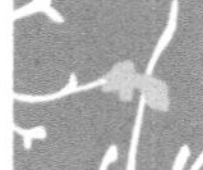

Yoga works on many levels, and aside from the obvious benefits of reducing physical, emotional and mental stress, it very intelligently works with the fascia of the body. Fascia is everywhere and gives form to the physical characteristics of our bodies. Fascia has a very sophisticated nervous system. It plays a role in how the body responds to the various kinds of stretching. So please remember, that this book is more than just a physical book: It has a very beautiful blog that helps to bring all your work into a beautiful, dynamic platform. I encourage you to review the various videos and other supportive materials on our website at www.alightfromwithin.net

For now, remember that the length of time any exercise or pose should be held is about 20 to 40 seconds. Moreover, the number of repetitions will depend on the user's goals (muscular balancing and overall toning, building muscle mass, or increasing flexibility). It is very important to know that different forms of stretching produce and have different effects on the muscles, tendons, fascia and ligaments of the body. Yin and restorative yoga poses may sometimes be held for a full minute or more. Generally, the greater number of repetitions, the shorter period of time each exercise or pose should be held. The darker muscle tissues of the body require longer holding times, while lighter muscle tissues require less. All muscle groups of the body should be worked so that one's body feels fully balanced. As an example, notice the deltoids of boxers, the large thighs of speed skaters, or the lats of swimmers. Therefore, depending on the imposed demand, there are also primary and secondary correlations, which should be considered.

Practice yoga poses on an empty or almost empty stomach. Intention and breath are very important, if not everything. Although it feels really great to go very deeply into a yoga pose, you must remember, nonetheless, to always breathe consciously. You may remember from high school physics that there are three kinds of levers involved in physical movement: first-, second- and third-class levers. On page 161 you will see an example of each class. It is important to understand that good form equates itself with good physics and an efficient use of energy. It is important to know one should feel more energetic upon the completion of their yoga practice-- not fatigued or tired. Therefore, be judicious in your efforts. Have fun. I like to think of yoga as something we journal ourselves into. As a matter of fact, this is why ALFW exists. This book is a place to relax and unwind, to record your experience(s), and then observe the many beautiful facets of you being alive!

Just as with the workbook questions and journal entry spreads, we have a spreads for all of the yoga poses too. The left side of every spread spells out all the instructions as to how to best execute or perform each of the 52 yoga poses, while the right side of the spread has miscellaneous supportive text, anatomy and other relative information. Beginning on page 182, you will see the start of the winter poses, the ace card: Tadasana. In addition to the instructions of the pose there is also a table of benefits, precautions and modifications. This same table includes a reference to a recommended counter pose. Lastly, you will see at the bottom of the page there is a suggested use of props to incorporate and use while doing the pose. On the right side of the spread you will see that we have included an anatomical illustration of the human spinal cord and all the major nerve plexuses and connections thereof. To illustrate the major components of human anatomy and physiology, we have created 45 different handdrawn sketches throughout the 52 different yoga poses in this book.

In addition to the alphabetical index of poses on page ix there is also an index of anatomical illustrations that may be helpful to reference anatomy used in the book. And lastly, regarding the right side of all the asana pages, you will see that on the same Winter Ace of spades spread, there is a place to experiment and practice your mudras. In this case, we have listed Trisula mudra, which, for the second time, shows a picture of the mudra (with the pronunciationand its most basic meaning. Immediately below each mudra you will see a place to record all your experiences. To the left of every mudra dialog box you will see a place to keep track of the number of times you have held that particular mudra. There are 13 slots upon which to place an "X" to record each and every sitting. We suggest you hold each mudra at least 12 times (on different occasions)for a minimum of 5 minutes, and then on the 13th time, journal that experience in the mudra dialogue box. Each mudra exercise is equivalent to about an hour or more.

Holding mudras tends to discipline the mind-- it gives it something constructive to focus on. All 52 mudras contained throughout this book should provide at least 52 hours of a mindfully based meditation practice—all in small steps of course. As you move further along through the book, you will find that your tolerance for peace and quite builds. At some point you begin to look forward to your practice. Therefore, let me introduce a few ideas on the principles and practice of how to cultivate a mindfully based mudra meditation practice. Meditation could be defined as any technique whose prime intention is to promote mental clarity and overall greater awareness. As mentioned many times throughout this book, wellness, is, in part about making responsible shifts in the patterns of your everyday thinking and feeling. It is about incorporating a healthy diet, increased exercise and fitness, and living in the context of a consciously social life. Remember, being in wellness requires a lot of self-discipline!

Here are two principle techniques that relate to our everyday yoga poses, meditation and mudra stillness:

1- Exclusive techniques

    One incorporates a singular focal point for better concentration—usually with eyes closed.

    Intensive sense-withdraw such as pratyahara (see p. 157).

    Refinement of attention such as the mental repetition of japa (mantra), visual concentration such as tratak (focusing the eyes toward the third-eye or tip of the nose), the recitation of sound such as the beja mantra, physical repetition such as mala japa (mala beads), and through things like skilled yoga and tai chi.

2- Inclusive techniques are more mindfully based. For example, within this yoga journal and workbook we use haikus, affirmations and other workbook exercises such as conscious observation of emotions as they present themselves. You see, inclusive meditation is much more accessible to everyday people.

Introduction to the Bandhas

Background

As explained in the pranayama chapter, bandhas are energetic "locks" or interconnecting energy points within the pranic body at the most subtle level. On the physical level, the bandhas have corresponding gross focal points not unlike other yogic tools and practices and have an impact on the mental and physical state of the body. The internal actions sustained by bandha activation within the body have the following effects:

Bandhas

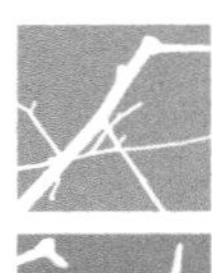

1. Help generate and maintain heat in the body.

2. Support the four natural curves of the spine.

3. Help to focus awareness on subtle energetic experiences.

4. Help set the way for meditative/contemplative absorption.

Bandhas may also be included in one of the eight limbs called pratyahara (sense withdrawal). Learning to change the energetic sensations both internally and intuitively requires a deeper commitment to both presence and attention to the details from awareness. Initially, the concept of a "lock" may be useful however, the andhas are as much (if not more) an "energetic intention" than a physical muscular contraction. In fact, as one develops and advances the use of bandhas, less "physical energy" is used to achieve the same (and sometimes even greater) subtle results.

Main Bandhas of the Body

Jalandhara bandha-— (chin) Upward Pulling

Uddiyana bandha— (navel) Upward Flying

Lock Mula bandha- (perineum) Root Lock

Mahabandha- The incorporation of all three bandhas used at the same time.

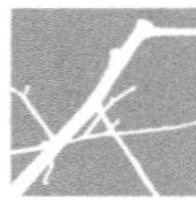

Jalandhara bandha

The throat or chin lock is engaged on either the inhale or exhale. For beginners, the recommendation is on the inhalation only. The chin lock can be activated by beginning with lifting the sternum upward and drawing the chin slightly back toward the occipital ridge at the back of the neck. Allow the space at the back of the ears to tilt upward slightly until the skin of the sides and back of the neck feels taunt. Finally, lower the chin down slightly toward the space at the center of the throat.

Jalandhara bandha corresponds to the Vishuddhi Chakra and raises air and space energy up the central channel. It draws prana vayu (upward flowing energydownward for mixing with apana vayu). The throat lock stimulates the thyroid and parathyroid glands. It is used to keep the collected elemental energies and prana from escaping the central nadhi channel. On a physical level, the bandha is associated with keeping the pressure in the carotid sinuses in the neck artificially elevated. The result of the increase in pressure in the throat allows the brain's natural defense against high blood pressure to be reset temporarily as the practitioner holds the breath for longer periods than would be possible without using the technique. With careful practice, the use of Jalandhara can reduce the heartbeat and help establish a feeling of meditative or contemplative awareness.

Uddiyana bandha

The upward flying lock is engaged best on the exhalation of breath down to the residual volume capacity (the amount of air still contained within the lungs once you have exhaled as much as possibleand the root lock is engaged. In order for the middle lock to be effective, the root lock engages automatically (for most)and the chin/throat lock must be used to seal the vacuum from above in the glottis. This seal causes the internal breathing diaphragm to lift upward. Hold in emptiness and keep the Jalandhara lock in place. Attempt to inhale to lift and expand the thoracic ribs laterally but do not inhale, hold the breath out. Uddiyana bandha corresponds to the swadisthana, manipura, and anahata chakras. It raises water energy up the central channel. The upward flying lock tones the abdominal organs and stimulates the heart and thymus.

Mula bandha

The root lock is engaged best on the exhalation for most beginners although it can be activated on the inhalation. Bring awareness to the abdomino-pelvic floor region. Initially work toward contractions in the urogenital and rectal triangles combined. As your ability to refine the core lift develops, become more centered on lifting at the baseline that connects these two triangles, located medially between the genitals and the coccyx. In this space are the deep pelvic floor muscles, shaped like a hammock that supports the pelvic floor organs. Hold the lift briefly and then inhale, allowing it to relax. The root lock corresponds to the Muladhara (root chakra)and raises earth and fire energies upward along the central channel. The root lock draws apana vayu (downward) flowing energy upward. The deep toning of the pelvic floor muscles with mula bandha helps pelvic and lumbar stabilization in many positions. Many poses can be facilitated with greater ease using the root lock, and some poses are next to impossible to perform without the technique.

Maha bandha

The integrated involvement of all the bandhas at once is called the great lock. The Mahabandha, also known as Tri Bandha, offers the integration of all the aforementioned principles and moves the individual practices to a new space of awareness where the parts no longer equal the whole. The use of all three locks is said to break down the three psychic knots believed to exist within the subtle body. The knots are detailed as:

1) Brahma granthi— the knot that has us attached to the material realm.
2) Vishnu granthi— the knot that has us attached to our emotions.
3) Rudra granthi— the knot that has us attached to our individuality.

The use of Maha Bhanda offers the yogic practitioner the opportunity to deepen awareness of the inner realm in addition to the external based explorations of asana and other elements. It is a factor in yogic lore of chakra activation and kundalini or pranic flow into the primary subtle channel, called Sashumna Nadhi.

Basic guidelines

1. Begin with Mulabandha, Jalandhara, and finally Uddiyana bandha in sequencing the introduction of the bandhas.
2. External breath retention (holding with breath out of the body) is considered a more advance technique and not appropriate for beginners. The Bandhas may increase intracavity pressure and are not appropriate for those with acute conditions of the pelvic floor or the abdominothoracic and cranial regions.
3. Offer easier exploration of all the bandhas by positional work previous to seated bandha work.
4. We can get a feeling for the Jalandhara bandha and prepare our energy and physical structures by holding a rolled-up sock, a small beanbag, pad, or the like in between the chin and sternal notch.
5. Practice bandhas after you have demonstrated skill at basic pranayama techniques previously introduced.

Winter

Tadasana

[Mountain Pose]

(tah-DAHS-anna)

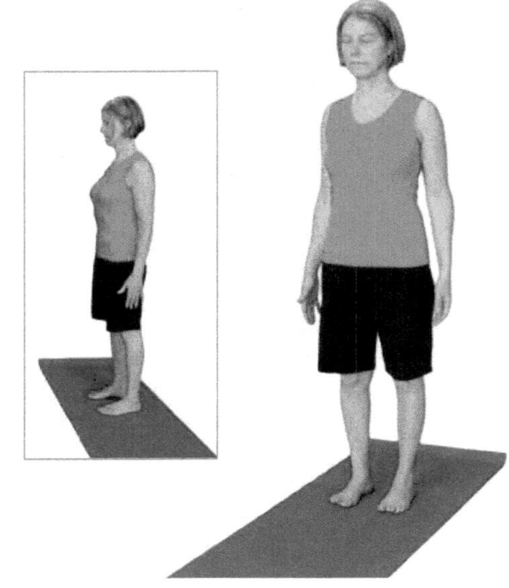

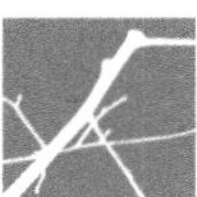

1 Stand in a neutral posture with feet about hip-distance apart. The outside edges of both feet are parallel to each other and the weight is evenly distributed between the four corners of the feet: the big toe ball mount, little toe ball mount and both sides of the heel. Relax the toes and spread each one from the next. Keep the arches lifted by engaging the inner calf muscles.

2 Inhale. Engage the legs by contracting the thigh muscles, which will draw the kneecaps up. Do not lock (hyperextend) the knees.

3 Exhale. Engage the core lift by extending the tailbone to the floor and aligning the hips in a neutral position. Gently engage the abdominal muscles.

4 Inhale. Raise the sternum (breastbone) gently, allowing the ribs and chest to open. Open the heart. Relax the shoulders, allowing them to fall away from the ears as the scapulae (shoulder blades) slide down the back and toward each other.

5 The arms hang easily at each side with the palms facing the body. Imagine tiny weights pulling gently on the fingers, arms and shoulders.

6 Inhale: Lengthen throughout the spine. Feel a silver-like thread lifting up through the crown of the head creating space between each vertebra. Keep the chin parallel to the floor and the eyes and ears level. Relax the jaw.

7 Bring awareness to the breath.

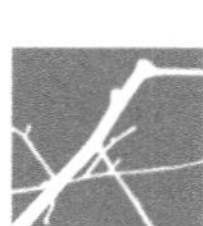

✚ BENEFITS

- ✚ Improves one's sense of balance and posture.
- ✚ Proper alignment helps prevent joint injury.
- ✚ Develop a sense of groundedness.
- ✚ Uplifts the ribcage allowing more room for respiration and creates space for improved functioning of the internal organs.
- ✚ Helps to relieve sciatica.

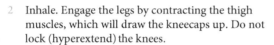

▲ PRECAUTIONS

- ▲ Headache
- ▲ Insomnia
- ▲ Low blood pressure
- ▲ Pronated/supinated feet

✳ COUNTERPOSE

- ✳ Child's pose

✪ MODIFICATIONS

- ✪ Block between inner thighs
- ✪ Block to back of legs (at thigh bones) while pressing it into the wall

OPTIONAL PROPS: ✓foam block balanced at crown of head

Pearls of Wisdom

In Sanskrit, tada means "mountain." The word "TAT" means "that," in reference to "That which is," the eternal. We refer to this pose as mountain pose. In making the body as firm and steady as a mountain, the mind stills, connecting us to the experience of the eternal.

Tadasana is the foundation for all of the standing asanas. Practicing it teaches us to seek out the balance between discipline and freedom, which is the basis of asana as outlined by Patanjali in the yoga sutras. Standing evenly on both feet, distributing the weight equally throughout each foot, creates balance and strength through the whole body. Proper alignment creates space for the organs and vascular system to function effectively. A strong, aligned spine permits freedom in the breath. As the feet press into the ground and the spine extends, muscles which have weakened from improper use are strengthened, and those which have been constricted are freed.

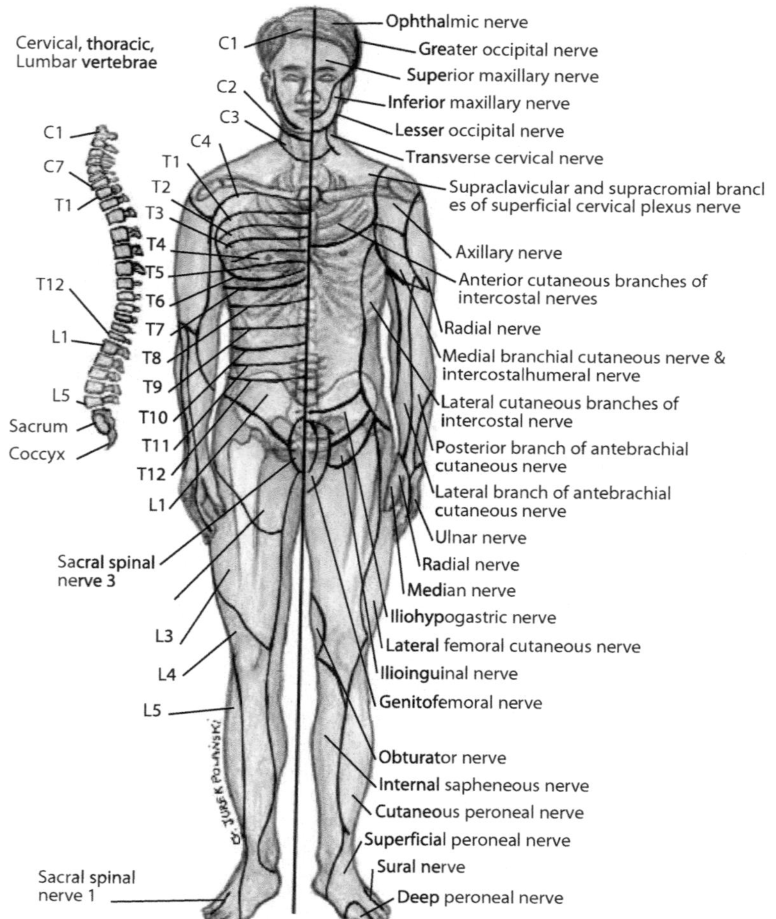

We highly recommend that you hold this mudra for at least 5 minutes in a seated meditation. Perform it at least 13 different times. Mudras may also be utilized while holding a yoga pose. Remember, mudras tend to be subtle and are very powerful in their own way.

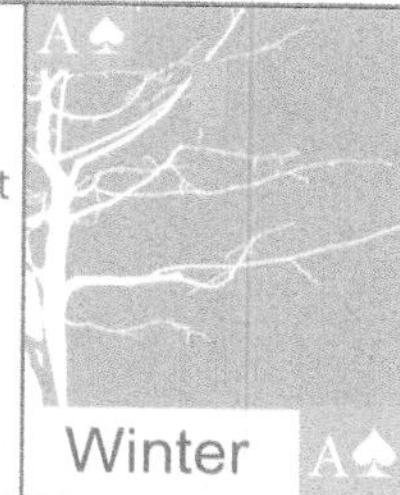

After holding this mudra for 5 minutes, place an X in the box below. After 13 sessions, please journal your experience.

Trisula
[tri-soo-lam]

Trisula symbolizes the trident, a uniting of three singles into a unity, a trinity.

X Mudra experience:

2♠

Winter

Virabhadrasana II

[Warrior 2 Pose]

(veer-ah-bah-DRAHS-anna)

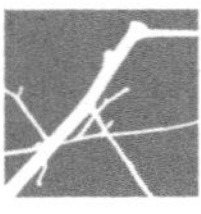

1 Step into Tadasana. Inhale.

2 Exhale. Step into Five Pointed Star.

3 Turn the left foot out 90° and the right foot in 45°. Align the left heel with the instep of the right foot.

4 Keep the shoulders and hips turned to the front wall.

5 Inhale raising the arms to shoulder height, palms down. Extend out through the fingertips.

6 Exhale. Bend the left knee bringing it directly over the ankle, while keeping the pelvis level. Extend through the right leg grounding firmly into the foot. Attempt to bring the right thigh parallel with the floor and the left shin perpendicular.

7 Inhale. Gently lift the sternum.Exhale and drop the tailbone to the floor. Extend out through the crown of the head.

8 Gaze out over the left fingertips with the chin parallel to the floor.

9 Come out of the posture as slowly as you went in. Inhale straightening the left knee.

10 Exhale, bringing the toes of the right foot back to facing the front.

11 Inhale as you step back into Tadasana.

12 Repeat on the opposite side.

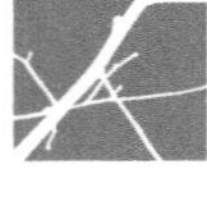

✚ BENEFITS	▲ PRECAUTIONS	✪ MODIFICATIONS
✚ Strengthens the legs. ✚ Opens the hips and pelvic area. ✚ Increases the flexibility of the spine and shoulders. ✚ Tones the kidneys and adrenal glands. ✚ Helps to develop strength, balance, and groundedness.	▲ Lower-body joint problems (ankle, knee, hip) ▲ Low back/disc problems ▲ Uncontrolled hypertension or a cardiac condition ✳ COUNTERPOSE ✳ Uttanasana	✪ Practice supine leg stretch series. ✪ Use a chair to support arm, or place chair under front thigh of leg. ✪ Use wall. ✪ Keep the hands on the hips. ✪ Support the back of the right thigh on a chair. ✪ Keep gaze toward the front.

OPTIONAL PROPS: Block for under the front foot, flat side down.

No. 10 Tao Te Ching
Nurture the darkness of your soul until you become whole. Can you do this and not fail? Can you focus your life breath until you become supple as a newborn child? While you cleanse your inner vision will you be found without fault? Can you love people and lead them without forcing your will on them? When Heaven gives and takes away can you be content with the outcome? When you understand all things can you step back from your own understanding? Giving birth and nourishing, making without possessing, expecting nothing in return. To grow, yet not to control: This is the mysterious virtue.

Superficial Front Muscle

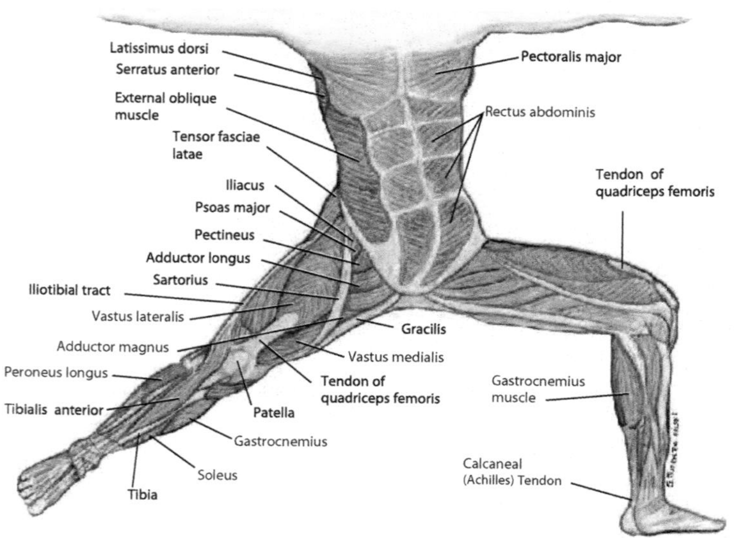

SUPERFICIAL FRONT MUSCLES
(Virabadrasana)

We highly recommend that you hold this mudra for at least 5 minutes in a seated meditation. Perform it at least 13 different times. Mudras may also be utilized while holding a yoga pose. Remember, mudras tend to be subtle and are very powerful in their own way.

After holding this mudra for 5 minutes, place an X in the box below. After 13 sessions, please journal your experience.

Sikhara
[si-kha-ram]

Sikhara is the "spire" mudra. It signifies a pillar, phallic symbol (shivalinga, an upward pulse, a release of weapons, a bow, sounding a bell, the act of embrace, an untying, to question, as well as a silence.

X	Mudra experience:

Winter

Virabhadrasana I

[Warrior I Pose]

(veer-ah-bah-DRAHS-anna)

1 Step into Tadasana. Inhale.

2 Exhale. Step into Five Point Star.

3 Turn the right foot out to 90° and the left foot in 45°.

4 Square the shoulders and hips over the right knee, turning the left foot in more deeply, if necessary, to level the hips.

5 Exhale. Bend the right knee into alignment directly over the ankle. Extend through the left leg standing firmly into the foot. Attempt to bring the right thigh more parallel to the floor.

6 Inhale. Gently lift the sternum. Exhale. Drop the tailbone to the floor.

7 Inhale. Raise the arms above the head with the elbows straight and the palms either facing each other or palms touching (palms touching is a more advanced pose).

8 Be sure your chest and shoulders are open enough to bring palms together.

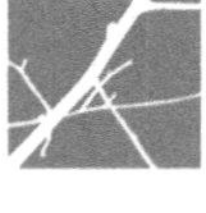

✚ BENEFITS

- ✚ Opens the chest and heart, improving respiration and circulation.
- ✚ Strengthens the entire leg, spine and shoulders.
- ✚ Opens the hips and pelvic area.
- ✚ Increases the flexibility of the spine and shoulders.
- ✚ Tones the kidneys and adrenal glands.
- ✚ Helps to develop strength, balance, flexibility and groundedness.

▲ PRECAUTIONS

- ▲ Structural injuries in the knee, lower back or shoulder areas.
- ▲ Uncontrolled hypertension or a cardiac condition.

✲ COUNTERPOSES

- ✲ Eagle pose
- ✲ Uttanasana

✪ MODIFICATIONS

- ✪ Keep the hands on the hips with hypertension or shoulder problems.
- ✪ Keep the hands shoulder-width apart.
- ✪ Raise the heel of the rear foot to bring the hips more squarely into alignment.
- ✪ Gaze straight ahead to protect the neck.
- ✪ Place back heel to wall for support, or block between front shin bone and wall (at front wall).

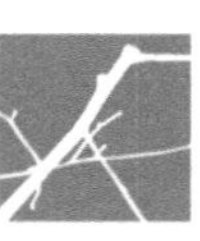

OPTIONAL PROPS: ✓ Block in between hands, or strap around upper arms

Pearls of Wisdom

No. 11 Tao Te Ching
Thirty spokes are joined together in a wheel, but it is the center hole that allows the wheel to function. We mold clay into a pot, but it is the emptiness inside that makes the vessel useful. We fashion wood for a house, but it is the emptiness inside that makes it livable. We work with the substantial, but the emptiness is what we use.

Lymphatics of the Body

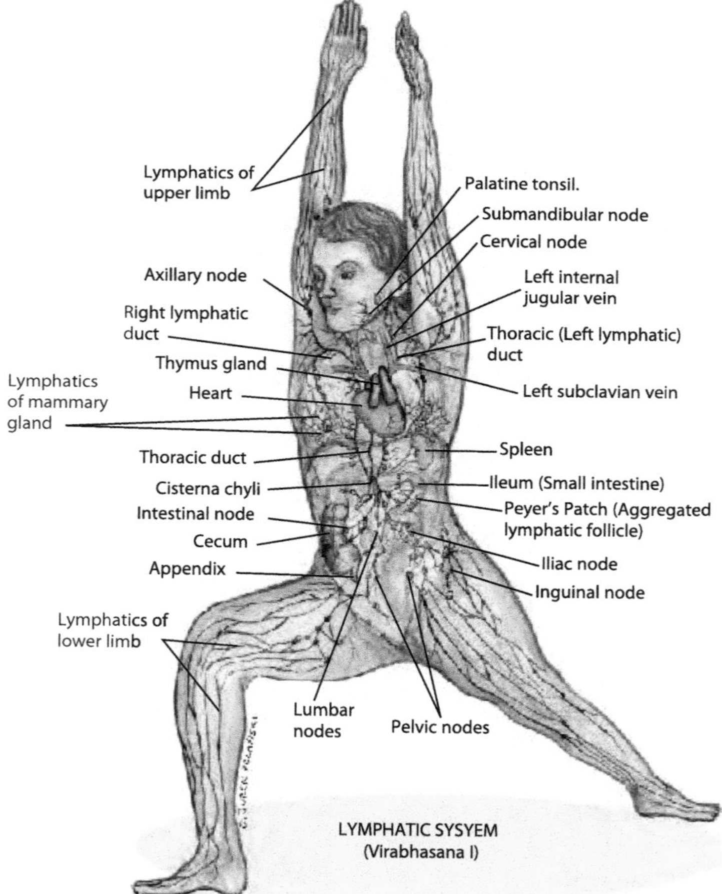

NOTE: The red marrow of the bones is also a major contributor within the fine and decentralized network of the lymphatic system.

We highly recommend that you hold this mudra for at least 5 minutes in a seated meditation. Perform it at least 13 different times. Mudras may also be utilized while holding a yoga pose. Remember, mudras tend to be subtle and are very powerful in their own way.

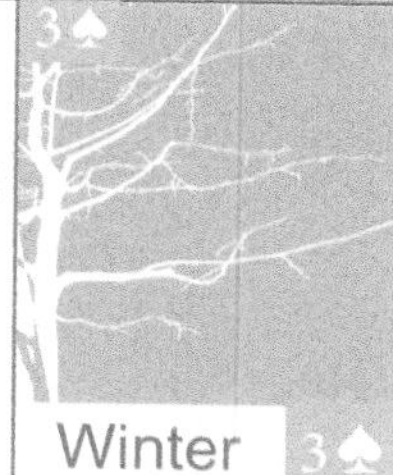

After holding this mudra for 5 minutes, place an X in the box below. After 13 sessions, please journal your experience.

Candrakala
[chan-dra-kha-lahm]

Candrakala or "Moon-time" mudra signifies oars tusks as well as eyebrows. It imitates a crescent of the moon—a fundamental, interpretive pattern. As a dance gesture, it further denotes the face, the crown of shiva, a cudgel.

X	Mudra experience:

Winter

Virabhadrasana III

[Warrior III Pose]

(veer-ah-bah-DRAHS-anna)

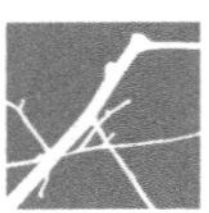

1 Step into Tadasana. Inhale.

2 Step the right foot out in front of you about 14-16 inches.

3 Stabilize your left foot and then balance on its toes.

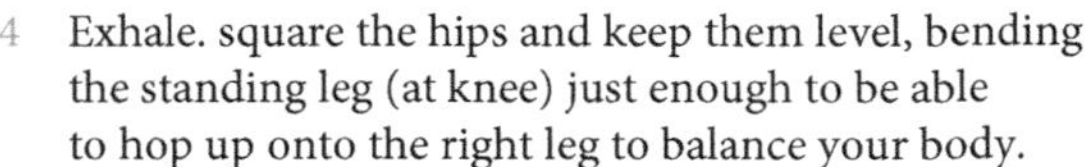

4 Exhale. square the hips and keep them level, bending the standing leg (at knee) just enough to be able to hop up onto the right leg to balance your body.

5 Keep your gaze out in front of you on the floor long enough to stabilize and concentrate your efforts.

6 Shift your gaze out toward the hands.

7 Be sure to keep the standing leg very active, but a microbend in the knee so that the inner calf muscle is activated to help keep the integrity of the truss of the foot. The leg and body should be stable and feel victorious.

☆ BENEFITS	▲ PRECAUTIONS	✪ MODIFICATIONS
✚ Strengthens the hip, knee and ankle joints. ✚ Tones the lateral hip rotors. ✚ Tones the abdomen. ✚ Improves balance. ✚ Helps to increase concentration. ✚ Strengthens bones of the standing leg.	▲ Pronated or supinated feet ▲ Weak knees ▲ High blood pressure ✳ COUNTERPOSE ✳ Janu sirsasana	✪ Use a wall for the hands, fingertips or a foot from behind. ✪ Stand in front of a wall and set back foot up on wall for stability. ✪ Use the support of the back of a chair to rest the arms. ✪ Place the arms at the side of the body.
OPTIONAL PROPS: ✓Chair ✓Wall ✓Block in between hands		

Pearls of Wisdom

As the gods and demons were diligently churning the ocean of milk and the ocean began to change, the demons sampled the liquid and doubled over in great pain because the first product was sheer poison…in order to prevent further trouble, Siva swallowed the remaining poison. It remained in his throat and turned it blue. When the universe (macrocosm) is mentioned, it is also a reference to man (microcosm). And under "gods and demons" we must understand the forces that are manifest in man on the psychic, mental, and physical levels.[1]

Thus the churning of the ocean is, generally speaking, a process in yoga. This milk ocean symbolizes the brain. In the course of yoga training there occurs a transformation of consciousness from the "milk of devotional thinking" through the "poison of imperfect development" to the "nectar of enlightenment." In the state of incomplete evolution lies the greatest danger, i.e., premature action resulting from erroneous, ill-formed judgment… and this is poison, especially for further development.[2]

Tendons and Muscles of Leg

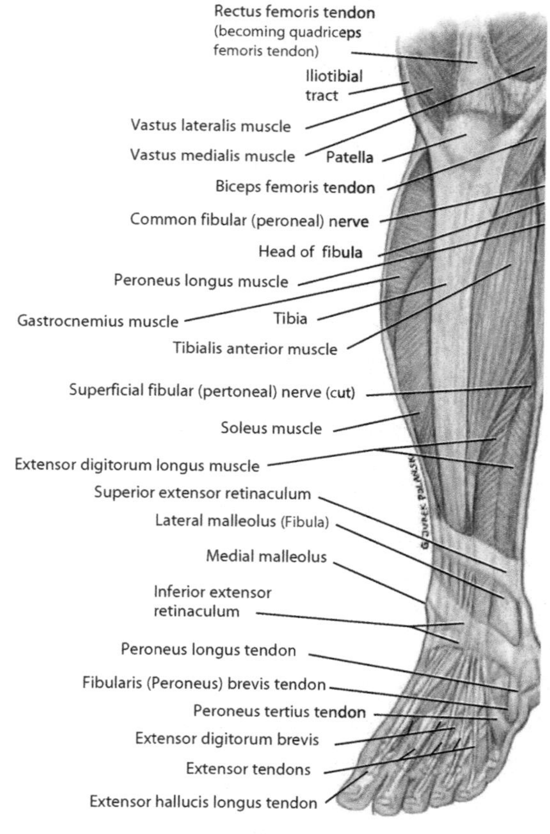

TENDONS & MUSCLES OF THE LEG AND FOOT

1 Hatha Yoga Praddapika, translated by Hans-Ulrich Reiker, P. 52

2 Ibid., pg. 52-53.

We highly recommend that you hold this mudra for at least 5 minutes in a seated meditation. Perform it at least 13 different times. Mudras may also be utilized while holding a yoga pose. Remember, mudras tend to be subtle and are very powerful in their own way.

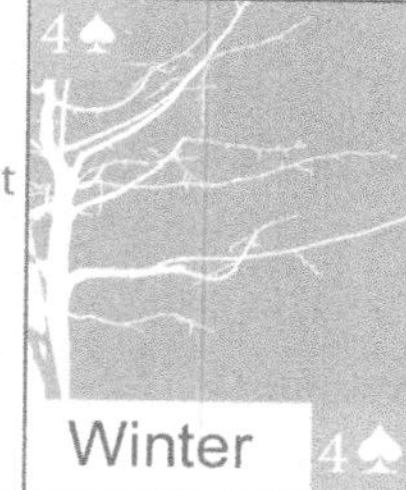

After holding this mudra for 5 minutes, place an X in the box below. After 13 sessions, please journal your experience.

Katarimukha

[cat-are-ee-muh-kha-lahm]

Katakamukha symbolizes the opening of a link. It can signify applying scents, glance, or even speech. It represents pulling reins, or the grasping of a garment.

X	Mudra experience:

Utkatasana

[Chair Pose]

(OOT-kah-TAHS-anna)

1. Step into Tadasana. Inhale lengthening through the spine.
2. Raise the arms above the head with the palms facing each other.
3. Relax and pull the shoulders swiftly down, away from the ears.
4. Exhale. Bend the knees and extend the buttocks back and down as if sitting in a chair behind you. Make sure the knees do not extend too far in front of the feet and that knees are aligned with ankles.
5. Maintain a forward gaze or look slightly upward toward the hands or ceiling.
6. Engage the legs, contracting the thigh muscles into the bone.
7. Stabilize the weight equally throughout the feet. Maintain the extension of the spine. Tuck and soften the tailbone slightly.
8. Hold and breathe.
9. To release, inhale slowly coming back to Tadasana.

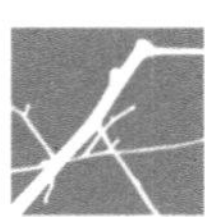

✚ BENEFITS	▲ PRECAUTIONS	✪ MODIFICATIONS
✚ Strengthens and tones thigh and calf muscles. ✚ Elongates the spine. ✚ Tones the kidneys and adrenal glands. ✚ Stimulates abdominal muscles and organs. ✚ Improves balance and body awareness.	▲ Headaches ▲ Structural injury or pain, especially knees, ankles and lower back. ▲ Uncontrolled hypertension, hypotension, or cardiac history. ✳ COUNTERPOSE ✳ Prasarita padottanasana	✪ Place hands on the hips or extend the arms out in front of the body at shoulders height with palms facing each other. ✪ Allow the hips to be supported by placing the chair (with blocks) under the buttocks for support.

OPTIONAL PROPS: ✓Chair ✓Wall ✓Block either between the thighs and/or in between feet supporting the ankles

Pearls of Wisdom

It was stated that prana should enter the hairline channel of sushumna; but prana cannot move any lower than the diaphragm, while apana finds its upper boundary below the diaphragm.
If we can tie these two streams together, one continuous flow reaches from the nostrils to the end of the spinal cord, thus constituting a single unit able to fulfill its task.[1]

Muscles of Respiration

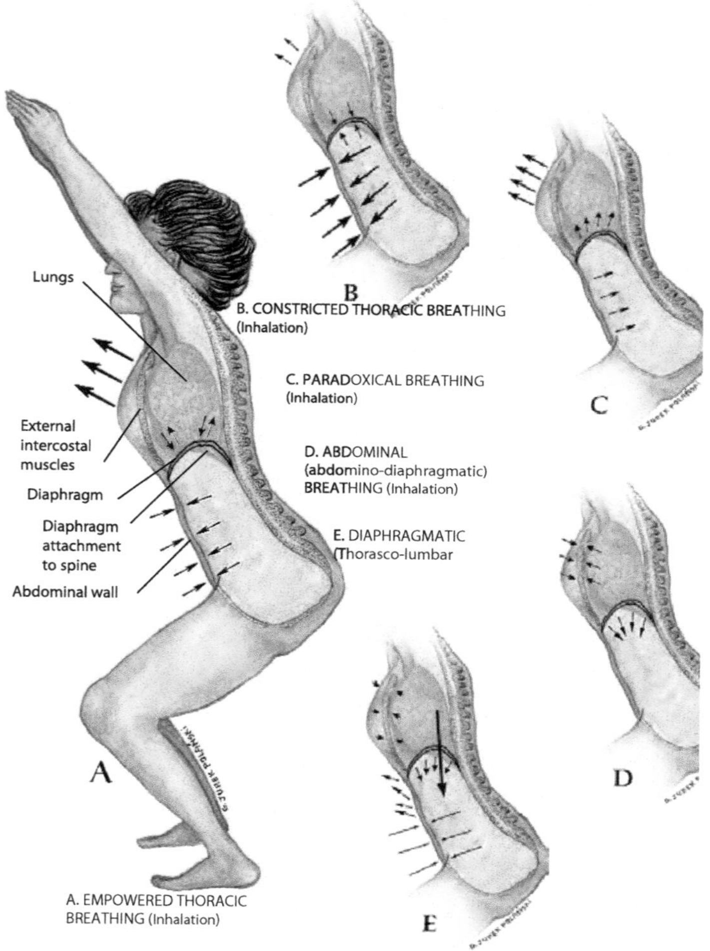

We highly recommend that you hold this mudra for at least 5 minutes in a seated meditation. Perform it at least 13 different times. Mudras may also be utilized while holding a yoga pose. Remember, mudras tend to be subtle and are very powerful in their own way.

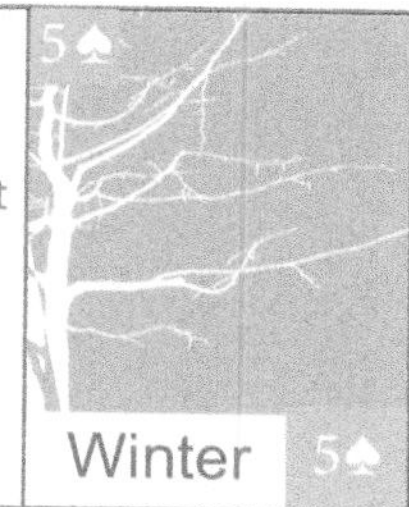

After holding this mudra for 5 minutes, place an X in the box below. After 13 sessions, please journal your experience.

Pataka
[pah-tah-kahm]

The Pataka mudra or "streamer" hand pose is the most basic gesture. It can denote driving force, joy, pride, even rain or a shower of blossoms. It is also used to bless or address a person In its execution, the arms are often held to the side.

X	Mudra experience:

1 Hatha Yoga Praddapika, translated by Hans-Ulrich Reiker, P. 60

Tadasana Urdhva Hastasana

[Half Moon Pose]

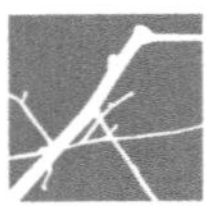

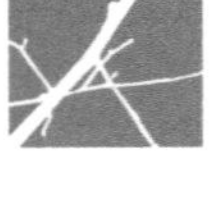

1 Step into Tadasana. Inhale lengthening through the spine.

2 Raise both arms above the head. Relax the shoulders away from the ears.

3 Exhale. Slowly begin to bend to the right side while pressing the hips to the left, keeping both sides of the torso long throughout the pose.

4 Keep the body aligned as if it were pressed between two panes of glass.

5 Extend the entire side from the feet to the fingertips.

6 Engage the legs, contracting the thigh muscles into the bone.

7 Stabilize the weight equally throughout the feet. Maintain the extension of the spine.

8 Hold and breathe.

9 To release, inhale slowly coming up into Tadasana.

10 Repeat on the opposite side.

✚ BENEFITS	▲ PRECAUTIONS	✪ MODIFICATIONS
✚ Stretches the muscles in the lower extremities. ✚ Improves the flexibility of the spine. ✚ Expands the ribs and increases the stretch in the intercostal muscles. ✚ Tones the arms and shoulders. ✚ Improves balance. ✚ Improves circulation of the feet. ✚ Helps release sciatica.	▲ Structural injury or pain, especially the hip or lower back. ▲ Uncontrolled hypertension or cardiac conditions. ▲ Advanced pregnancy. ▲ Eye strain. ✳ COUNTERPOSE ✳ Parivrtta prasarita podattanasana	✪ Place hands on the waist in cases of hypertension. ✪ Use a tie between the hands or only raise one arm to alleviate shoulder pain. ✪ Do on the floor in a supine position. ✪ Stand with the feet hip-distance apart for easier balance.

OPTIONAL PROPS: ✓ Table or bar to stabilize hips for lateral bend

Pearls of Wisdom

"It is not as important to withhold potency as it is to know how to manage it and, above all, how to transform it into spiritual potency. Celibacy without transformation of the preserved potencies only forces them to find their own outlet, mostly where it is least desired, at the weakest point of the whole organism." [1]

We highly recommend that you hold this mudra for at least 5 minutes in a seated meditation. Perform it at least 13 different times. Mudras may also be utilized while holding a yoga pose. Remember, mudras tend to be subtle and are very powerful in their own way.

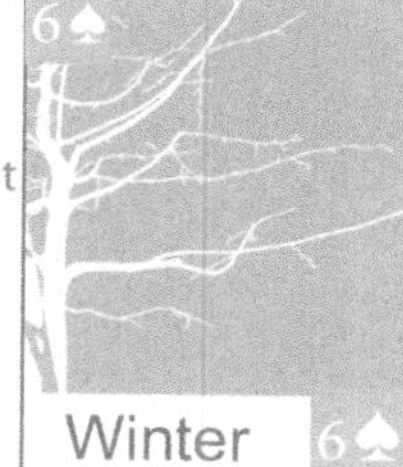

Winter 6♠

After holding this mudra for 5 minutes, place an X in the box below. After 13 sessions, please journal your experience.

Ardha Chandra
[Ardha-chan-dra-kha-lahm]
Ardha Chandra denotes a half moon. It can symbolize origin, consecrting, an idol, meditation or prayer,or the salutation of the common people.

X Mudra experience:

Abdominal Organs

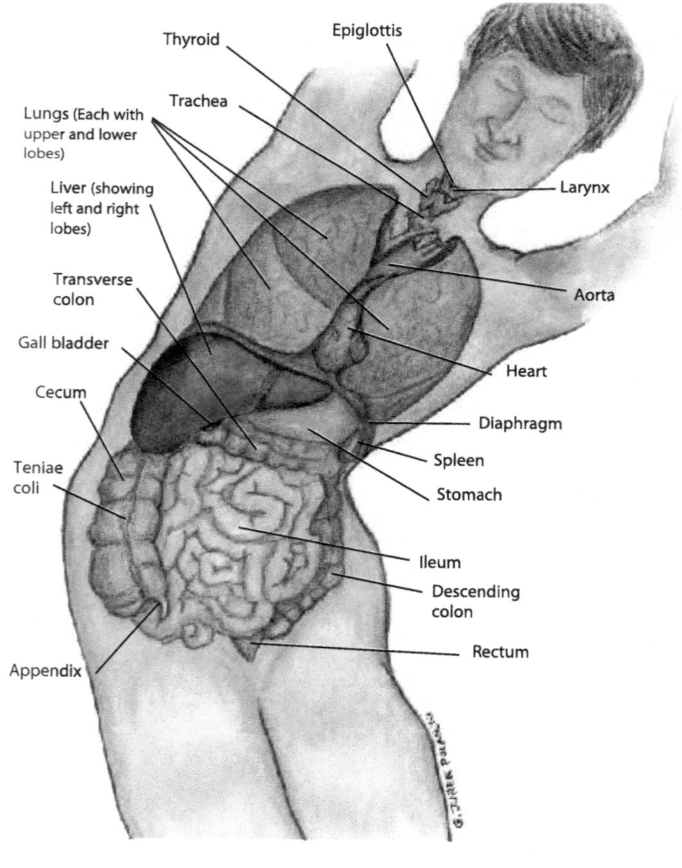

MAJOR ABDOMINAL ORGANS
(Lateral bend)

1 Hatha Yoga Praddapika, translated by Hans-Ulrich Reiker, P. 64

Vrkshasana

[Tree Pose]

(vrik-SHAHS-anna)

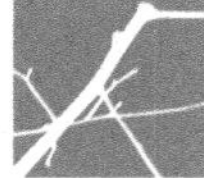

1. Step into Tadasana. Inhale, lengthening through the spine.
2. Shift the weight into the left foot.
3. Find a focal point approximately 8 feet in front of you.
4. Inhale. Bend the right knee and rest the sole of the right foot on the calf, or inner thigh of the left leg. If necessary, use your hand to place and secure the right foot.
5. Do NOT place the foot against the opposite knee.
6. In this balanced stance, gently move the right knee toward the back to bring both hips into alignment.
7. Exert counter-pressure between the raised foot and the standing leg.
8. Exhale, bringing the hands into prayer position at the chest.
9. Inhale. Raise both arms above the head. Relax the shoulders away from the ears.
10. Stabilize the weight equally throughout the left foot.
11. Elongate the spine with each inhalation. Keep the tailbone tucked toward the floor.
12. Maintain focus and concentration.
13. To release, inhale slowly and bring the hands back to prayer position. Lower the hands and right foot to resume Tadasana.
14. Repeat on the opposite side.

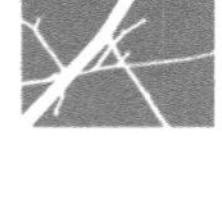

✚ BENEFITS	▲ PRECAUTIONS	✪ MODIFICATIONS
✚ Strengthens and tones thigh and calf muscles. ✚ Elongates the spine. ✚ Tones the kidneys and adrenal glands. ✚ Stimulates abdominal muscles and organs. ✚ Improves balance and body awareness. ✚ Helps to flush toxins from the knee.	▲ Headaches ▲ Structural injury or pain, especially knees, ankles and lower back ▲ Uncontrolled hypertension hypotension, or cardiac history (Optional: do not raise arms overhead) ▲ Low blood pressure **✳ COUNTERPOSE** ✳ Ardha chandrasana	✪ Place hands on the hips or extend the arms out in front of the body at shoulder height with palms down. ✪ Allow your body to be perpendicular to a wall so that the knee of the bent leg can slightly push into the wall for greater stability.

OPTIONAL PROPS: ✓ Blocks or belt

Pearls of Wisdom

Hatha yoga is a refuge for all those who were scorched by the 3 fires. To those who practice yoga, hatha yoga is like the tortoise that supports the world. These 3 fires are well known to us: they are the fire of self-created suffering, the fire of suffering through higher powers, and the fire of suffering that is caused by other beings. Nobody can eliminate the influences that create such sufferings from this world.

What we can and should do is prepare the physical-mental-spiritual soil in such a way that the seed of impressions cannot sprout into suffering. Sufferings are unfulfilled desires. The realization of these desires depends not only on ourselves— it is subject to external influences, and we always desire something, even if it is the desire for the happiness of a desireless state. But yoga does not mean to learn self-satisfaction. Rather, it means to strive for such a state of perfection that some day it will be our nature to be desirelessly happy and to have good reason for it.[1]

Muscles of the Buttock and Back Leg

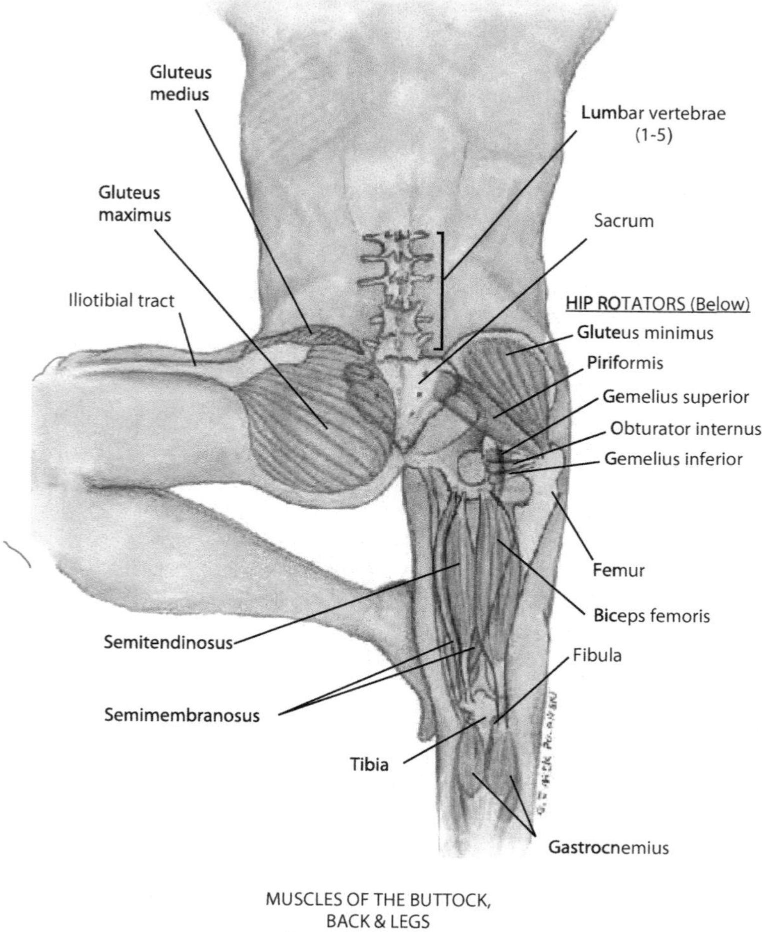

MUSCLES OF THE BUTTOCK, BACK & LEGS (Prasita Padottanasana)

1 Hatha yoga praddapika, translated by Hans-Ulrich Reiker.

We highly recommend that you hold this mudra for at least 5 minutes in a seated meditation. Perform it at least 13 different times. Mudras may also be utilized while holding a yoga pose. Remember, mudras tend to be subtle and are very powerful in their own way.

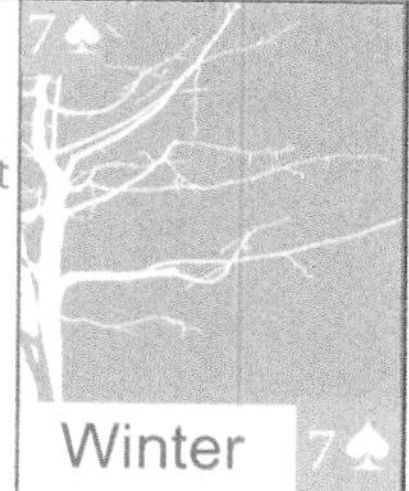

Winter 7♠

After holding this mudra for 5 minutes, place an X in the box below. After 13 sessions, please journal your experience.

Anjali
[.ahn-jha-leh-ahm]

Anjali is a gesture widespread throughout Asia to express salutation, especially toward a deity. It also expresses humility, and is used when receiving presents.

X	Mudra experience:

Utthita Tadasana

(Five-Pointed Star)

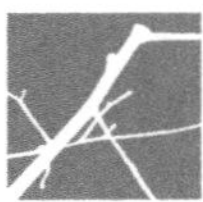

1. From Tadasana (and with slightly bent knees) jump or walk your feet about three to three and half feet apart (the distance of about one leg), as shown in picture.
2. Be sure to point the big toes slightly inward while pressing the outside edges of the feet into the floor.
3. At this point your legs should be very active and all the muscles working.
4. Rotate the front of the thighs internally so that the upper legs spiral inward. (Be sure the hips are not leaning forward or in front of the knees.)
5. While exhaling, pull the navel back toward the spinal column and then feel the extension in the torso.
6. While maintaining all of the above, externally rotate the shoulder blades down and toward the floor (at the same time spreading the back of the shoulders laterally away from each other).
7. Lift and spread the arms out and away from the body. (Be sure to keep a slight bend in the elbows, yet at the same time, stretch the fingertips from the elbows only.)
8. Lengthen the back of the neck and dip the nose slightly down toward the floor.
9. At this point you should feel the whole body being activated. This pose should correct any excess curvature of the spinal column.

✚ BENEFITS

- ✚ Unites the kinetic myofascial slings of the body.
- ✚ Strengthens the legs.
- ✚ Keeps the curves of the spine healthy.
- ✚ Improves circulation.

▲ PRECAUTIONS

- ▲ Sacroilliac problems
- ▲ Knee issues
- ▲ Supinated feet

✳ COUNTERPOSES

- ✳ Uttanasana
- ✳ Tadasna

✪ MODIFICATIONS

- ✪ Put one foot and one hand of the same side of the body at a wall for better support.
- ✪ Can be practiced while laying flat on the floor (backside of the body down) with a folded blanket to support under the back.

OPTIONAL PROP: ✓ Wall

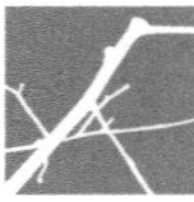

"When the breath wanders, i.e., is irregular, the mind also is unsteady. But when the breath is calmed, the mind too will be still..." When the nadis are impure, breath cannot penetrate into the sushumna. Then the yogi achieves nothing, nor can he reach the state of deep concentration. Therefore, one should practice pranayama with the mind in sattvic condition until the sushumna is free from impurities.[1]

Spinal Cord of Backside

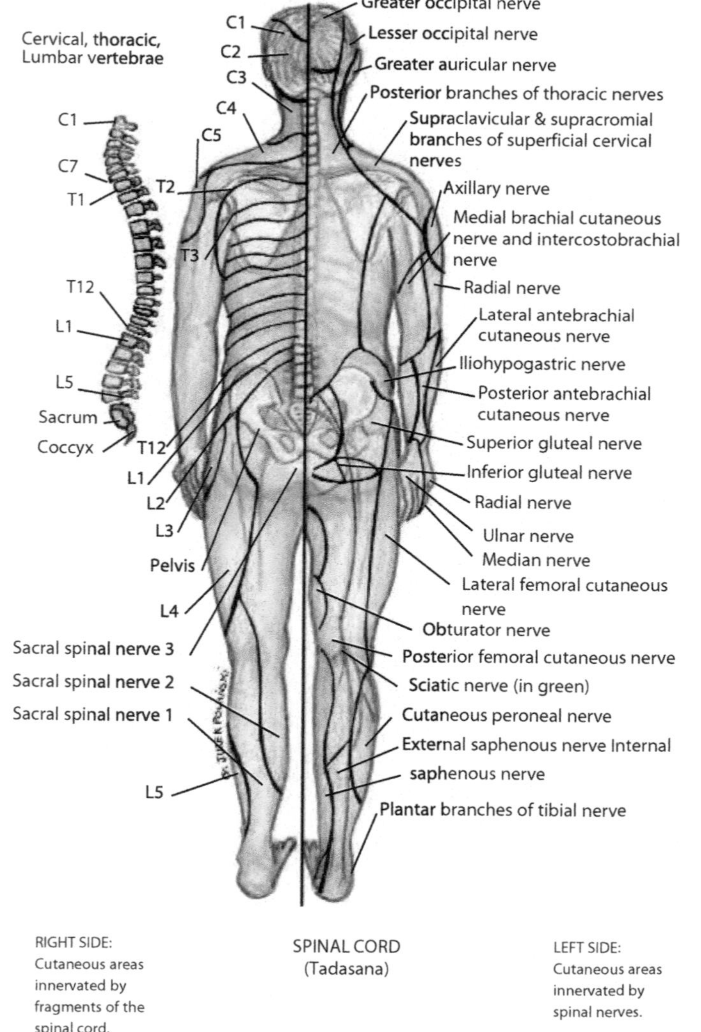

1 Hatha Yoga Praddapika, translated by Hans-Ulrich Reiker, pgs. 71-73.

We highly recommend that you hold this mudra for at least 5 minutes in a seated meditation. Perform it at least 13 different times. Mudras may also be utilized while holding a yoga pose. Remember, mudras tend to be subtle and are very powerful in their own way.

8♠ Winter 8♠

After holding this mudra for 5 minutes, place an X in the box below. After 13 sessions, please journal your experience.

Suci

[su-chee-ahm]

Suci is the "needle" hand pose and stands for the number 1, to point, to think, to threaten, the decline of the day, the world, beating drums, a rod, the potter's wheel, the circumference of a wheel, the cosmos, and astonishment.

X	Mudra experience:

Winter

Utthita Parsvakonasana

[Extended Side Angle Pose]

1 Step into Tadasana. Inhale.

2 Exhale. Step into 5-pointed star. The space between the feet may be slightly wider when practicing bent knee poses.

3 Turn the right foot out to 90° and the left foot in 45°. Align the right heel with the instep of the left foot.

4 Keep the shoulders and hips turned to the front wall.

5 Inhale, raising the arms to shoulder height, palms down. Extend out through the fingertips.

6 Exhale. Bend the front knee, bringing it directly over the ankle. Extend through the rear leg, grounding firmly into the foot. Attempt to bring the front thigh parallel with the floor and the shin perpendicular.

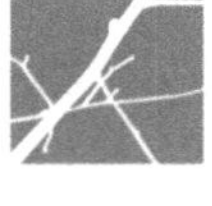

7 Inhale. Gently lift the sternum and drop the tailbone to the floor. Extend out through the crown of the head.

8 Exhale. Bend laterally from the waist, placing the right elbow onto the right thigh. If possible, release the elbow from the thigh and place the right hand on the mat on the outside of the right foot.

9 Draw the right shoulder down away from the ear.

10 Rotate the torso and roll the left ribs upward.

11 Inhale the left arm up along the left arm and extend out through the fingertips, palm facing down.

12 Extend through the back foot, pressing the outside of the foot into the mat.

13 Gaze up and past the left underarm. Keep the head and neck aligned with the spine.

14 Breathe evenly, continuing to lengthen the tailbone down and extend out through the crown of the head.

15 Come out of the posture very slowly. Inhale, straightening the front knee.

16 Exhale, bringing the toes of the right foot back to facing front.

17 Inhale as you step back into Tadasana.

18 Repeat on the opposite side.

✚ BENEFITS

- ✚ Strengthens and lengthens spine.
- ✚ Tones the legs and arms.
- ✚ Opens the chest and back, increasing lung capacity.
- ✚ Opens the pelvic area.
- ✚ Massages and tones the internal organs.
- ✚ Allows the body to feel extended and grounded.
- ✚ Improves digestion.
- ✚ Strengthens the diagonal slings of the body.

▲ PRECAUTIONS

- ▲ Uncontrolled hypertension or cardiac history.
- ▲ Structural injury or pain, especially the neck, knees, hips or lower back.
- ▲ Avoid with abdominal issues or inflammation.

✳ COUNTERPOSES

- ✳ Child's pose
- ✳ Tadasana

✪ MODIFICATIONS

- ✪ Use a block under the hand on the outside of the forward foot.
- ✪ Keep the elbow resting on the thigh of the bent leg.
- ✪ Support the back of the front thigh on a chair.
- ✪ Keep the upper arm on the waist.

OPTIONAL PROPS: ✓Block ✓Chair

YOGIC DIET AND MIND

Maintenance: There is constant wear and tear in our body cells as we age. The old cells are constantly replaced with new cells, and a harmony between degeneration and regeneration is maintained by a proper and balanced diet. Energy supply: Our body needs a constant supply of energy, which is obtained by the breaking down of food particles we ingest. The more simple and less processed the food items are, the more direct energy they have.

DIET AND MIND

According to the Yoga Sutra, there is a deep relationship between our diet and our mind. Scientific evidences have proved that an individual diet has a deep influence on his or her mind. The basic qualities of mind are sattva (virtue), Raja (aggressive desire) and Tama (ignorant sloth). Satvaguna expresses strengthening, invigorating and vitalizing. This Guna expresses essence, understanding, purity, clarity, compassion and love. Rajoguna implies movement, aggressiveness and extroversion, and it operates on a sensual level. Tamoguna manifests ignorance, inertia, heaviness and dullness.

Satvaguna is a positive virtue and it strengthens and calms the mind. Rajoguna and Tamoguna are negative qualities, which weaken and destabilize the mind. Yet all the three qualities are needed of course for a balanced state, having a strong control over Satvaguna for a normal functioning of the mind. As the final aim of yoga practitioner is elevation and uplifting of mental faculties to attain eternal bliss or peace, an individual should try to enhance his Satvaguna through proper diet and good conduct. In *Bhagavad-Gita* Lord Krishna says, " Yoga becomes the destroyer of all the woes and sorrows and can be accomplished only by those who are regulated and moderate."

In yogic cooking, the most satisfying part of the meal comes from the freshness and the "prana,"or the life force existing in the food being prepared. When the food is cooked or made, consumed and digested inside our body with an awareness, grace, acceptance and respect, our body will get the "life force" of health and wellness. The food should always be taken in a pleasant state of mind for a positive effect on the body. According to Ayurveda, the six tastes, which are the sweet, sour, salty, bitter, pungent and astringent, should be included in every meal . . . because each has a distinct flavor and sufficient nutritional value. It renders a sense of overall balance and helps to prevent the cravings and overeating to maintain the body's natural weight and health.

IDEAL FOOD FOR YOGA PRACTITIONERS

Foods that are sweet, bland, oily, fresh, natural, nourishing and agreeable are a Satvik diet and promote health, longevity, intelligence, happiness, vigor and vitality. Eating right provides a well-balanced base and fuel for our body in the right proportion, just like an over-oiled machine or a well-tuned car.
Ideal food types for a yoga practitioner include the following items:

1. All nuts and fruits, especially those with a sweet and slightly sour taste
2. All kinds of vegetables and edible green leaves
3. All kind of lentils or pulses
4. Milk, slightly sour curds, butter and ghee
5. Dates, honey, jaggery and all types of spices in moderation.
6. Wheat, unpolished rice, oats and barley
7. Sprouted pulses and cereals

Food should be freshly prepared and served. Very bitter, sour, spicy, oily and fried food should be avoided. Food items that are semi- cooked or burnt, stale or impure should be avoided as they produce Tamoguna.

The yogic food which is comprised mainly of dal when combined with rice or bread, provides a complete protein, low in fat. Having six tastes, it is full of taste and flavor with the blend of ancient healing spices from India. The most important spices that contribute to good health and balanced nutrition are ginger, turmeric, cardamom, cumin, asafetida.

We highly recommend that you hold this mudra for at least 5 minutes in a seated meditation. Perform it at least 13 different times. Mudras may also be utilized while holding a yoga pose. Remember, mudras tend to be subtle and are very powerful in their own way.

9♠ Winter 9♠

After holding this mudra for 5 minutes, place an X in the box below. After 13 sessions, please journal your experience.

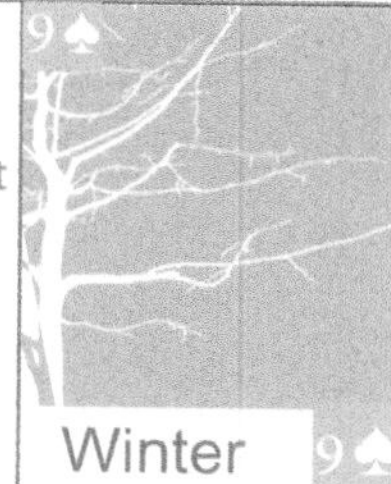

Tamracuda

[tah-mra-koo-dahm]

Tamracuda denotes the "red crest of the cock," but its use is extended to the cock, crane, crow, calf, camel, and a pen. Tamracuda is the gesture both of beckoning to children and of rebuke.

X	Mudra experience:

Winter

Garudasana

[Eagle Pose]

(gah-rue-DAHS-anna)

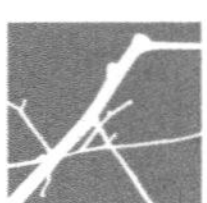

1. Step into Tadasana.
2. Shift weight into the left foot.
3. Find a focal point out in front.
4. Inhale. Bend the right knee and cross the right leg over the left. Wrap the right foot behind the left calf. Allow the left knee to bend.
5. In the balanced state, extend both arms in front of the body. Place the left arm on top of the right. Bend both at the elbows and place the palms together.
6. Stabilize the weight equally in the left foot.
7. Elongate the spine with each inhalation. Keep tailbone tucked toward the floor.
8. Maintain focus and concentration.
9. To release, inhale slowly releasing the arms. Lower hands and feet.
10. Repeat on the opposite side.

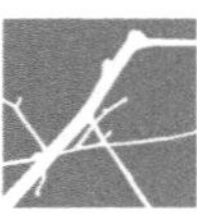

✚ BENEFITS	▲ PRECAUTIONS	✪ MODIFICATIONS
✚ Strengthens muscles and bones of the legs. ✚ Increases flexibility in the hips and shoulders. ✚ Tones the spine. ✚ Helps with sciatica. ✚ Strengthens the lower back and ✚ Improves balance, coordination, and postural awareness. ✚ Focuses the mind.	▲ Upper and lower body joint pain ▲ Uncontrolled hypertension or cardiac conditions ▲ Structural injury or pain, especially shoulders, hips, knees or ankles ▲ Hip replacement/surgery ✳ COUNTERPOSES: ✳ Downward-Facing Dog ✳ Tadasana	✪ Practice pose in a supine position. ✪ Practice against a wall until balance is developed. ✪ Practice the arm and leg components separately. ✪ Place the toes of the raised leg on a block.
OPTIONAL PROP: ✓ Block		

"Just as all the multitude of asanas aim at the spinal column, so the essence of prana is centered in kumbhaka, the period when there is no breathing. From this as well as by later indications we can recognize that it is not the breath air that carries the current but that the current is being produced during the breathing process.

Just as the plunging waters in a power plant are only the means of releasing the energy through which the brushes of the stationary turbins are activated, so prana also does not originate in breath but in the 'turbins,' the chakra wheels with which the nadis have an inductive relationship." [1]

There are 5 forms of prana (Vayu).
They have different names according to
the bodily functions with which they correspond.
These forms of prana are:

- **u**dana-vayu, corresponding to the throat region and the function of speech
- **p**rana-vayu, corresponding to the chest region
- **s**amana-vayu, corresponding to the central region of the body and is related to the function of digestion
- **a**pana-vayu, corresponding to the region of the lower abdomen and the function of elimination
- **v**yana-vayu, corresponding to the distribution of energy into all the different areas of the body

We highly recommend that you hold this mudra for at least 5 minutes in a seated meditation. Perform it at least 13 different times. Mudras may also be utilized while holding a yoga pose. Remember, mudras tend to be subtle and are very powerful in their own way.

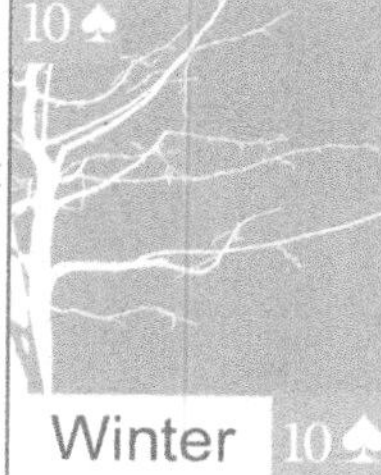

After holding this mudra for 5 minutes, place an X in the box below. After 13 sessions, please journal your experience.

Guruda
[gah-rood-ahm]

The Garuda mudra references the mount of Shiva. The Garuda is a fabulous bird for its upper torso, but half-man beneath. The Garuda symbolizes courage.

X	Mudra experience:

1 Hatha Yoga Praddapika, translated by Hans-Ulrich Reiker, pg. 75.

Winter

Uttanasana

[Standing Forward Fold Pose]

(OOT-tan-AHS-anna)

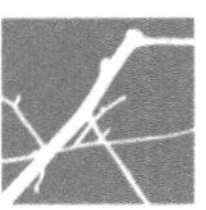

1 Step into Tadasana. Inhale lengthening through the spine.

2 Exhale. Slowly begin to bend forward, leading with the sternum. Hinge from the hips.

3 Extend out through the hands, placing the fingers or palms to the floor if possible.

4 Engage the legs, contracting the thigh muscles into the bone. Note: please keep the knees slightly bent. Never hyperextend the knees.

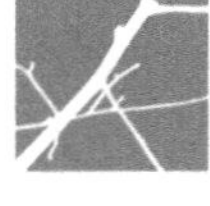

5 Release the head, neck and shoulders allowing gravity to gently extend the stretch.

6 Stabilize the weight equally throughout the feet. Maintain the extension of the spine.

7 With each inhalation, extend the torso. With each exhalation, visualize and feel as if you are coming down a little further each time.

8 To release, inhale, slightly bend the knees while coming back to Tadasana with a straight back.

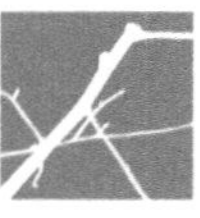

✚ BENEFITS	▲ PRECAUTIONS	✪ MODIFICATIONS
✚ Stretches the leg muscles, especially the hamstrings, and the entire spine. ✚ Tones the kidneys and adrenal glands. ✚ Regulates digestive processes. ✚ Increases blood flow to the brain, calming and oxygenating it. ✚ Develops a sense of balance and groundedness.	▲ Back injury ▲ Hamstring pulls/sciatica ▲ Glaucoma. ▲ Headache ✳ COUNTERPOSE ✳ Ustrasana	✪ Bend the knees slightly to release the hamstrings and lower back. ✪ Place the hands on the hips when coming out of the pose. ✪ Stand at the wall, allowing the back of the hips to be supported for balance. ✪ Place blocks under the hands. ✪ Rest the head on a block to help alleviate hypertension or stress-related headaches.

OPTIONAL PROP: ✓ Tadasana

The Origins of Space

Life. So many dimensions. Endless possibilities. Wherefore the landscapes roam our bodies and minds adore. Abstract is its form unrehearsed.

Let us great friends, let go and forget about the many words and symbols that have no heartfelt meaning. And, in its stead, let us pray to remember to become the form with which our light reflects the luminous heart. Let our Light help generate and guide the truth from within the deepest ravines of our most humble being.

And in our great reform, let us remember that Light seeks Life. It is through the laws of the stars we forge forth the truth and essence of our being.

It is through the understanding of our presence that we learn to empty the cluttered rooms of our mansion— our inner being. Once through the interior doors, it is here that we come to meet and greet our sacred second self. More often than not, the forgotten self! And it is here, in this wondrous village, that we come into Light of a *second sight.*

A second sight seeks. It engulfs and consumes the flames of distraction. It melts and burns away the smoke and mirrors of life's illusion.
It is through the sifting of our embers and ashes that we discover presence: Thus blooms the golden lotus. And, let us not forget, that from the essence of our presence is the key to awakening up to life. It is in this place of truth that we have become more ... with less.

And so my friends, from this moment on, let us, in all ways, remember how truly deep-rooted we are into the universal seed force of Love: that of which binds us all together one divine.

-Miguel Latronica, 2015

We highly recommend that you hold this mudra for at least 5 minutes in a seated meditation. Perform it at least 13 different times. Mudras may also be utilized while holding a yoga pose. Remember, mudras tend to be subtle and are very powerful in their own way.

Winter

After holding this mudra for 5 minutes, place an X in the box below. After 13 sessions, please journal your experience.

Mrgasirsa
[mrah-gasir-sham]

The Mrgasirsa or "deer head" mudra draws action toward stasis. It thus represents traditional manners, a place of residence, an anchoring of feet, patterns drawn in solid soil, and something well loved.

X	Mudra experience:

Winter

Utthita Trikonasana

[Triangle Pose]

(oo-TEE-tah trik-cone-AHS-anna)

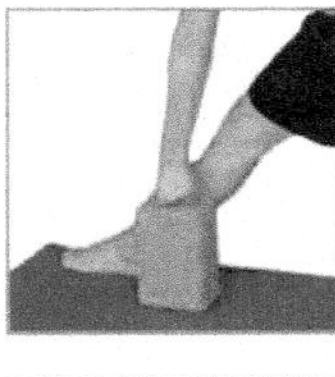

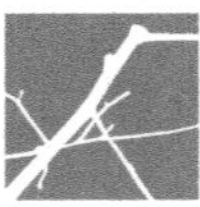

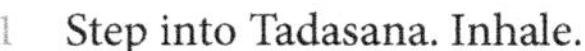

1 Step into Tadasana. Inhale.

2 Exhale. Step into Five-Pointed Star. Turn the right foot out to 90° and the left foot in 45°. Align the right heel with the instep of the left foot.

3 Keep the shoulders and hips facing forward, feeling an openness in the pelvis and the front of the thighs.

4 Exhale. Shift the left hip slightly to the left while extending the torso to the right, creasing at the hip.

5 Only bend as far laterally as possible without moving the left hip forward.

6 Exhale. Windmill the arms extending the right hand towards the floor and the left arm to the ceiling.

7 Align the head and neck as an extension of the spine and turn the gaze toward the upper hand, or at the lower shoulder to release neck tension.

8 Hold and breathe evenly. Continue to rotate the torso upward and elongate the spine.

9 To release the pose, inhale using the left arm to lift you back to a standing position.

10 Exhale, bringing the toes of the right foot back to facing forward.

11 Inhale as you step back into Tadasana.

12 Repeat on the opposite side.

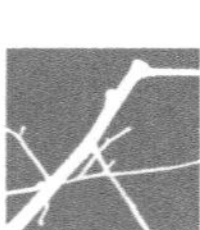

✚ BENEFITS

- ✚ Strengthens and lengthens entire spine.
- ✚ Flexes and rotates hips.
- ✚ Stretches and tones oblique abdominal muscles.
- ✚ Strengthens outer thighs while stretching inner thighs. Lengthens hamstring muscles.
- ✚ Lengthens and tones arms and upper back.
- ✚ Strengthens neck muscles.

▲ PRECAUTIONS

- ▲ Uncontrolled hypertension, hypotension, or cardiac history
- ▲ Structural injury or pain, especially in the knees or lower back
- ▲ Not suggested during menstruation

✳ COUNTERPOSE

- ✳ Utkatasana

✪ MODIFICATIONS

- ✪ Slightly bend front knee.
- ✪ Place hand on block placed on the outside of the bottom calf.
- ✪ Rest gaze toward floor or straight ahead.
- ✪ Practice posture against the wall.
- ✪ Place back of outer heel at wall for stability and ease.

OPTIONAL PROPS: ✓ Block ✓ Wall

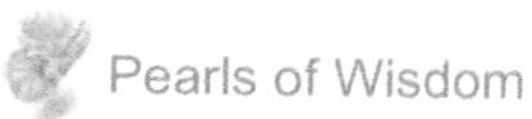

Hatha yoga is comprised of jyoti (light) and mantra (sound). The powers are awakened by means of the upper sphere of vibrations (light), which extend from the cosmic ether rays through the ultra colors to infrared, the rays of heat; and they are also awakened through the lower sphere of vibrations, from supersonic sound down to the lowest plane of vibrations. [1]

Deep Muscles of the Hip and Thigh

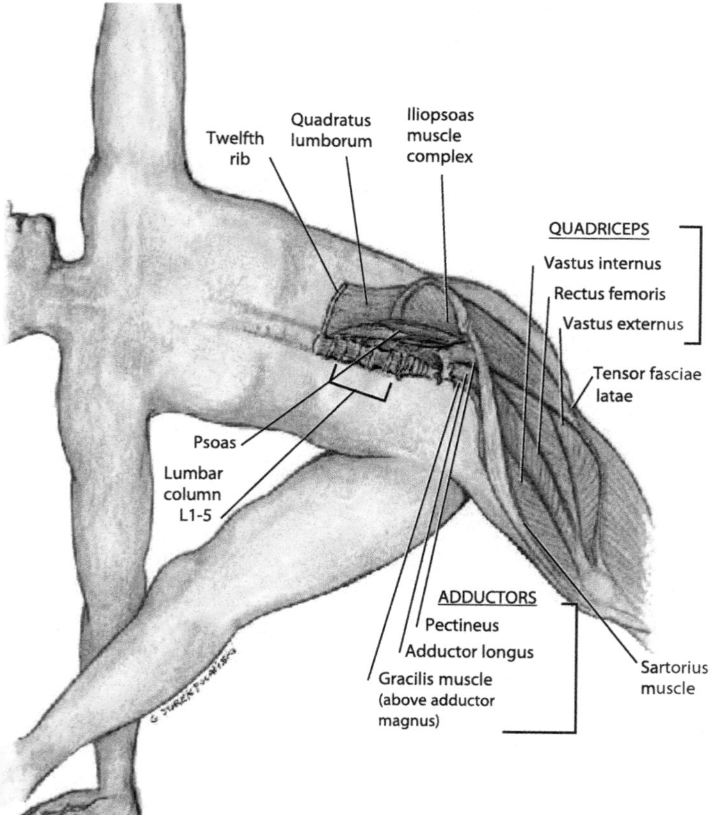

DEEP MUSCLES OF HIP AND THIGH
(Utthita Trikonasana)

We highly recommend that you hold this mudra for at least 5 minutes in a seated meditation. Perform it at least 13 different times. Mudras may also be utilized while holding a yoga pose. Remember, mudras tend to be subtle and are very powerful in their own way.

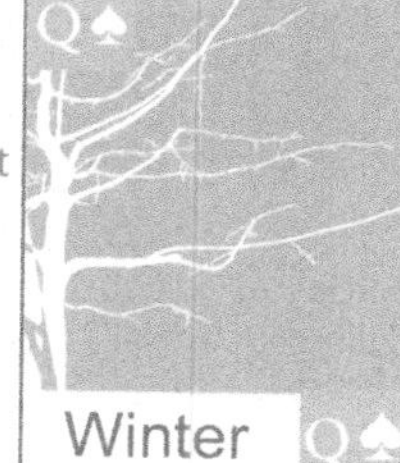

Winter Q♠

Ardhapataka
[ardha-patha-kam]

The Ardhapataka represents upright forms. It can denote the number 2 or a slab or a board, a knife or a spear, a tower, temple, and the bank of a river.

After holding this mudra for 5 minutes, place an X in the box below. After 13 sessions, please journal your experience.

X Mudra experience:

1 Hatha Yoga Praddapika, translated by Hans-Ulrich Reiker, Pg. 130.

Parivrtti Trikonasana

[Revolved Triangle Pose]

(par-ee-vrit-tah trik-cone-AHS-anna)

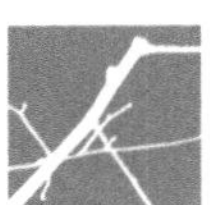

1 Step into Tadasana. Inhale.

2 Exhale. Step the left leg back about 2 - 3 feet.

3 Keep the right foot pointed forward and the outer edge parallel to the side of the mat.

4 Turn the left foot in 45° so that the hips and shoulders are now squared.

5 Exhale. Inhale, extend through both legs, standing firmly onto each foot.

6 Inhale. Gently lift the sternum to get greater lengthening through the entire spinal column.

7 Inhale. Exhale, bring the right hand to the right hip or up toward the sky.

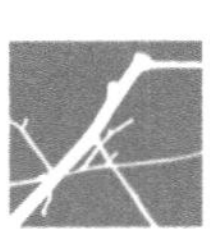

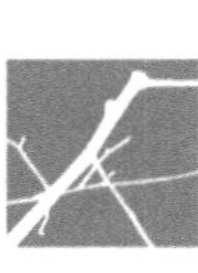

✚ BENEFITS	▲ PRECAUTIONS	✪ MODIFICATIONS
✚ Tones and stimulates the abdominal organs. ✚ Releases tight diagonal myofascial slings of the body. ✚ Strengthens the hips, legs and spine. ✚ Improves the capacity for breath. ✚ Great for digestive problems.	▲ Low back issues ▲ Recent surgeries ▲ Low blood pressure ▲ Diarrhea ▲ Headache **✳ COUNTERPOSE** ✳ Tadasana ✳ Janu sirsasana	✪ Hand on block, chair or chin bone. ✪ Shorten stance. ✪ Keep front knee slightly bent while keeping the back leg more firm.

OPTIONAL PROPS: ✓ Blocks, chairs or other yoga props

Fifteen Important Tips for the Yogic Diet:

1. Eat to live but don't live to eat.
2. Eat food that is beneficial.
3. Eat food in moderate quantity.
4. Those foods not familiar to you should not be eaten .
5. Food should be eaten slowly and chewed well before swallowing. Always eat in a peaceful and happy state of mind.
6. The stomach should be filled half with food, one fourth with water and the remaining with air.
7. The yoga asanas should not be done immediately after taking food.
8. The most suitable times for yoga are in the morning and the evening, on an empty stomach.
9. One should not go to bed immediately after taking supper, but rather 2 - 3 hours later.
10. According to Ayurveda, a well-balanced diet consists of foodstuffs having 6 tastes, or Rasa namely: Madhura (sweet), Amla (sour), Lavana (salty), Katu (pungent), Tikta (bitter) and Kasya (astringent).
11. Modern dieticians say that a well-balanced diet should have vitamins and minerals in such a required quantity that provides needed calories to the body.
12. Food should be planned giving consideration to each of the 3 concepts (Yogic, Ayurvedic and Modern) related to diet, and ultimately coming to a final conclusion for the diet plan.
13. Food should always be cooked on a low flame to preserve it's nutrients.
14. Vegetables should be cut into big pieces for cooking to maintain its food value and fiber content.
15. Iron utensils are healthy for yogic cooking in place of chemically coated or processed steel body utensils which may react with food ingredients by producing toxic substances harmful to the body.

We highly recommend that you hold this mudra for at least 5 minutes in a seated meditation. Perform it at least 13 different times. Mudras may also be utilized while holding a yoga pose. Remember, mudras tend to be subtle and are very powerful in their own way.

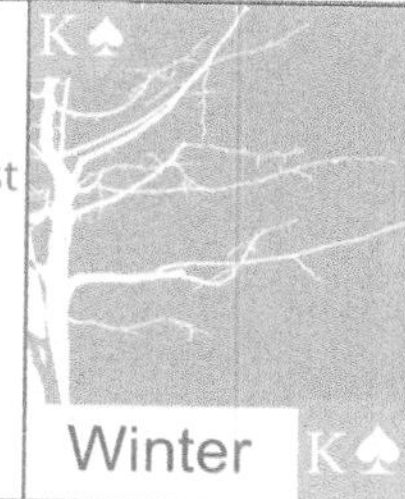

After holding this mudra for 5 minutes, place an X in the box below. After 13 sessions, please journal your experience

Padmakosa

[pad-mah-ko-sam]

Padmakosa symbolizes a lotus-bud, essential fruit, a cooking pot, an ant hill, an egg, a ball, to suggest a circular movement, and the round breasts of a woman.

X	Mudra experience:

Bhjangasana
[Cobra Pose]

(boo-jang-GAHS-anna)

Spring

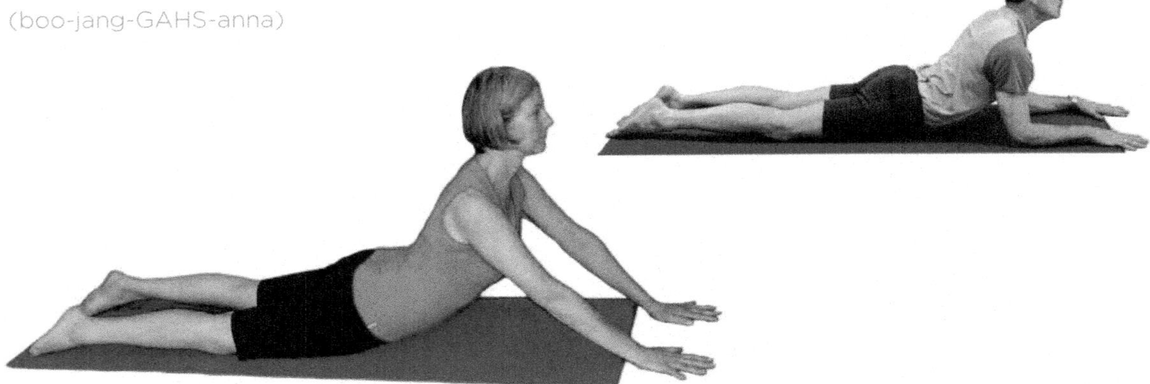

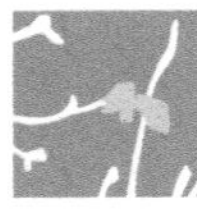

1 Lie down on the mat belly side down (prone).

2 Keep hips, torso, shoulders and arms on the ground.

3 Lift left leg up off floor and slither it further back behind the right foot.

4 Keeping the left leg fully engaged, lift the right leg up and move it back to meet the left tips of the left foot.

5 Legs should be about 6 inches from each other.

6 Place hands slightly out in front (or under) the shoulders, while keeping the elbows lined up with the sides of the torso.

7 On an inhalation, begin to straighten out the arms so that the head and torso lift up off the floor.

8 Be sure not to pinch the lower back. Keep the tailbone tucking in toward the floor and pubis toward the navel.

9 While keeping the buttocks soft, inhale and lengthen the spine, but again, be sure not to increase the lordosis in the low back or at the neck (cervical).

10 As the hands press the floor down and away, be sure to broaden the back of the shoulder blades away from each other.

11 Keep the eyes and face soft.

12 Hold the pose anywhere from 10-40 seconds.

✚ BENEFITS	▲ PRECAUTIONS	✪ MODIFICATIONS
✚ Strengthens the spinal column. ✚ Opens the front side of the body. ✚ Invigorates the heart and lungs. ✚ Helps to release sciatica. Tones the buttocks.	▲ Back injury/issues ▲ Carpel tunnel syndrome ▲ Pregnancy ▲ Headaches ✳ COUNTERPOSE ✳ Forward bend or child's pose	✪ Place blanket under hips. ✪ Place block in between thighs. ✪ Place forearms on two half blocks.

OPTIONAL PROPS: ✓ Blanket(s) ✓ Block

Bhujanga means cobra in Sanskrit. The snake, or serpent, embodies the life of the spine. Kundalini, the serpent goddess, the symbol of our divine potential energy, is said to lie sleeping at the base of the spine. In this pose, we seek out our relationship to gravity, using consciousness to rise with great discrimination, as the cobra does, to meet opportunities. Bhujangasana strengthens, tones, and lengthens the muscles of the spine and back, helps to align the spinal disks, stimulates the thyroid, kidneys, adrenals, tones the uterus and helps to regulate the endocrine system, assisting in reproductive and menstrual problems. As the chest opens, lung capacity is increased, also helping to massage the heart. For the front body to open, the pubic bone must press into the ground, lengthening the low back, which makes more energy available to rise along the spine, allowing the heart to open to feeling, and the mind to open to intuition and discrimination, allowing the choices we make to become more conscious.

Front View of Hips

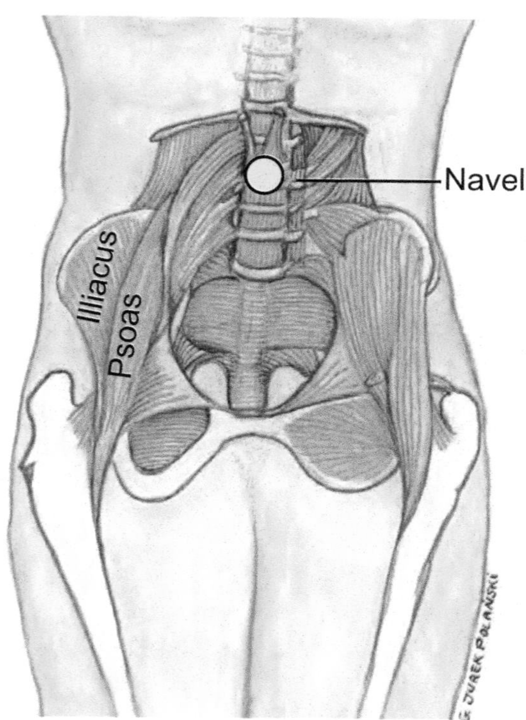

We highly recommend that you hold this mudra for at least 5 minutes in a seated meditation. Perform it at least 13 different times. Mudras may also be utilized while holding a yoga pose. Remember, mudras tend to be subtle and are very powerful in their own way.

After holding this mudra for 5 minutes, place an X in the box below. After 13 sessions, please journal your experience.

Kangula
[kan-gu-lam]

The Kangula or "tail" mudra signifies the small or diminutive. It is the gesture of holding up a child's face by the chin; representing a bird, little bells worn by children, pills, a coconut, the betal nut tree or fruits.

X	Mudra experience:

Spring

Classical Natarajasana

[Lord of the Dance Pose]

(na-tara-jahs-anna)

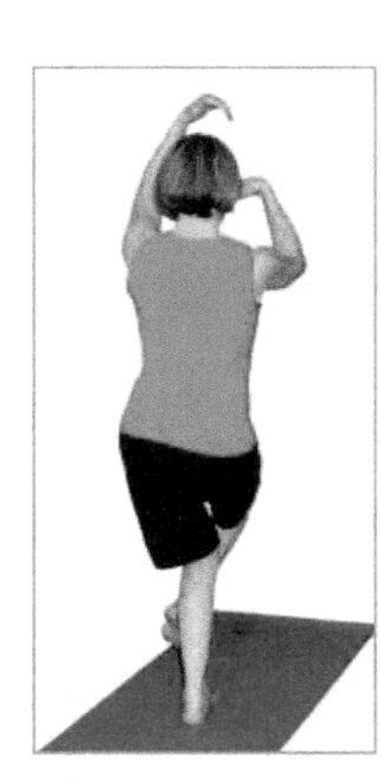

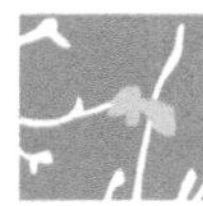

1 Step into Tadasana. Inhale, lengthening through the spine.

2 Shift the weight into the left foot.

3 Find a focal point approximately 8 feet in front of you.

4 Exhale. Bend the left knee slightly and lift the heel of the right leg, bending at the right knee. Continue to lift the right leg away from the floor until the knee is even with the hip.

5 Bring the right knee into the midline without moving the hips.

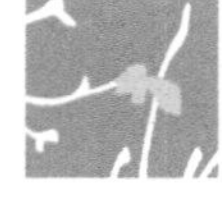

6 In the balanced state, extend both arms in front of the body. Allow the arms to bend at the elbows. Inhale. Bring the right arm up so that the wrist is in line with the forehead. The right elbow is at shoulder height. The left wrist is at the same height as the right elbow.

7 Relax the shoulders and drop them away from the ears.

8 Elongate the spine with each inhalation. Keep the tailbone tucked toward the floor.

9 Maintain focus and concentration. Gaze forward with the eyes soft.

10 To release, inhale slowly, releasing the arms. Lower the hands and foot to resume Tadasana.

11 Repeat on the opposite side.

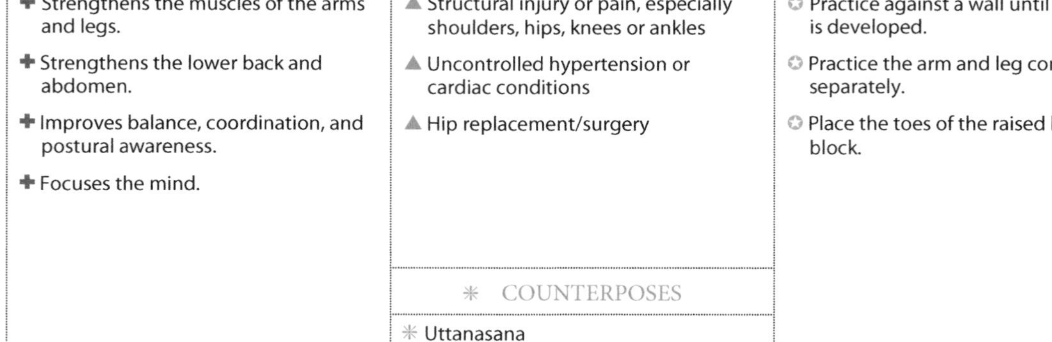

✚ BENEFITS	▲ PRECAUTIONS	✪ MODIFICATIONS
✚ Strengthens the muscles of the arms and legs. ✚ Strengthens the lower back and abdomen. ✚ Improves balance, coordination, and postural awareness. ✚ Focuses the mind.	▲ Structural injury or pain, especially shoulders, hips, knees or ankles ▲ Uncontrolled hypertension or cardiac conditions ▲ Hip replacement/surgery ✳ COUNTERPOSES ✳ Uttanasana ✳ Dandasana	✪ Practice against a wall until balance is developed. ✪ Practice the arm and leg components separately. ✪ Place the toes of the raised leg on a block.

OPTIONAL PROPS: ✓ Block ✓ Wall

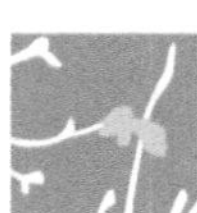

"The practice of yoga aims to overcome the limitations of the body. Yoga teaches us that every individual's goal is to take the inner journey to the soul. Yoga offers both the means and the goal to reach it." - BKS Iyengar

Sacroiliac/Lumbar Complex

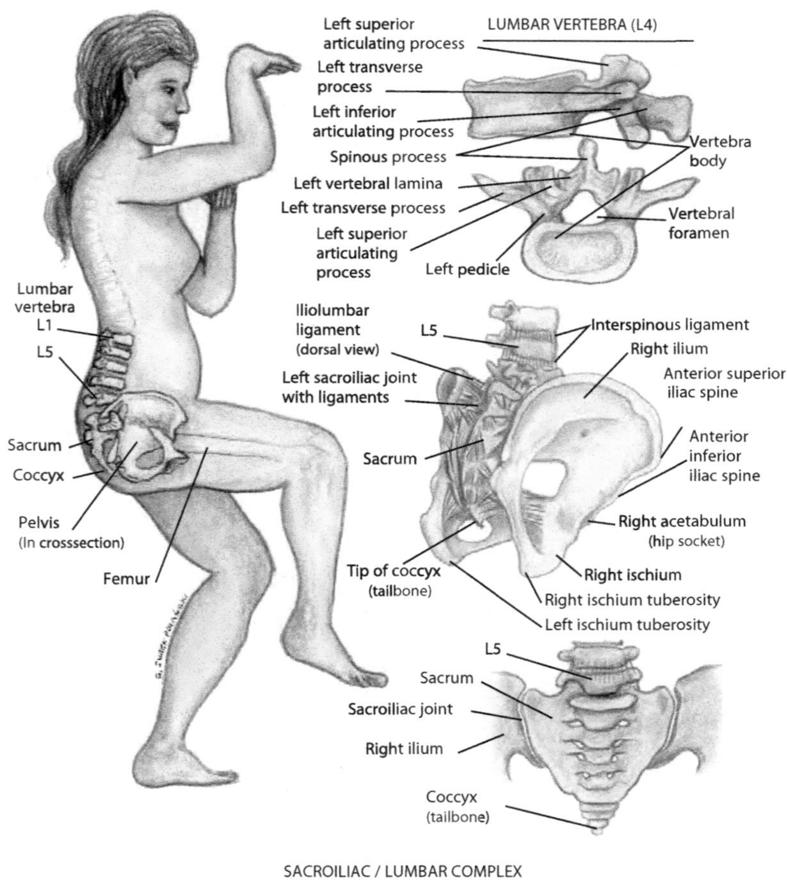

SACROILIAC / LUMBAR COMPLEX
(Natrasana)

We highly recommend that you hold this mudra for at least 5 minutes in a seated meditation. Perform it at least 13 different times. Mudras may also be utilized while holding a yoga pose. Remember, mudras tend to be subtle and are very powerful in their own way.

Spring 2♥

After holding this mudra for 5 minutes, place an X in the box below. After 13 sessions, please journal your experience.

Shakti

[shahk-tahm]

Shakti (S'akti references the divine and universal power inherent in a deity. It further signifies a javelin or spear, and thus denotes active potency.

X	Mudra experience:

Spring

Dandasana

[Staff Pose]

(dan-dah-sah-anna)

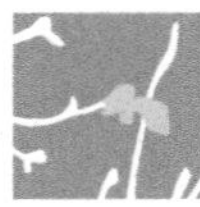

1 Sit on the floor on the sitz bones with both legs extended to the front. Extend out through the heels.

2 Place the palms or fingertips to the sides of the hips.

3 Inhale, lifting the ribs and sternum. Bring the scapulae together gently and drop the shoulders away from the ears.

4 Exhale, extending out through the heels. Activate the legs, turning the tops of the thighs in slightly while gently pressing them down toward the floor. The kneecaps should be very engaged!

5 Inhale, extending up through the spine.

6 The neck should also be lengthening as the tip of the nose slightly drops.

✚ BENEFITS	▲ PRECAUTIONS	✪ MODIFICATIONS
✚ Strengthens the muscles of the back, legs, and arms.	▲ Wrist or ulnar nerve issues.	✪ Turn the hands (fingers backwards) for wrist pain.
✚ Allows for greater spinal extension.	▲ Slipped discs or other low back problems.	✪ Bend the knees or elevate the hips for tight hamstrings or hips or low back pain.
✚ Opens up the shoulders and chest.		✪ For shorter arms or tight shoulders, use a block, half block, or rolled mat or blanket under the hands.
✚ Allows for balanced hamstrings.		✪ Practice with the spine against a wall to find and support proper alignment.
	✳ COUNTERPOSE	✪ Place a rolled-up blanket under the back of the knees to help prevent hyper-extending.
	✳ Setu Bhandasana	

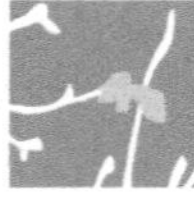

OPTIONAL PROPS: ✓ Block ✓ Blanket

Danda means "staff" in Sanskrit. The staff is a symbol of power and sovereignty, and in Vedic iconography is wielded by Vishnu to preserve the universe. The staff also refers to the spine, the preserver and pathway of the nervous system. As the basis of all seated forward bends, dandasana teaches us to own our power so that we may utilize it in the process of surrender.

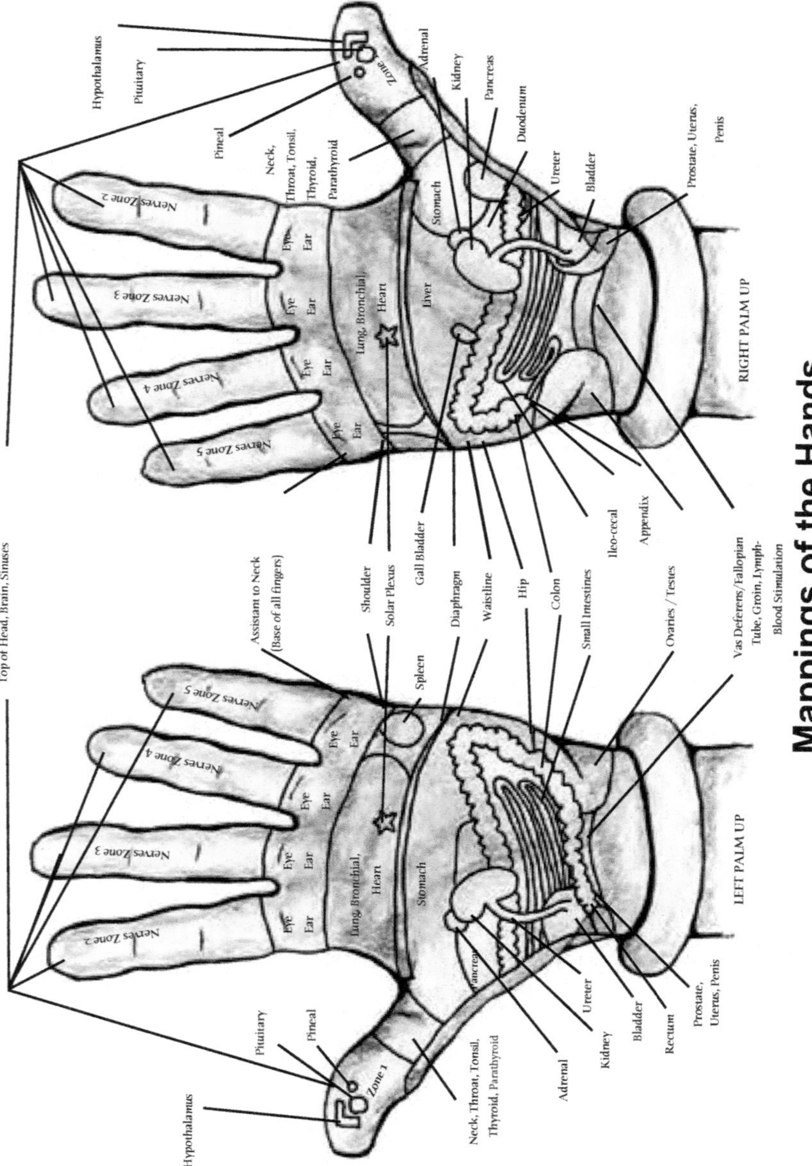

Mappings of the Hands

We highly recommend that you hold this mudra for at least 5 minutes in a seated meditation. Perform it at least 13 different times. Mudras may also be utilized while holding a yoga pose. Remember, mudras tend to be subtle and are very powerful in their own way.

After holding this mudra for 5 minutes, place an X in the box below. After 13 sessions, please journal your experience.

Katakavardhana

[kata-kavar-da-nahm]

Katakavardhana signifies a "link of increase." It symbolizes speaking the truth, a marriage blessing, worship, a coronation or profound ritual.

X	Mudra experience:

4♥ Spring

Parsvattonasana

[Intense Side Stretch Pose]

(parsh-voh-tahn-AHS-anna)

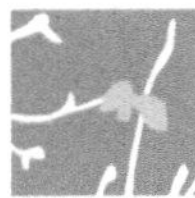

1. Step into Tadasana. Inhale.
2. Exhale. Step into Five-Pointed Star.
3. Turn right foot out to 90° and left foot in approximately 45°.
4. Square shoulders and hips over the right knee. Interlace the fingers behind the back.
5. Inhale. Gently lift the sternum and drop the tailbone to the floor, elongating the spine.
6. Exhale. Slowly bend forward at the hips coming to flat back parallel to the floor, while gently raising the arms towards the ceiling.
7. Inhale, elongating the spine.
8. Exhale, folding deeper into the pose extending the torso over the front thigh.
9. Find the breath as you relax into the posture.
10. To release the pose, slowly inhale raising the body to an upright position.
11. Release the arms to the sides.
12. Bring the feet back to a parallel stance.
13. Inhale bending the right knee as you step back into Tadasana.
14. Repeat on the opposite side.

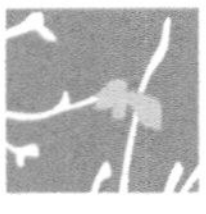

✚ BENEFITS	▲ PRECAUTIONS	✪ MODIFICATIONS
✚ Opens the chest, improving respiration. ✚ Increases blood flow to the brain. ✚ Stretches and strengthens the muscles of the legs and buttocks, especially the hamstrings and adductors.	▲ Structural injuries in hips, lower back, wrists or shoulder areas ▲ Uncontrolled hypertension or cardiac condition ▲ Eye conditions (detached retina, glaucoma) ✳ COUNTERPOSE ✳ Ustrasana	✪ Keep hands on either side of the front foot, using blocks if necessary. ✪ Hold the opposite elbow behind the back. ✪ Raise the heel of the rear foot to bring hips squarely into alignment. ✪ Slightly bend the front knee. ✪ Increase the width between the feet for a more stable stance.

OPTIONAL PROPS: ✓ 2 blocks

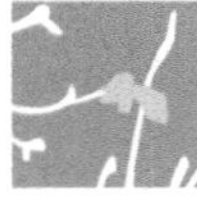

Pearls of Wisdom

The source of the nectar is the "moon" in the area of the brain stem. The "cooling beams of the moon," a term known in the mythologies of all countries, drip into the "fire of the sun" that burns in the region of the diaphragm and, so to speak, represents the flame of life (solar plexus). But the nectar is not fuel for this fire; to the contrary, it subdues and regulates the embers that are constantly being fanned into new life by the vata current. It is a direct, active messenger of consciousness to the functions of the vegetative system. When the supply is impeded, we have fever; with an oversupply, the fire becomes weak. When the demons of coarse bodily nature, while churning the ocean of milk, prematurely sampled the nectar before it had been wisely apportioned to them by the gods of mind, they poisoned themselves because the organic balance was disturbed. In order to fan the fire of "burning asceticism," the nectar has to be diverted from its usual course into the fire of life. But the stream is not only diverted; it is also utilized in other ways.[1]

Lateral View of Leg Muscles

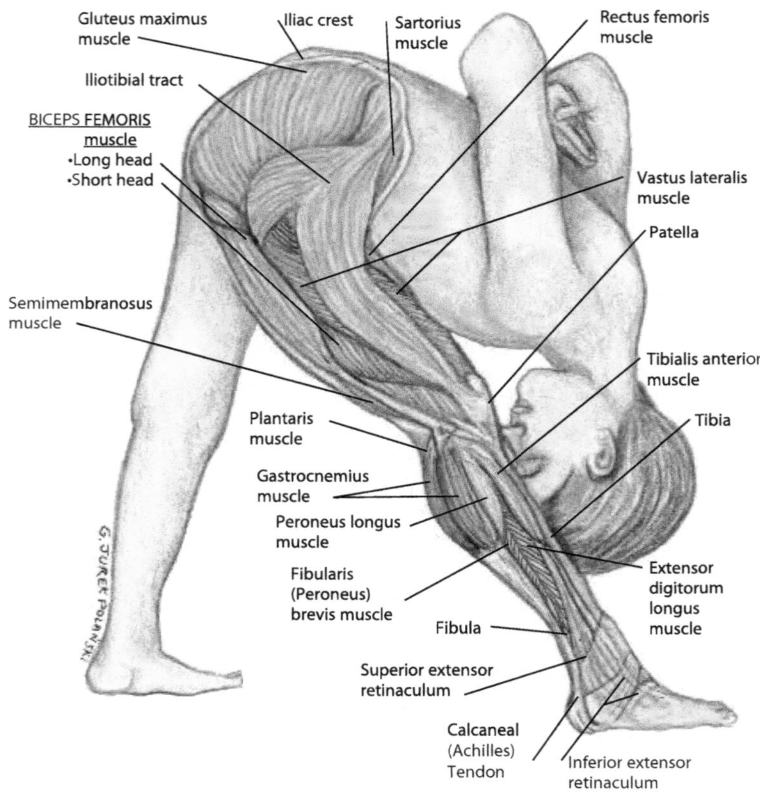

LATERAL VIEW OF LEG MUSCLES
(Parsvottanasana)

1 Hatha Yoga Praddapika, translated by Hans-Ulrich Reiker Pgs.116-118.

We highly recommend that you hold this mudra for at least 5 minutes in a seated meditation. Perform it at least 13 different times. Mudras may also be utilized while holding a yoga pose. Remember, mudras tend to be subtle and are very powerful in their own way.

4♥

Spring 4♥

After holding this mudra for 5 minutes, place an X in the box below. After 13 sessions, please journal your experience.

Svastika

[swa-sti-kam]

The Svastika means "crossed" and symbolizes expansive things such as the firmament, oceans, jungles, the earth itself. It is a sign of auspiciousness. It can reference praise, dispute, and even speech.

X Mudra experience:

Ardha Shalambhasana

[Grasshopper/Locust Pose]

(ARE-dah-Shal-ab-HAHS-anna)

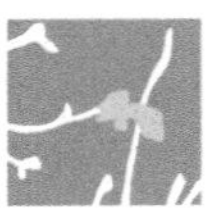

1 Lie down on the mat, belly side down.

2 Palms down, place the arms to the side of the torso.

3 While engaging the arms into the floor, gently stabilize the hips to lift and lengthen the head and neck. Let head then rest on the floor.

4 With stable hips, arms and hands, lift one leg and let it lengthen away from the parallel hips.

5 Either continue to hold the pose this way and then switch leg, or otherwise, have both legs lifted up off of the mat as shown in picture above, to the right. mat as shown in picture above, to the right.

6 Take the pose to the next level: Simply lift the torso up off the mats with the legs.

7 It is imperative to keep your hips stable and pressing downwards into the floor.

8 Hold for 20 - 40 seconds.

9 Repeat with opposite leg in the air.

✚ BENEFITS	▲ PRECAUTIONS	✪ MODIFICATIONS
✚ Stimulates abdominal organs ✚ Stretches arms, shoulders, belly, thighs and anterior tibialis ✚ Helps with indigestion ✚ Stimulates interstitial pressure	▲ Back or neck injury ▲ Headache ✳ COUNTERPOSE ✳ Child's pose	✪ Folded blanket under the hips and/or forehead ✪ Work one leg at a time ✪ Keep arms at side of torso ✪ Place two blocks in front for hands

OPTIONAL PROPS: ✓ Blanket ✓ Blocks

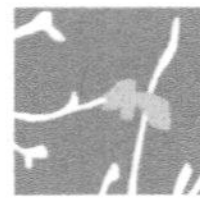

We highly recommend that you hold this mudra for at least 5 minutes in a seated meditation. Perform it at least 13 different times. Mudras may also be utilized while holding a yoga pose. Remember, mudras tend to be subtle and are very powerful in their own way.

Mulabhanda

The root lock is engaged best on the exhalation for most beginners although it can be activated on the inhalation. Bring awareness to the abdomino-pelvic floor region. Initially, contractions in the urogenital and the rectal triangles are combined. As your ability to work with the core develops, the focus is more centered on lifting the baseline that connects these two triangles, located medially between the genitals and the coccyx. In this space are the deep pelvic floor muscles, shaped like a hammock that supports the pelvic floor organs. Hold the lift briefly and then inhale, allowing it to relax.

The root lock corresponds to the Muladhara (root chakra) and raises earth and fire energies upward along the central channel. The root lock draws apana vayu (downward flowing energy upward) upward. The deep toning of the pelvic floor muscles with mula bhanda helps pelvic and lumbar stabilization in many positions. Many poses can be facilitated with greater ease using the root lock, and some poses are next to impossible to perform without utilizing this technique.

Sciatic Nerve Pathway

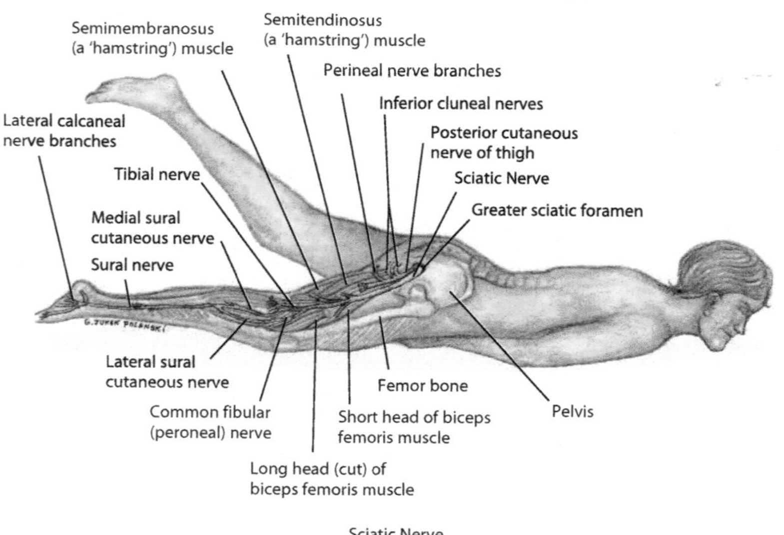

Sciatic Nerve
(Ardha Shalambhasana)

After holding this mudra for 5 minutes, place an X in the box below. After 13 sessions, please journal your experience.

Sandamsa
[san-dam-sham]

Sandamsa denotes the number 5, the belly or navel, great fear, to worship, and making an offering to deities.

X Mudra experience:

6♥

Spring

Prasarita Padottanasana

[Wide-Angle Standing Forward Bend]

(pra-sa-REE-tah pah-doh-tahn-AHS-anna)

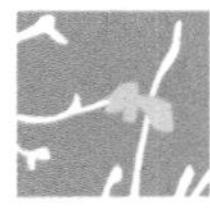

1. Step into Tadasana. Inhale, lengthening through the spine.
2. Exhale into Five-Pointed Star.
3. On the next exhale slowly begin to bend forward, leading with the sternum and folding forward from the hips.
4. Place the palms on the floor (below the shoulders) between the feet. Elbows are bent and kept close to the torso.
5. Engage the legs, contracting the thigh muscles very firmly.
6. Stabilize the weight equally throughout the feet. Maintain the extension of the spine. Gaze between the legs.
7. Hold and breathe.
8. Step into Tadasana.

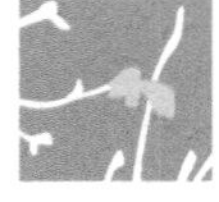

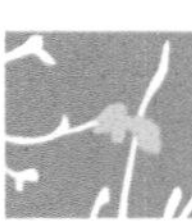

✚ BENEFITS

- ✚ Stretches the leg muscles, especially the hamstrings and the entire spine.
- ✚ Opens the hips and stretches the inner groin.
- ✚ Tones the kidneys and adrenal glands.
- ✚ Regulates menstrual processes.
- ✚ Improves digestive functions.
- ✚ Increases blood flow to the brain, calming and oxygenating the brain.
- ✚ Develops a sense of groundedness.

▲ PRECAUTIONS

- ▲ Structural injury or pain, especially hamstring and lower back
- ▲ Uncontrolled hypertension, history of strokes or glaucoma
- ▲ Headaches

✳ COUNTERPOSE

- ✳ Gauradasana

✪ MODIFICATIONS

- ✪ Bend knees slightly to release hamstrings and lower back.
- ✪ Place hands on the hips.
- ✪ Maintain the extended spine parallel to the floor.
- ✪ Stand at a wall allowing the back of the hips to be supported for balance.
- ✪ Place blocks under the palms.
- ✪ Rest the head on a block to help alleviate hypertension or stress-related headaches.

OPTIONAL PROPS: ✓ 2 Blocks

Pearls of Wisdom

6 Primary Characteristics of Witness Consciousness

1. There is no duality; ultimately only the experience of each moment.
2. There is no judgment of that which is only the observing.
3. The entirety of one's being is used to be with what is.
4. The potentiality for witnessing is always possible.
5. The witness is the vehicle for interacting with that part of our nature which does not change, and cannot perish.
6. The witness is eternally present, transcends space and time.

Muscles of the Buttocks, Back and Legs

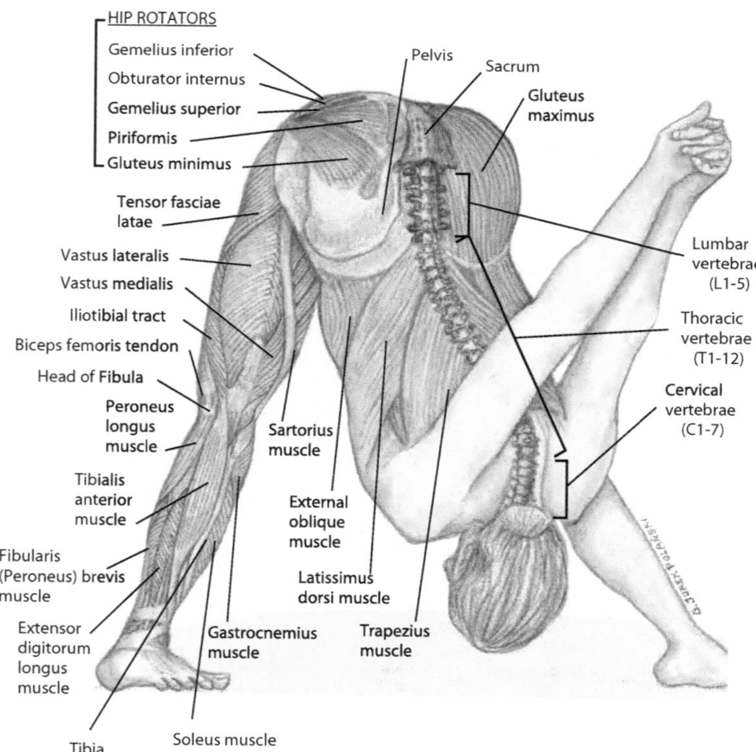

MUSCLES OF THE BUTTOCK, BACK & LEGS
(Prasita Padottanasana)

We highly recommend that you hold this mudra for at least 5 minutes in a seated meditation. Perform it at least 13 different times. Mudras may also be utilized while holding a yoga pose. Remember, mudras tend to be subtle and are very powerful in their own way.

After holding this mudra for 5 minutes, place an X in the box below. After 13 sessions, please journal your experience.

Musti
[mush-ti]

Musti is the "fist" mudra.
It represents focused holding:
holding a weapon, grasping the hair, even wrestling.
It can furthermore signify steadfastness to grasp

X	Mudra experience:

7♥ Spring

Adho Mukha Svanasana

[Downward-Facing Dog Pose]

(AH-doh MOO-kah shvah-NAHS-anna)

1 Begin in the table position with the spine extending back from the sacrum and out through the crown of the head. Keep the big toes active and pressing down into the floor more actively than the others. Be sure to keep the ceiling of each arch of the foot lifting by activating the inner calf muscles.

2 Inhale, pressing down into the palms (be sure to not over stretch the thumbs and keep the index fingers more active than the others). Extend the muscles of the inner arm.

3 Exhale, lifting the hips up and back. Engage and slowly straighten the legs.

4 Press into the heels and the palms.

5 Hold the pose for several long, slow breaths.

6 Continue to lengthen the spine.

7 Keep the heels slightly wider than the outsides of the little toes (this will encourage your thighs to want to internally rotate thereby keeping the sacrum from crunching.

8 To release, exhale, bending the knees to resume the table posture.

9 When practicing downward-facing dog, visualize your self working with all the different parts of your body by concentrating on all the acupressure points from within the mapping of the hands.

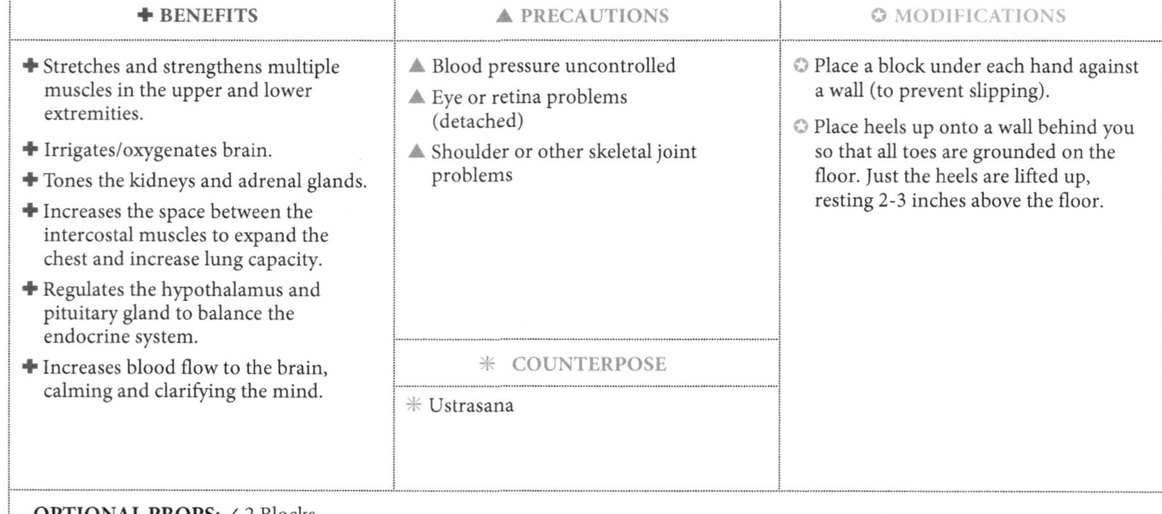

✚ BENEFITS	▲ PRECAUTIONS	✪ MODIFICATIONS
✚ Stretches and strengthens multiple muscles in the upper and lower extremities. ✚ Irrigates/oxygenates brain. ✚ Tones the kidneys and adrenal glands. ✚ Increases the space between the intercostal muscles to expand the chest and increase lung capacity. ✚ Regulates the hypothalamus and pituitary gland to balance the endocrine system. ✚ Increases blood flow to the brain, calming and clarifying the mind.	▲ Blood pressure uncontrolled ▲ Eye or retina problems (detached) ▲ Shoulder or other skeletal joint problems ✳ COUNTERPOSE ✳ Ustrasana	✪ Place a block under each hand against a wall (to prevent slipping). ✪ Place heels up onto a wall behind you so that all toes are grounded on the floor. Just the heels are lifted up, resting 2-3 inches above the floor.

OPTIONAL PROPS: ✓ 2 Blocks

Pearls of Wisdom

No. 6 Tao Te Ching
The spirit of emptiness is immortal.
It is called the Great Mother
because it gives birth to Heaven and Earth.

It is like a vapor,
barely seen but always present.
Use it effortlessly.

Muscles of the Wrists, Arms and Neck

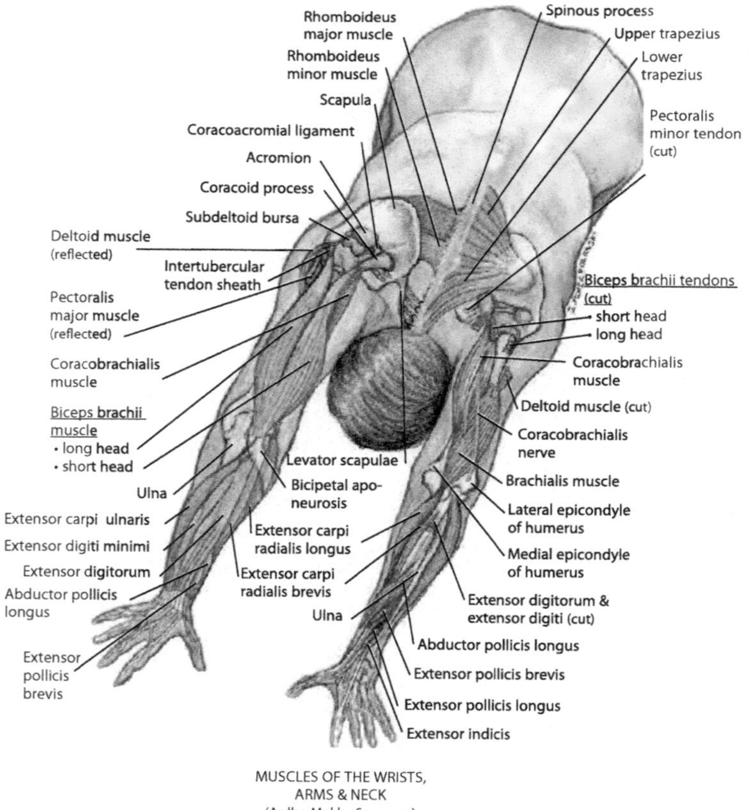

MUSCLES OF THE WRISTS, ARMS & NECK
(Ardho Mukha Savasana)
(Frontal view from above)

We highly recommend that you hold this mudra for at least 5 minutes in a seated meditation. Perform it at least 13 different times. Mudras may also be utilized while holding a yoga pose. Remember, mudras tend to be subtle and are very powerful in their own way.

Spring 7♥

After holding this mudra for 5 minutes, place an X in the box below. After 13 sessions, please journal your experience.

Bherunda

[ber-un-dahm]

Bherenda mudra signifies the holding of flowers at the time of making love, a pair of lovebirds.

X Mudra experience:

Matsyasana

[Fish Pose]

(mot-see-AHS-anna)

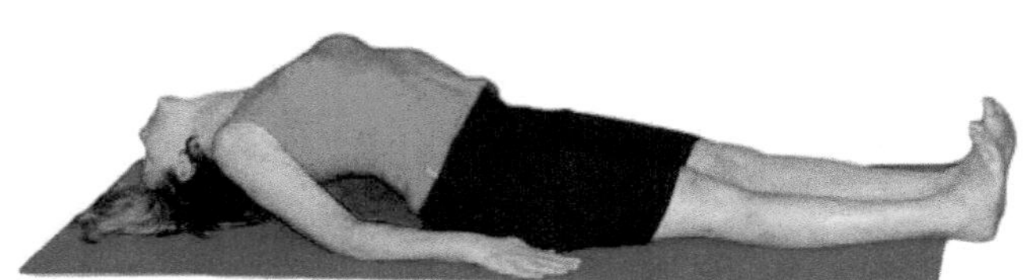

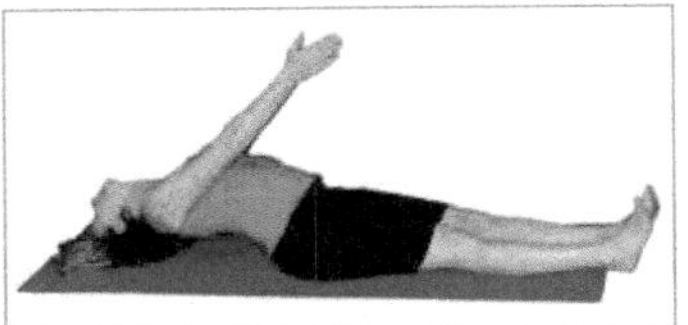

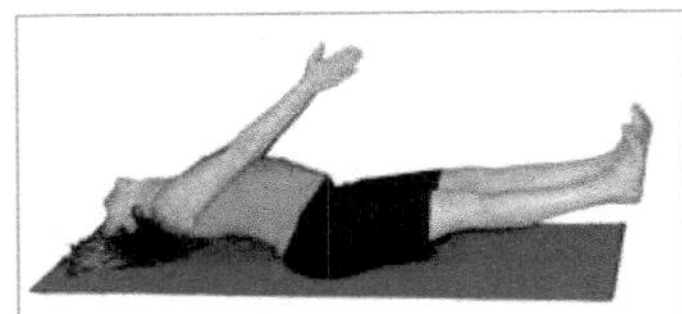

1 Sit in Sukhasana.

2 Walk you hands and arms behind you to lean back on your elbows and forearms—be sure to keep arms and hands just beside the skin of the torso itself.

3 Balancing on the arms and elbows, begin to bend only the right leg at the knee to bring the foot down to the floor near the hip. Press the foot into the floor to help adjust the hips for stability and comfort.

4 Once your hips are stable, extend the right leg back onto the floor and then allow the chest to puff on up higher towards the ceiling so that the upper torso is shaped like a dome.

5 Either keep the head lifted, or simply allow it to relax and slowly release it down toward the floor.

6 Be sure to keep the legs very active so that the thighs and heels press down into the floor while the legs continue to extend away from the hips. Feet should not be curled, but rather flat as if pressing into a wall.

7 To release the pose, bend one knee and then the other so that you can reposition your hands and arms to eventually push yourself back up and into a sitting position.

✚ BENEFITS	▲ PRECAUTIONS	✪ MODIFICATIONS
✚ Increases lung capacity. ✚ Opens the superficial front lines of the body. ✚ Helps to reset sacroilliac joint. ✚ Helps to balance hamstrings.	▲ High blood pressure ▲ Low back injury ▲ Cervical issues/neck injury ▲ Migraine **✳ COUNTERPOSE** ✳ Uttanasana	✪ Place a round bolster from under the upper back slightly beneath and off of the shoulder blades. ✪ Allow your feet to press into a wall. ✪ Position a block under the head before getting fully into the pose so that your head can relax on it.

OPTIONAL PROPS: ✓ Bolster ✓ Block

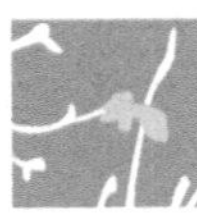

"Perfection in asana is achieved when the effort to perform it becomes effortless, and the infinite being within is reached."

Patanjali, sutra 11.47

Arterial Circulatory System

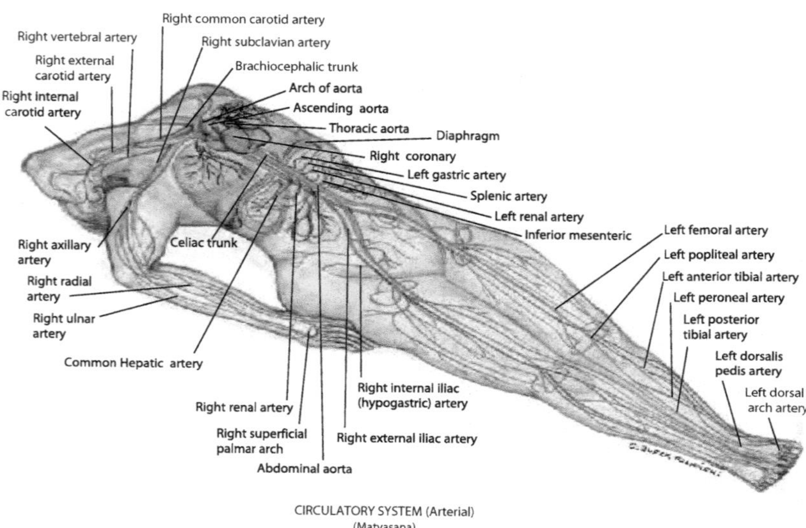

CIRCULATORY SYSTEM (Arterial)
(Matyasana)

Venous Circulatory System

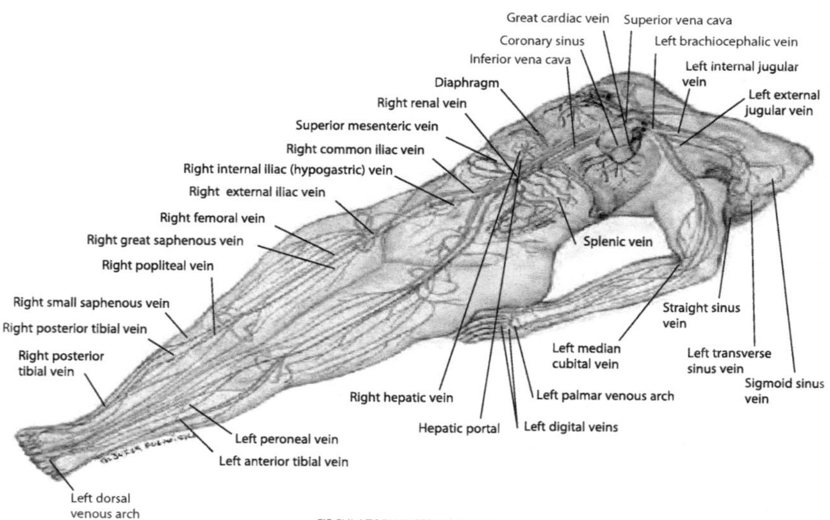

CIRCULATORY SYSTEM (Venous)
(Matyasana)

We highly recommend that you hold this mudra for at least 5 minutes in a seated meditation. Perform it at least 13 different times. Mudras may also be utilized while holding a yoga pose. Remember, mudras tend to be subtle and are very powerful in their own way.

After holding this mudra for 5 minutes, place an X in the box below. After 13 sessions, please journal your experience.

Matsya

[mhat-syah]

The Matsya or "fish" references the first incarnation of Vishnu in that form. It signifies how manifestation emerges from nonmanifestation.

X	Mudra experience:

Parighasana

[Gate Pose]

(par-ee-GOSS-anna)

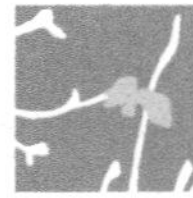

1 Come to your knees on the mat.

2 Extend the right leg laterally to the right side. The foot should be in line with the left knee.

3 Flex the right foot toward the floor so that it is almost perpendicular to the left knee. Rotate the right knee to face the ceiling.

4 Inhale both the arms up, the palms toward each other, finger tips to the ceiling. Drop the shoulders away from the ears on the exhale.

5 Inhale elongating the spine, lifting the sternum and extending out through the crown of the head.

6 Exhale bending the torso laterally over the right leg while pressing into the left hip.

7 The right arm slowly moves down the right leg with the palm facing up, as the left arm continues to extend up and away from the left hip. The left palm faces down and the arm remains alongside the left ear.

8 Keep the left hip in alignment with the right hip, both hips squared to the front.

9 The head is held in a natural alignment with the spine. Turn the gaze up under the left arm, or down at the lower shoulder for a more relaxed feeling into the neck.

10 Continue to extend through the torso with each breath.

11 On the inhale, bring the body to an upright posture.

12 Repeat on the opposite side.

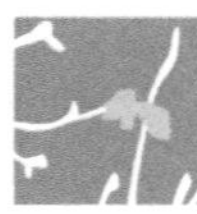

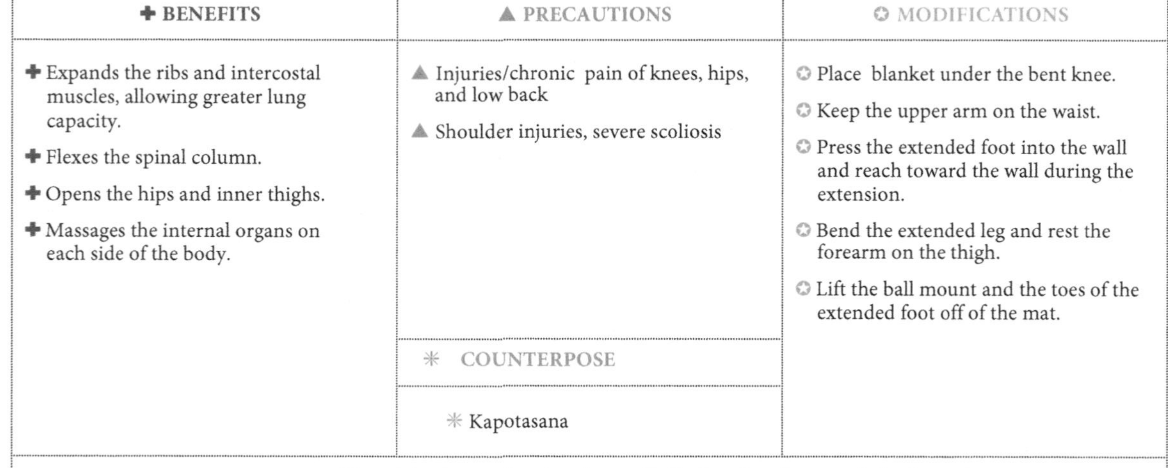

✚ BENEFITS	▲ PRECAUTIONS	✪ MODIFICATIONS
✚ Expands the ribs and intercostal muscles, allowing greater lung capacity. ✚ Flexes the spinal column. ✚ Opens the hips and inner thighs. ✚ Massages the internal organs on each side of the body.	▲ Injuries/chronic pain of knees, hips, and low back ▲ Shoulder injuries, severe scoliosis ✳ COUNTERPOSE ✳ Kapotasana	✪ Place blanket under the bent knee. ✪ Keep the upper arm on the waist. ✪ Press the extended foot into the wall and reach toward the wall during the extension. ✪ Bend the extended leg and rest the forearm on the thigh. ✪ Lift the ball mount and the toes of the extended foot off of the mat.

OPTIONAL PROPS: ✓ Blanket ✓ Two blocks under (and parallel) the shin bone of the bent leg

No.48 Tao Te Ching
One who seeks knowledge learns something new every day.
One who seeks the Tao unlearns something new every day.
Less and less remains until you arrive at non-action.
When you arrive at nonaction,
nothing will be left undone.

Mastery of the world is achieved
by letting things take their natural course.
You cannot master the world by changing the natural way.

Motor Reflex of Muscles and Nerve

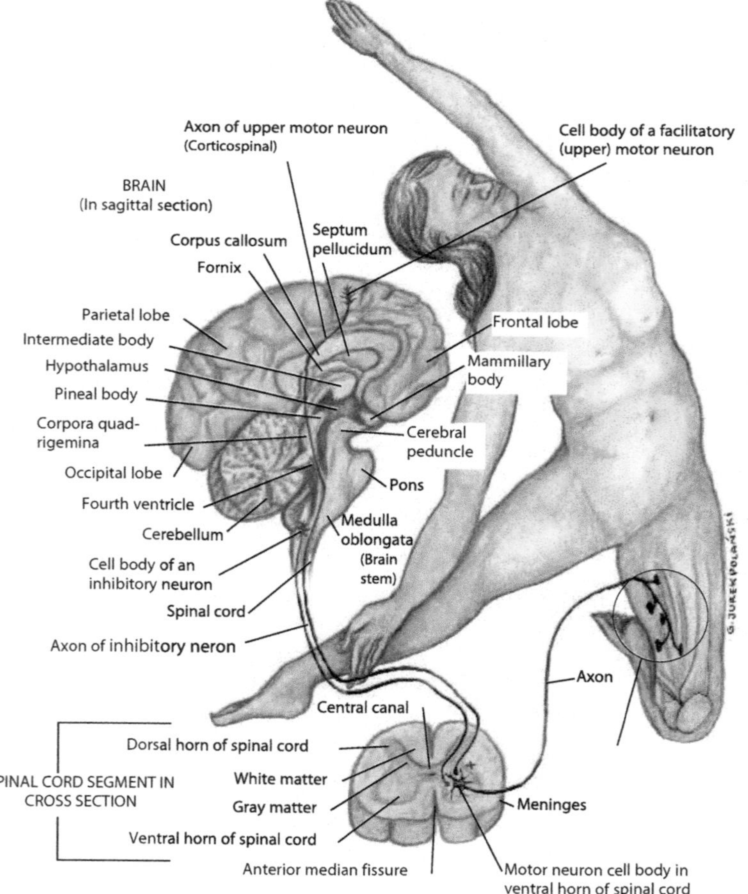

MOTOR REFLEX / MUSCLES AND NERVES
(Parigasana)

We highly recommend that you hold this mudra for at least 5 minutes in a seated meditation. Perform it at least 13 different times. Mudras may also be utilized while holding a yoga pose. Remember, mudras tend to be subtle and are very powerful in their own way.

After holding this mudra for 5 minutes, place an X in the box below. After 13 sessions, please journal your experience.

Karkala

[kar-ka-lam]

Karkala or "crab" mudra denotes yawning or stretching after sleep, the twisting or stretching or massaging of the limbs, and, as well, trumpeting a conch shell. When the fingers are turned inwards, it may depict anxiety; with the finger it denotes surprise.

X	Mudra experience:

10♥

Spring

Pashimottanasana

[Intense West Stretch Pose]

(POSH-ee-moh-tan-AHS-anna)

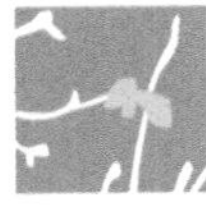

1. Sit on the floor with both legs extended to the front.
2. Extend out through the heels.
3. Inhale lifting the ribs and sternum. Elongate the spine from the sacrum through the crown of the head.
4. Activate the legs turning the tops of the thighs in slightly and gently pressing them down toward the floor.
5. Inhale, raising the arms up alongside the ears.
6. Exhale, bending forward from the hips.
7. Lengthen both the front torso and the back side evenly. Hold the head as a natural extension of the spine.
8. Extend the arms out along the legs toward the feet.
9. Inhale, again, lengthening the spine. Exhale, relaxing into the posture.
10. Inhale to slowly raise the torso back to a neutral seated position.

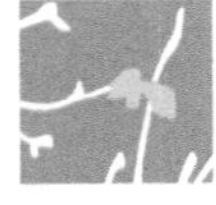

In Sanskrit, pashim means west, ut means intense, and tan means stretch. Traditionally, asana was practiced facing east, so the west side of the body is the back body. Thus, paschimotonasana means "intense west stretch of the body."

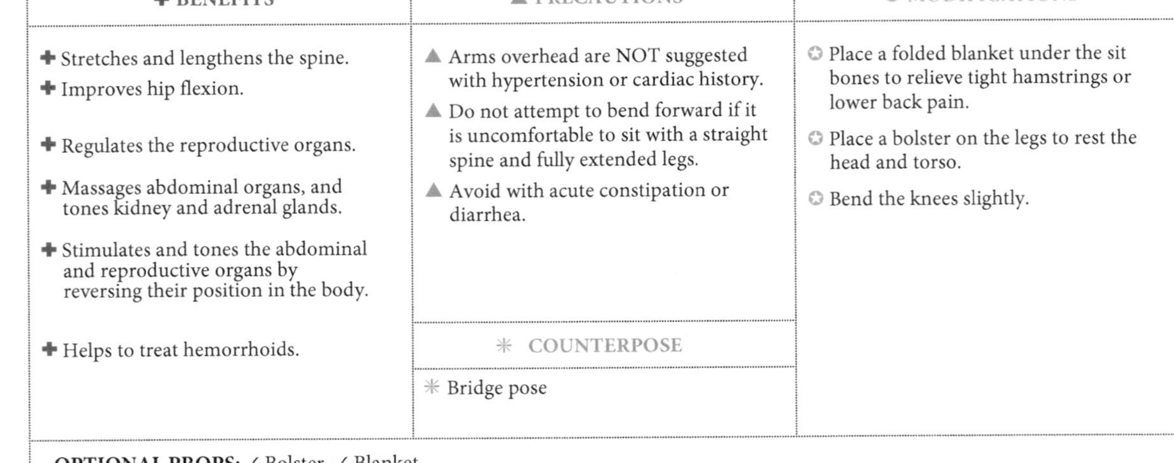

✚ BENEFITS	▲ PRECAUTIONS	✪ MODIFICATIONS
✚ Stretches and lengthens the spine. ✚ Improves hip flexion. ✚ Regulates the reproductive organs. ✚ Massages abdominal organs, and tones kidney and adrenal glands. ✚ Stimulates and tones the abdominal and reproductive organs by reversing their position in the body. ✚ Helps to treat hemorrhoids.	▲ Arms overhead are NOT suggested with hypertension or cardiac history. ▲ Do not attempt to bend forward if it is uncomfortable to sit with a straight spine and fully extended legs. ▲ Avoid with acute constipation or diarrhea. ✳ COUNTERPOSE ✳ Bridge pose	✪ Place a folded blanket under the sit bones to relieve tight hamstrings or lower back pain. ✪ Place a bolster on the legs to rest the head and torso. ✪ Bend the knees slightly.

OPTIONAL PROPS: ✓ Bolster ✓ Blanket

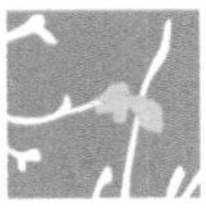

Nerve irritation or compression is often a serious consequence of bone and muscle misalignment. An important example of such interrelationships is the greater superior occipital nerve of the atlas-axis joint where the head balances on the neck vertebrae. The C2 dorsal root ganglion is covered by the obliquus interior muscle and runs between this and the atlantoaxial joint. While it does not enter into the posterior atlas-axial membrane, the C2 dorsal nerve root lies alongside it and ultimately branches into a dorsal and ventral root. The potential for pain and dysfunction arising from imbalance or abuse in such a closely knit and powerful arrangement can be clearly seen in the figure below.

The Atlas - Axis joint

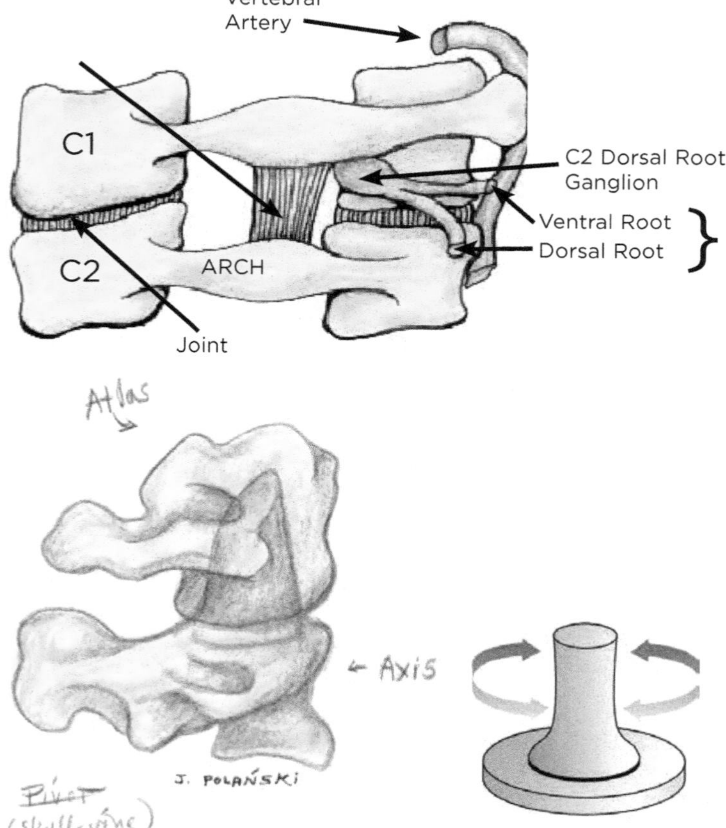

We highly recommend that you hold this mudra for at least 5 minutes in a seated meditation. Perform it at least 13 different times. Mudras may also be utilized while holding a yoga pose. Remember, mudras tend to be subtle and are very powerful in their own way.

After holding this mudra for 5 minutes, place an X in the box below. After 13 sessions, please journal your experience.

Pasa

[pahs-sam]

The Pasa or "noose" mudra symbolizes the noose, manacles, links, chains, and methods of constraint, and thus often denotes a fight or quarrel—enmity.

X	Mudra experience:

Spring

Baddha Konasana

[Bound Angle Pose]

(BAH-dah cone-AHS-anna)

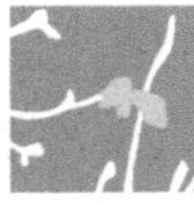

1 Sit on the floor with both legs extended to the front.

2 Bend both knees, drawing the soles of the feet together.

3 Inhale. Lengthen the spine, pressing the sacrum back and down while extending out through the crown of the head. Lift the sternum.

4 Inhale the arms up alongside the ears with the palms facing each other.

5 Exhale, bending forward, hinging at the hips.

6 Continue to extend the torso over as far forward as possible without losing spinal alignment.

7 Inhale, lengthening the spine. Exhale relaxing into the posture.

8 Inhale to slowly raise the torso back to a neutral seated position.

9 Place the hands on the outside of the knees and gently draw them together.

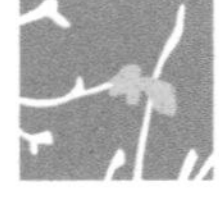

✚ BENEFITS	▲ PRECAUTIONS	✪ MODIFICATIONS
✚ Stretches and lengthens the spine. ✚ Opens the hips and stretches the inner thighs. ✚ Forward bends stimulate the abdominal organs, and tone the kidneys, prostate and adrenal glands.	▲ Arms overhead are NOT suggested with hypertension or cardiac history. ▲ If tight hamstring muscles or a weak lower back exists, sit on a folded blanket (under sit bones). ▲ Do not attempt to bend forward if bent knees are higher than the hips. ▲ Groin, knee injury/inflammation ✳ COUNTERPOSE ✳ Child's pose	✪ Support the outer thighs with blocks. ✪ Place a folded blanket under the sit bones to relieve tight hamstrings or lower back pain. ✪ Place the hands around the feet rather than raising the arms overhead. ✪ Press the entire length of the spine into a wall. ✪ Recline over a bolster for restorative benefit.

OPTIONAL PROPS: ✓ 2 Blocks ✓ Blanket ✓ Bolster

Inhalation in pranayama is called puraka, which literally means "the act of filling." Exhalation is called recheck, meaning "the act of emptying" Retention of breath is imbalances, deficiencies, called kumbhaka. Kumbha means a water pot. Just as a water pot holds water when it is filled with it, so in kumbhaka the breath is held after filling the lungs. Actually, kumbhaka can be practiced in two ways. We can hold the breath in after a puraka, or we can hold the breath out after a rechaka. The first variety is recommended much more in traditional books. It is called abhyantara kumbhaka or antah-kumbhaka. The second variety of kumbhaka is called babyakambhaka.[1]

Heart and Deep Abdominal Organs

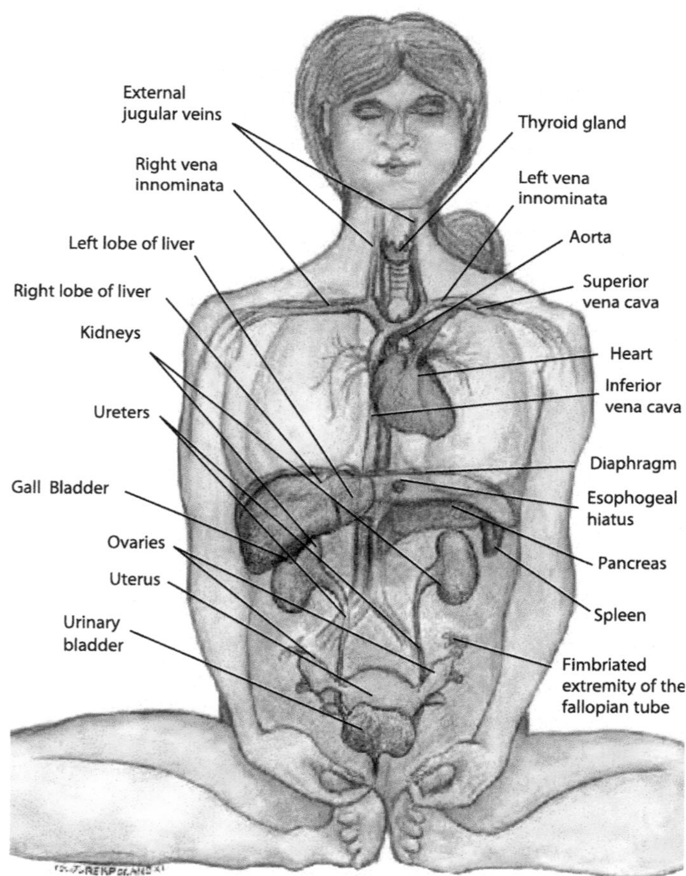

DEEP ABDOMINAL ORGANS & HEART
(Baddha Konasana)

1 Joshi Dr. KS. Yogic Pranayama.

We highly recommend that you hold this mudra for at least 5 minutes in a seated meditation. Perform it at least 13 different times. Mudras may also be utilized while holding a yoga pose. Remember, mudras tend to be subtle and are very powerful in their own way.

After holding this mudra for 5 minutes, place an X in the box below. After 13 sessions, please journal your experience.

Hakini
[hah-kee-nahm]

Hakini is a Hindu goddess who controls the subtle mind: it watches over the Ajna Chakra where our center of wisdom and clarity reside. It also helps to balance the five elements that work through our bodies and life.

X	Mudra experience:

Spring

Sukhasana

[Easy Sitting Pose]

(soo-KAH-sah-nah)

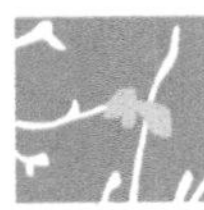

1 Sit on the floor with legs crossed to the front.

2 Place hands on the floor so that sit bones can be placed as far behind the vertical torso as is comfortable.

3 Inhale. Lengthen the spine while pressing the sacrum slightly back and down. Remember to keep extending out through the spine and crown of the head.

4 Inhale. Lift the sternum.

5 Exhale. Let the tip of the nose slightly dip so as to lengthen the back of the neck.

6 Continue to extend the torso over as far forward as possible without losing spinal alignment.

7 Place the hands on the top of the knees and gently let them rest.

8 Once finished, reverse the position of the legs and repeat on the opposite side.

✚ BENEFITS	▲ PRECAUTIONS	✪ MODIFICATIONS
✚ Helps to balance the nervous system. ✚ Strengthens the muscles of the back. ✚ Helps to release adductors. ✚ Calms the mind and helps to balance emotions.	▲ Sciatica ▲ Recent knee or hip injury. ✳ COUNTERPOSE ✳ Yoga Mudra	✪ Sit on one or two folded blankets. ✪ Place one block under each leg (just behind the knees) to support legs and SI joint.

OPTIONAL PROPS: ✓ Blanket ✓ Sand bags (2)

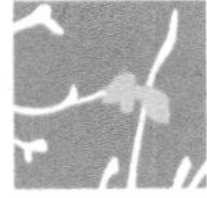

No.74 Tao Te Ching
If you do not fear death,
then how can it intimidate you?
If you aren't afraid of dying,
there is nothing you cannot do.

Those who harm others
are like inexperienced boys
trying to take the place of a great lumberjack.
Trying to fill his shoes will only get them seriously hurt.

Muscles/Tendons of the Hand, Wrist and Arm

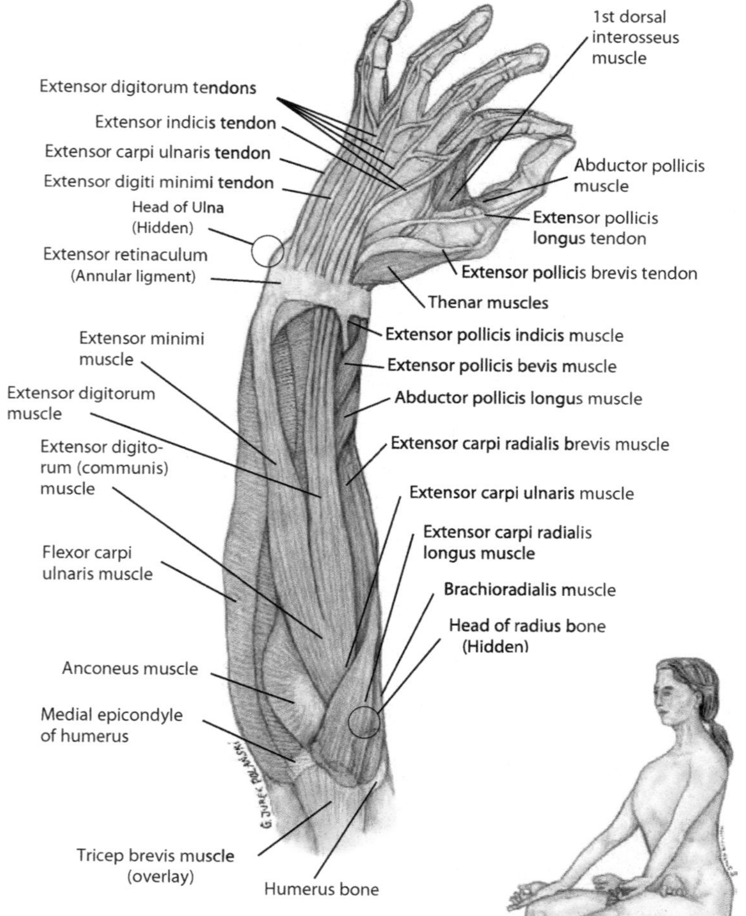

We highly recommend that you hold this mudra for at least 5 minutes in a seated meditation. Perform it at least 13 different times. Mudras may also be utilized while holding a yoga pose. Remember, mudras tend to be subtle and are very powerful in their own way.

After holding this mudra for 5 minutes, place an X in the box below. After 13 sessions, please journal your experience.

Hamsasya
[ham-sas-yam]

Hamsasya is the "swan-face" mudra. It denotes the beak of a bird, purity, pearls, jasmine, flowers, the act of writing or painting, steadfastness, and accomplishment, and hence is used to represent tying the marriage knot, the close examination of things, finess. It symbolizes "Tat tvam asi" ("thou are that"). An Indian precept that all is in unity.

X Mudra experience:

Spring

Janu Sirsasana

[Head-to-Knee Pose]

(JAH-new shear-SHAHS-anna)

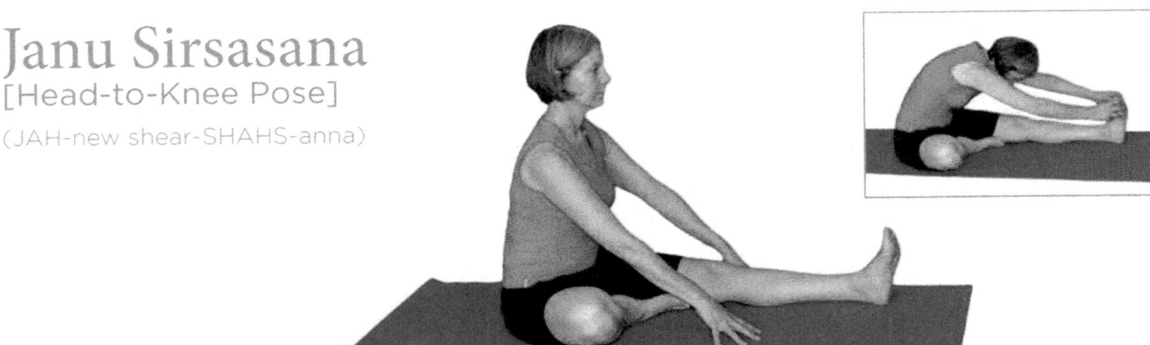

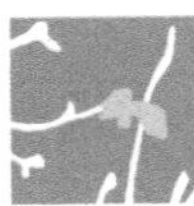

1 Sit in Dandasana.

2 Bend the right leg by bringing the right foot on the floor beside the inner left thigh. Then allow the right knee to descend down toward the floor. Sit and ground yourself.

3 Allow your hands and arms to safely retract back toward your hips so that you can press the hands down into the floor to allow that right hip to scoot back and make it more square with the left one (as if they were equal distance from the wall behind you, yet grounded).

4 Do not be so concerned with how far down you come into the pose, but rather extend out through the column of the spine.

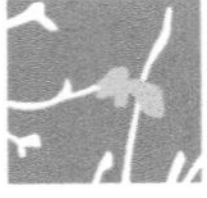

5 With a straight back allow your rib cage to descend toward the left thigh.

6 It should feel as if both sides of the torso extend evenly away from the square hips. Be patient. Be humble!

JANU SIRSASANA

In Sanskrit, janu means knee and sirsa means head. Directly translated, Janu Sirsasana is head-knee pose. Though often referred to as head-to- knee pose, it is perhaps more accurate to describe as head-to- the-knee pose, as rounding the back to get the head to the knee is not conducive to creating space in the spine. Think rather of sending the head of the bent knee into the ground to assist the opening in the hip and kidney area.

Janu sirsasana has all the benefits of a forward bend, but due to the slight asymmetry provides a gentle, twisting action which releases the kidney area in particular, as well as helping to tone the liver, the spleen, and the pancreas. The asymmetrical extension helps to align the spine, and opens the hips, the hamstrings, and all of the joints.

Caution should be used with back, neck, knee, and hip problems.

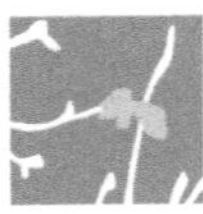

✚ BENEFITS	▲ PRECAUTIONS	✪ MODIFICATIONS
✚ Strengthens the muscles of the back. ✚ Releases the hamstrings. ✚ Releases tight hips.	▲ If tight hamstring muscles or a weak lower back exists, sit with a folded blanket under the sit bones ▲ Groin, knee injury/inflammation. ▲ Place a small rolled towel under knee. ✳ COUNTERPOSE ✳ Bridge pose	✪ Do the pose while laying down on your back and then extend both legs up on wall. Bend one leg so that it is folded into the inner thigh of the extended (opposite) leg. ✪ Place a block or folded blanket under the bent leg for support. ✪ Place a yoga belt around the foot of the extended leg so that with each hand the belt creates tensioning for a greater extension of the spine.

OPTIONAL PROPS: ✓ Yoga strap ✓ Block ✓ blanket ✓ Small hand towel

No.64 Tao Te Ching
Things are easier to control while things are quiet.
Things are easier to plan far in advance.
Things break easier while they are still brittle.
Things are easier hid while they are still small.

Prevent problems before they arise.
Take action before things get out of hand.
The tallest tree
begins as a tiny sprout.
The tallest building
starts with one shovel of dirt.
A journey of a thousand miles
starts with a single footstep.

If you rush into action, you will fail.
If you hold on too tight, you will lose your grip.

Therefore the Master lets things take their course
and thus never fails.
She doesn't hold on to things
and never loses them.
By pursing your goals too relentlessly,
you let them slip away.
If you are as concerned about the outcome
as you are about the beginning,
then it is hard to do things wrong.
The master seeks no possessions.
She learns by unlearning,
thus she is able to understand all things.
This gives her the ability to help all of creation.

Tailbone and Hip Assembly

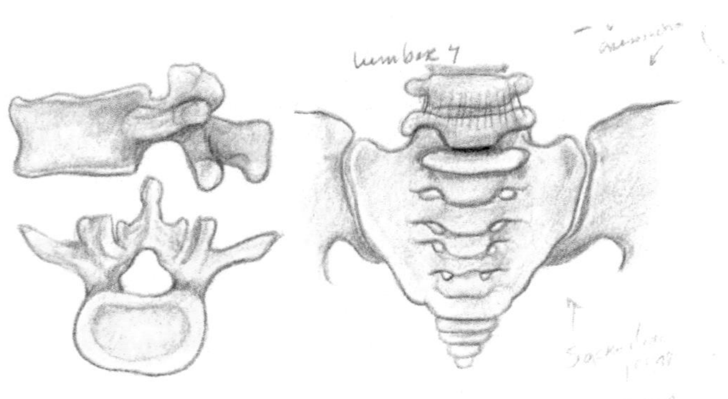

We highly recommend that you hold this mudra for at least 5 minutes in a seated meditation. Perform it at least 13 different times. Mudras may also be utilized while holding a yoga pose. Remember, mudras tend to be subtle and are very powerful in their own way.

After holding this mudra for 5 minutes, place an X in the box below. After 13 sessions, please journal your experience.

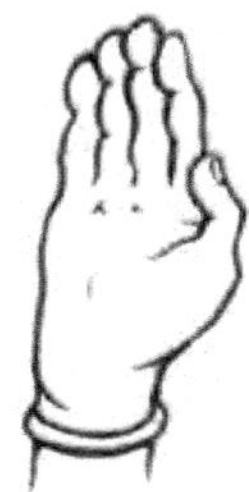

Hamsapaksa
[Ham-sa-pak-sha-ka

The Hamsapaksa or "swan-feather" mudra denotes arranging, hence tying up the hair, and even bridge-making. It can further symbolize the number 6, a bridge, and a covering.

X	Mudra experience:

A♣

Summer

Marichyasana I

[Ray of Light Pose]

(mar-ee-chee-AHS-anna)

1 Sit on the floor with both legs extended to the front.

2 Bend the right leg at the knee and draw the foot as close as possible to the body. The right foot is flat to the floor along the left inner thigh.

3 Inhale reaching forward with the right arm. Internally rotate the right shoulder while bending the elbow.

4 Exhale, wrapping the right arm around the right leg just under the knee.

5 Activate the left leg turning the top of the thighs in slightly, gently pressing the left thigh down toward the floor. Extend out through the left heel.

6 Inhale, lifting the left hand above the head. Elongate the spine from the sacrum through the crown of the head.

7 Exhale as you wrap the left arm around the back, catching the right wrist if possible.

8 Inhale lifting the sternum. Maintain the head position as a natural extension of the spine.

9 Exhale and slowly extend the upper torso down and over the extended leg. Hinge from the hips, which remain squared. Continue to press the extended leg into the mat.

10 Extend the spine with each inhalation; relax deeper into the asana with each exhalation.

11 Inhale to slowly raise the torso back to a seated position. Release the arms and straighten the right leg.

12 Repeat on the opposite side.

✚ BENEFITS	▲ PRECAUTIONS	✪ MODIFICATIONS
✚ Stretches and lengthens the spine. ✚ Improves hip flexibility. ✚ Regulates the reproductive organs. ✚ Provides deep abdominal massage.	▲ Low back conditions/sciatic nerve pain ▲ Mid-back pain/scoliosis ▲ Shoulder conditions (torn rotator cuff, etc.) ▲ Avoid with acute constipation or diarrhea ▲ Knee strain or injury ✳ COUNTERPOSE ✳ Paripurna navasana	✪ Assume lower body portion of pose while lifting arms overhead. ✪ Use a strap to assist binding arms behind the back. ✪ To keep pelvis stabilized, use padding beneath bent-leg buttock. ✪ Keep the arms lifted overhead to alleviate shoulder pain. ✪ Place a folded blanket under the hips.

OPTIONAL PROPS: ✓ Yoga strap ✓ Blanket

Samkhya/Yoga/ Ayurveda Cosmology Overview

Prakriti- Primary Nature

1. Brahman- The singular background intelligent principle (spirit) of all that is manifest which is unmanifest.

2. Atman- The individual spirit (becomes conscious) that it has "separated" from Brahman and takes on Individual Consciousness. It develops subtle impressions of the mind:
Subtle impressions of mind:

   Thoughts
   Desires
   Actions
   Memory
   Habits
   Destiny

3. Three levels of mind combine to form the ego or Ahamkara:
   1) Inner Mind - Chitta- concepts beliefs, ideas
   2) Middle Mind - Buddhi- Intelligence, discrimination.
   3) Outer Mind - Manas- Sensory input

4. Five Sensory Abilities (Tanmatras)- Not the faculties directly but the energy that provides them with their subtle energy:
   1) Sound
   2) Touch
   3) Sight
   4) Taste
   5) Smell

5 Five Sensory Organs (Karmendriyas) "Organs of action":
   1) Speech
   2) Hands
   3) Feet
   4) Reproductive
   5) Excretive

6. Five Faculties of Perception (Jnanendriyas) "Organs of wisdom":
   1) Ear
   2) Skin
   3) Eye
   4) Tongue
   5) Nose

7. Five Great Elements (Panchatattvas or Mahabhutas):
   1) Space
   2) Air
   3) Fire
   4) Water
   5) Earth

We highly recommend that you hold this mudra for at least 5 minutes in a seated meditation. Perform it at least 13 different times. Mudras may also be utilized while holding a yoga pose. Remember, mudras tend to be subtle and are very powerful in their own way.

After holding this mudra for 5 minutes, place an X in the box below. After 13 sessions, please journal your experience.

Kilaka

[Kila-kam]

Kilaka is the "bond" mudra and signifies the conversation of lovers, and thus affection.

X	Mudra experience:

2♣ Summer

Marichyasana II

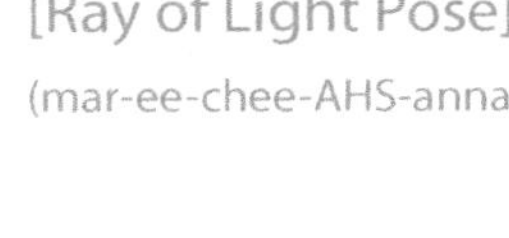

[Ray of Light Pose]

(mar-ee-chee-AHS-anna)

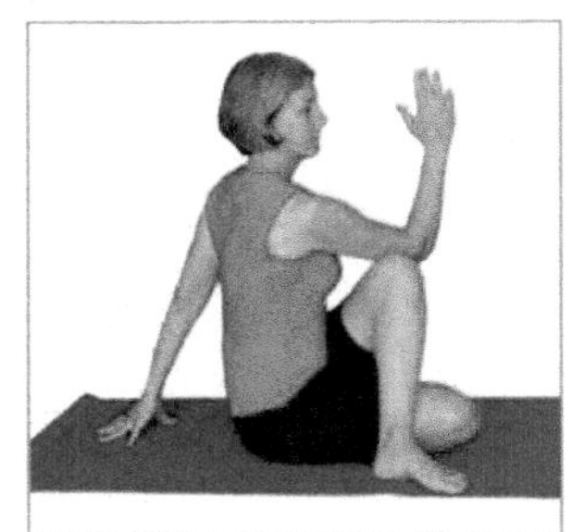

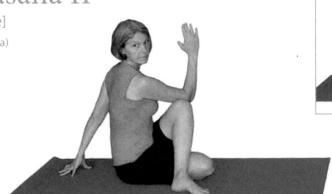

1. Sit on the floor with both legs extended to the front.
2. Bend the right leg at the knee and draw the heel of the foot as close as possible to the left sit bone. (The outside edge and top of the right foot should lay flat on the floor.)
3. Inhale. Exhale, and carefully set the left leg to the outside of the right leg as shown in picture above. (Be sure to not torque the knees while moving into, holding or exiting the pose.)
4. Once the hips are somewhat level on the floor, scoot the hips back toward the wall behind you so that the spinal column is vertical and balanced above the hips.
5. While inhaling, place the left hand/arm behind the left hip.
6. Once the body is fully supported by the left arm, reach up and place the right upper arm (close to the elbow portion) to the front of the left knee as pictured above.
7. Use the breath and the left arm to stabilize the body so that while in this twist the diagonal myofascial slings are thoroughly worked.
8. Lastly, while keeping the ear lobes level, begin to turn the head to the right to help take any excess slack out of the spinal column.
9. Repeat on the opposite side.

✚ BENEFITS	▲ PRECAUTIONS	✪ MODIFICATIONS
✚ Opens the hips. ✚ Allows for greater flexibility and lubrication of the spine. ✚ Flushes out toxins and other cellular waste and allows a new flood of fresh organs, muscles and fascia	▲ Structural injury or pain, especially shoulders, hips, knees or ankles ▲ Uncontrolled hypertension or cardiac conditions ▲ Hip replacement/surgery. blood and oxygen to permeate the ▲ Slipped disc(s) ▲ Low back pain. ✳ COUNTERPOSE ✳ Baddha konasana	✪ Hips resting on a folded blanket(s). ✪ Use two yoga blocks at the side of the body to help stabilize the torso and hips to get proper stability and elongation.

OPTIONAL PROPS: ✓ Blanket(s)

Marichi's name means "the Lord of the Dawn". In the Bhagavad Gita, chapter 10, sutra 6, he is one of the original seven great soul teachers (Maharishis).

In Sutra 21, Marichi is identified as the chief of the 49 winds, the source of prana. It enhances circulation around all the abdominal organs.

Superficial Back Muscles

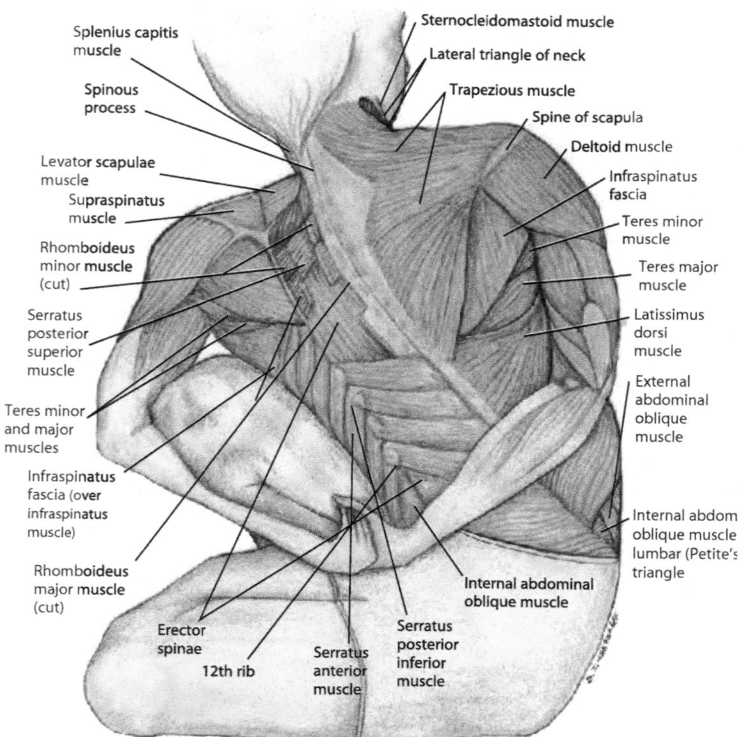

SUPERFICIAL UPPER BACK MUSCLES
(Marichyasana II)

We highly recommend that you hold this mudra for at least 5 minutes in a seated meditation. Perform it at least 13 different times. Mudras may also be utilized while holding a yoga pose. Remember, mudras tend to be subtle and are very powerful in their own way.

2♣

Summer 2♣

After holding this mudra for 5 minutes, place an X in the box below. After 13 sessions, please journal your experience.

Bharmaram

[Bhra-ma-ram]

The Bhramara or "bee" mudra represents the gesture of picking flowers or picking out thorns. It also signifies the bee, cuckoo, crane, parrot, and other birds.

X	Mudra experience:

3♣

Summer

Parivrtta Prasarita Podattonasana

[Wide-Legged Forward Bend]

(pah-doh-tahn-AHS-anna)

1. From Tadasana come into Five-Pointed Star.
2. Lower your torso and place your left hand on the floor just below your chest.
3. Place and slightly press your right palm onto your sacrum to help keep your spinal column in a straight line parallel to the floor.
4. Press the left hand and arm down toward the floor while rotating the shoulder blades (both) internally.
5. While feeling open at the collarbones, extend your upper arm to the ceiling while continuing to be soft around the shoulders.
6. Extend the tips of the fingers of the right hand away from the elbow to get a sense of widening across the front of the chest and torso (both vertically and horizontally).

✚ BENEFITS	▲ PRECAUTIONS	✪ MODIFICATIONS
✚ Tones legs and hips. ✚ Strengthens upper back. ✚ Improves spinal flexibility. ✚ Massages the internal organs. ✚ Opens up shoulders and tones the neck muscles. ✚ Releases tight diagonal myofascial slings of the body.	▲ Herniated disks ▲ Sciatica ▲ Vertigo ▲ If twisting into the pose be sure to protect shoulder joints ✳ COUNTERPOSE ✳ Yoga mudra.	✪ Set a block under hand on floor. ✪ Allow hips to rest against wall for greater stability.

OPTIONAL PROPS: ✓ Block ✓ Place lower forearm on the seat of a chair for support

Joint Types (Arthrology):

A. Fibrous – bone-fibrous connective tissue–bone

1. Sutures – skull only
2. Schindylesis – nasal septum
3. Gomphosis – peg–socket (teeth)
4. Syndesmosis – bone-ligament-bone

B. Cartilagenous – bone-cartilage-bone

1. Synchondrosis – hyaline cartilage
2. Symphasis – fibrocartilage

C. Synovial

1. most common
2. freely moveable
3. characteristics

fibrus capsule lined with synovial membrane.

joint space.

hyaline cartilage lines articular surfaces

synovium – lubricant

D. Types (based on bony surfaces)

E. planar (flat) – nonaxial (gliding movement) – vertebral facet joints.

F. ginglymus (hinge) – uniaxial (flexion/extension) – elbow, finger

G. trochoid (pivot) – uniaxial (rotation) – atlas/axis

H. Condylar – 2 concave surfaces join 2 convex surfaces with movement basically in 1 axis (uni-axial) (sometimes only one convex/concave surface) – occipital bone on atlas

I. Ellipsoid – convex/concave surfaces with movement in 2 axes (bi-axial) –usually do not have rotation (first knuckle of the finger) (flex/extend; abduct/adduct).

J. Sellar (saddle) – both bony surfaces are convex and concave biaxial allowing circumduction without rotation) – 1st carpal-meta carpal joint in hand (thumb)

K. Spheroidal (ball and socket) – tri-axial (allowing circumduction with independent movements in all 3 planes) – hip, shoulder

L. Compound – characteristics of more than one type of joint i.e., knee

We highly recommend that you hold this mudra for at least 5 minutes in a seated meditation. Perform it at least 13 different times. Mudras may also be utilized while holding a yoga pose. Remember, mudras tend to be subtle and are very powerful in their own way.

3♣

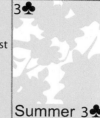

Summer 3♣

After holding this mudra for 5 minutes, place an X in the box below. After 13 sessions, please journal your experience.

Katakamukha
[kata-kamu-kam]

Katakamukha symbolizes the opening of a link. It can signify applying scents, a glance, or even speech. Katakamukha represents pulling reins, or the grasping of a garment.

X	Mudra experience:

Gumakhasana

[Cow Face Pose]

(go-moo-KAHS-anna)

1 Sit down on your mat and place the right leg over the left as shown in photo above.

2 Gently position the sit bones slightly behind the hips. Maybe place folded blanket under the hips.

3 Inhale, and position the spinal column in its most vertical and upright position.

4 Once comfortable, elongate the back of the neck as the tip of the nose slightly dips or lowers itself.

5 As the front of the shoulders and chest laterally broaden and come alive, be sure to widen the back of the shoulders as well.

6 Place the left arm up and over the backside of the left shoulder as pictured above.

7 Once the left arm is in place simply reach the right arm behind from below the chest to grip the opposite hand.

8 If grabbing the hand is not possible, simply hold a strap in the left hand and then grab it with the right hand for a firm hold.

9 Repeat on the second side by reversing the position of the arms and legs.

✚ BENEFITS	▲ PRECAUTIONS	✪ MODIFICATIONS
✚ Stretches the shoulders, arms, hips and side of the body. ✚ Helps to keep lymphatic system open. ✚ Helps to strengthen nervous system. ✚ Releases tight fascia of the upper body.	▲ Wrist, elbow, shoulder or neck issues ▲ Recent knee injury ✳ COUNTERPOSE ✳ Ustrasana	✪ Sit on one or two blankets. ✪ Try the pose in a standing position, or even while seating on a chair. ✪ Use a belt instead of trying to reach for the other hand.
OPTIONAL PROPS: ✓ Blanket ✓ Belt ✓ Chair		

Yoga Sutras of Patanjali

A collection of brief but complex thoughts regarding the ultimate reality. There is evidence to support the idea that not only did Patanjali simply act as a compiler of the techniques that are now considered classically yoga, but that the disciplines, which are a large part of the Yoga Sutras may very well have existed previously and were an overall part of the compilation process. In any case, the Sutras are succinctly designed to address the needs of spiritual development. The Sutras are divided into four sections, called padas. Translated pada means foot, or part, or in my mind path. Thus each book is a part or path to a specific topic.

-Book one is Samahdi Pada or the path on contemplation

-Book two is Sadhana Pada or the path on practice

-Book three is Vibhuti Pada or the path on divine powers

-Book four is Kaivalya Pada or the path on absolute freedom

Ellipsoidal Joint of the Wrist (Condylar)

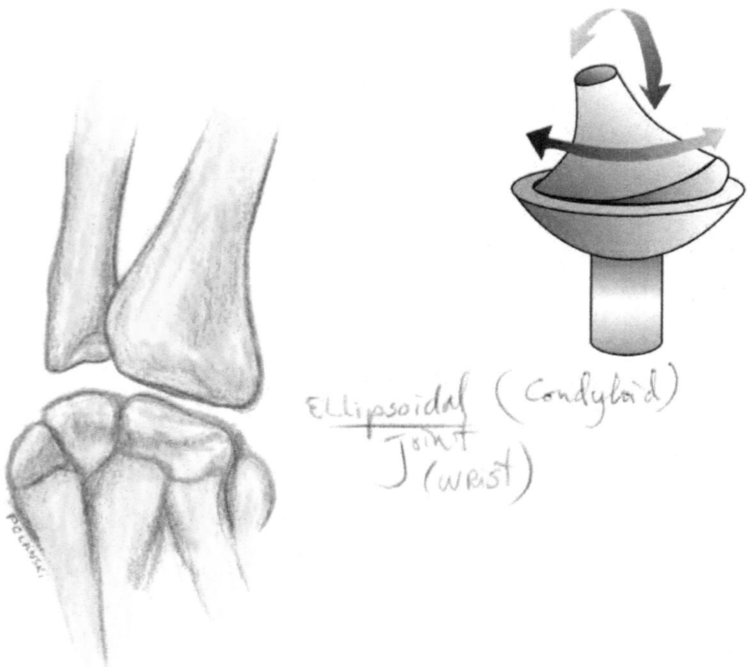

We highly recommend that you hold this mudra for at least 5 minutes in a seated meditation. Perform it at least 13 different times. Mudras may also be utilized while holding a yoga pose. Remember, mudras tend to be subtle and are very powerful in their own way.

4♣

Summer 4♣

Ganesha

[Ghan-ah-shaum]

The Uttar Abodhi mudra is a gesture of supreme enlightenment.

After holding this mudra for 5 minutes, place an X in the box below. After 13 sessions, please journal your experience.

X	Mudra experience:

Ustrasana

[Camel Pose]

(oosh-TRAHS-anna)

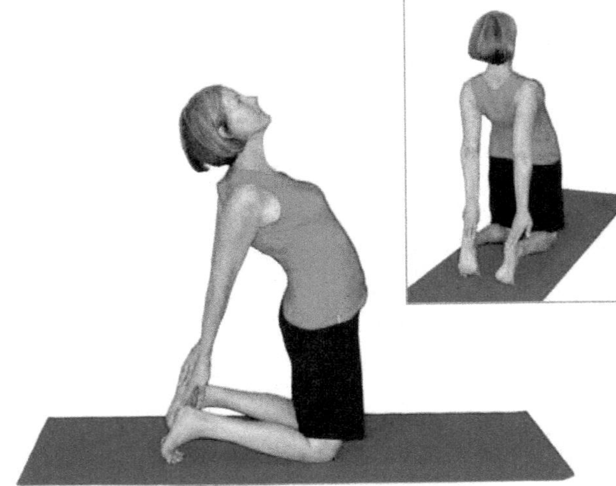

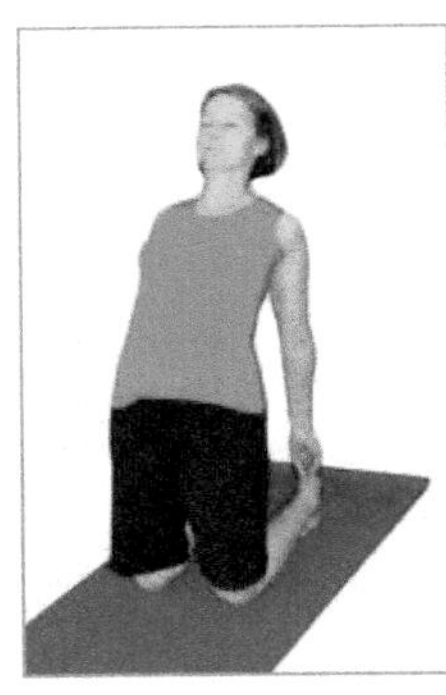

1. From kneeling position, align knees with hips.
2. Extend the tops of the feet on the floor while heels point slightly outward.
3. Place hands on hips and lengthen the sternum up and away from the naval and knees. (Keep the belly and lower ribs soft.)
4. Lengthening the spine vertically, slowly move the shoulder girdle behind the hips while rotating the inner thighs internally. (Keep the glutes soft.)
5. Keep the back and front of the neck evenly extending and draw the crown center away from the central axis of the spine.
6. Inhale slowly and continue to lift the chest and sternum forward and upward.
7. Gently arch the back so as to increase the space between each and every vertebra.
8. Exhale, reach back and place the hands either onto the blocks (on the outside of your heels) or on the heels as shown in the picture above
9. Inhale to slowly release the posture, elongating the spine as the hands, torso and shoulders return to center.

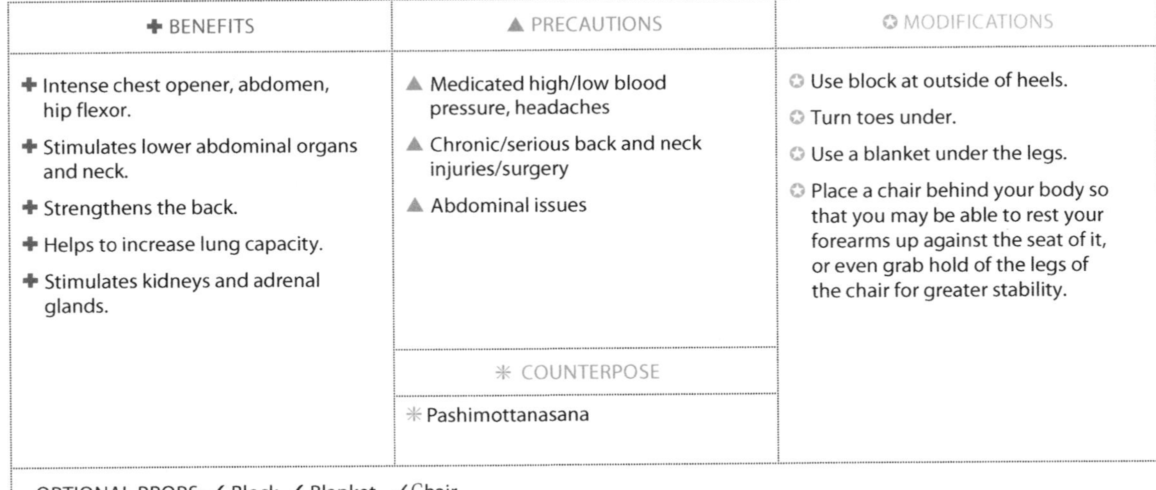

✚ BENEFITS	▲ PRECAUTIONS	✪ MODIFICATIONS
✚ Intense chest opener, abdomen, hip flexor. ✚ Stimulates lower abdominal organs and neck. ✚ Strengthens the back. ✚ Helps to increase lung capacity. ✚ Stimulates kidneys and adrenal glands.	▲ Medicated high/low blood pressure, headaches ▲ Chronic/serious back and neck injuries/surgery ▲ Abdominal issues ✳ COUNTERPOSE ✳ Pashimottanasana	✪ Use block at outside of heels. ✪ Turn toes under. ✪ Use a blanket under the legs. ✪ Place a chair behind your body so that you may be able to rest your forearms up against the seat of it, or even grab hold of the legs of the chair for greater stability.

OPTIONAL PROPS: ✓ Block ✓ Blanket ✓Chair

SOFT TISSUE OF NECK

Platysma muscle – superficial muscle originating from skin and fascia over the pectoralis major, deltoid muscle and clavicle. It then courses superiorly over the neck, inserting along the inferior border of the mandible several muscles of facial expression and into the skin around the mouth. The platysma muscle increases intravenous pressure, which increases intravenous flow in the neck.

LATERAL VIEW OF BODY MUSCLES

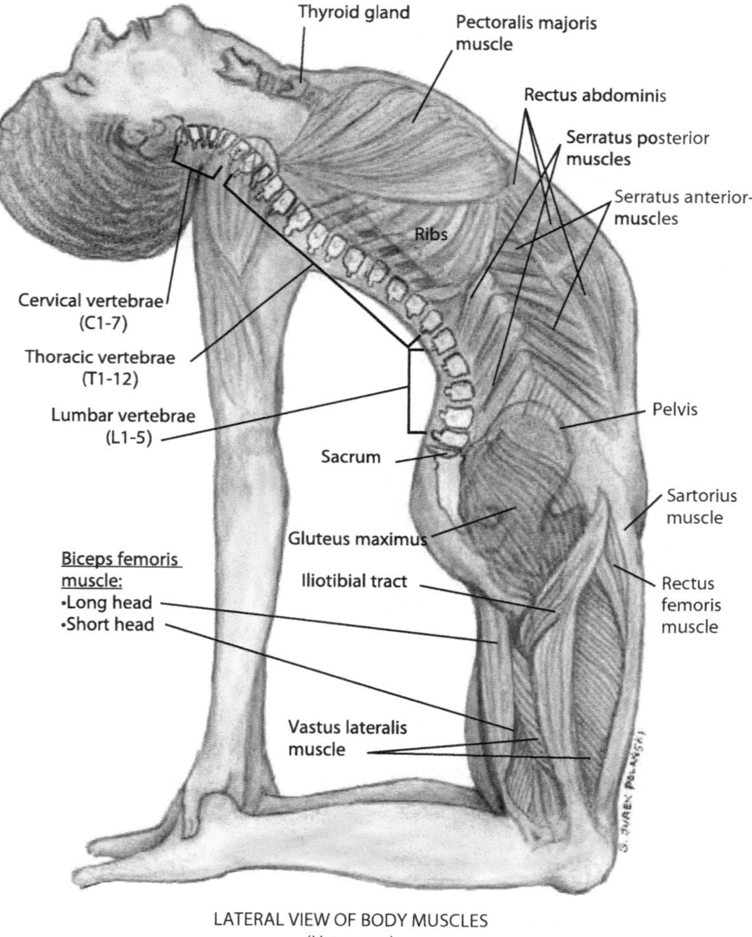

LATERAL VIEW OF BODY MUSCLES
(Ustrasana)

We highly recommend that you hold this mudra for at least 5 minutes in a seated meditation. Perform it at least 13 different times. Mudras may also be utilized while holding a yoga pose. Remember, mudras tend to be subtle and are very powerful in their own way.

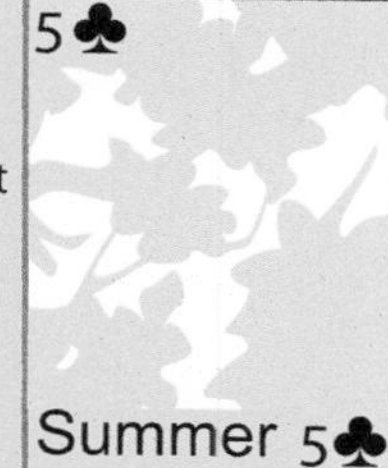

After holding this mudra for 5 minutes, place an X in the box below. After 13 sessions, please journal your experience.

Makara

[Mahk-kar-rham]

The Makara is a "fish" mudra. It can signify flesh-eating animals such as the shark and similar fish, the crocodile, and by extension, the lion or tiger.

X	Mudra experience:

Eka Pada Rajakapotasana

[Pigeon Pose]

(aa-KAH pah-DAH rah-JAH-cop-poh-TAHS-anna)

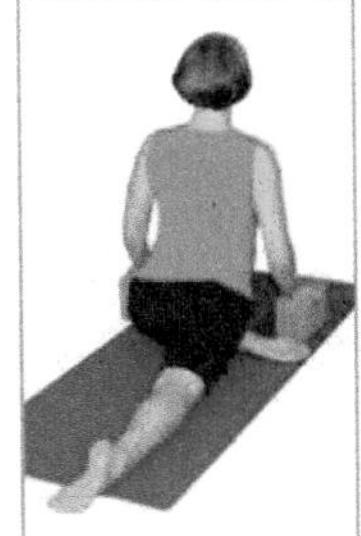

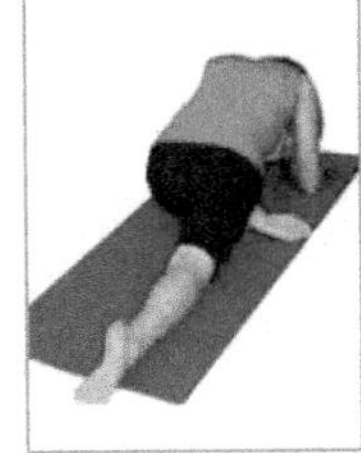

1 Begin in table posture.

2 Inhale and bring the right knee between the hands while extending the left leg straight behind you. Rest the front of the left thigh, the shin and the top of the left foot on the floor.

3 Move the right foot forward, attempting to bring the right shin parallel with the front of the mat.

4 Engage the core and press the pelvis toward the mat. Align both hips on the same plane.

5 Exhale, extending the arms out along the floor in front of you. Elongate the torso as you lower it to the mat.

6 Breathe and relax into the posture.

7 Inhale, bringing the hands under the shoulders with the elbows kept close to the body. Exhale.

8 Inhale, gently lifting the upper body from the sternum and drawing the scapulae slightly together.

9 Find a balanced stance. Exhale and bring the arms open to the sides.

10 To release the posture, bring the hands to either side of the front knee and come back to table posture.

11 Repeat on the opposite side.

✚ BENEFI TS	▲ PRECAUTIONS	✪ MODIFICATI ONS
✚ Stimulating front body bend that deepens respiration and strengthens low back. ✚ Improves lower body circulation. ✚ Lengthens psoas, hip flexor mobility. ✚ Strengthens the lower back. ✚ Tones the kidneys. ✚ Stimulates the adrenal gland.	▲ Hip or low back conditions ▲ Knee sensitivity ▲ Sciatic pain ▲ Structural injury or pain, especially the knees, hips or lower back ✳ COUNTERPOSE ✳ Shavasana	✪ Use support beneath buttock of flexed leg. ✪ Draw flexed leg and foot back close to body. ✪ Keep hands on floor.

OPTIONAL PROPS: ✓ Blanket ✓ Block ✓ Yoga wedge

Major Glands of the Body

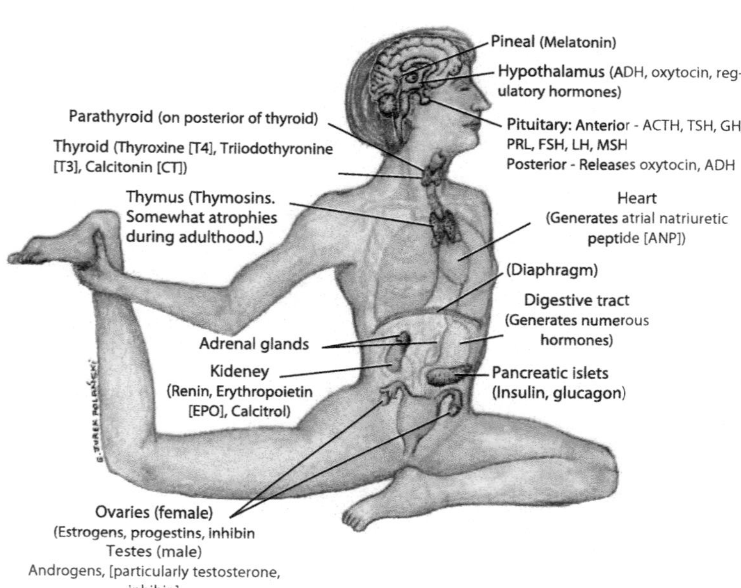

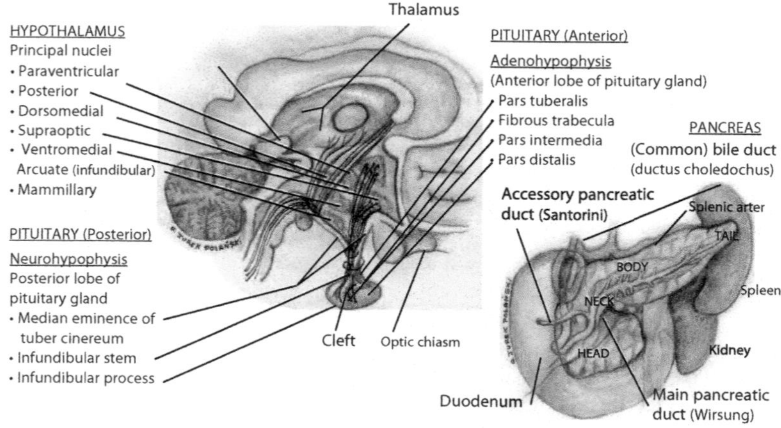

The adrenal glands are further divided into:
· Adrenal medulla (Epinephrine (E), norepinephrine)
· Adrenal cortex (Cortisol, corticosterone, cortisone, aldosterone, androgens)

Major Glands
(Kapotasana)

We highly recommend that you hold this mudra for at least 5 minutes in a seated meditation. Perform it at least 13 different times. Mudras may also be utilized while holding a yoga pose. Remember, mudras tend to be subtle and are very powerful in their own way.

6♣

Summer 6♣

After holding this mudra for 5 minutes, place an X in the box below. After 13 sessions, please journal your experience.

Cakra

[Cha-kr ahm]

The Cakra mudra signifies the "discus," which was used as a sharp weapon in ancient warfare. It later extended to represent "wheel." The Cakra mudra symbolizes power and protection.

X	Mudra experience:

Chaturanga Dandasana

[Four-limbed Staff Pose]

(chaht-tour-ANG-ah don-DAHS-anna)

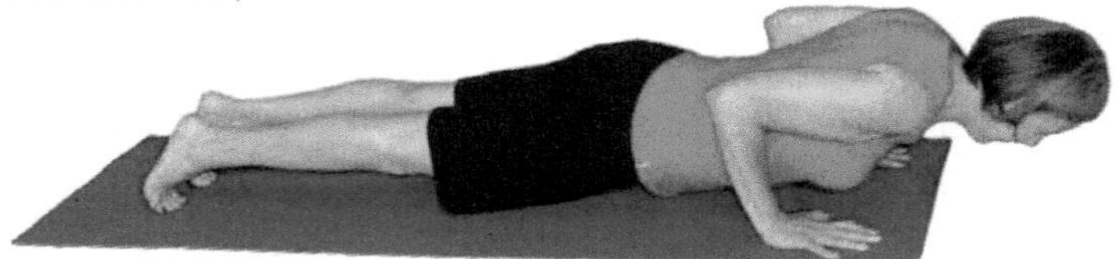

1 From the table posture, fully extend both legs straight back with the toes turned under on the inhale.

2 The palms are spread on the floor beneath the elbows, which are drawn close to the body.

3 Engage the legs and extend out through the heels.

4 Engage the core and contract the abdominal muscles.

5 Exhale gently drawing the shoulder blades together and down the back. Inhale, lifting the sides of the waistline up.

6 Exhale, lowering the body until the upper arms are parallel to the floor, keeping the neck in line with the spine.

7 Continue to extend out through the crown of the head and the heels with each breath.

8 Exhale to slowly release the posture, elongating the spine as the forehead and hips lower to the floor.

✚ BENEFITS	▲ PRECAUTIONS	✪ MODIFICATIONS
✚ Increases body heat. ✚ Irrigates/oxygenates the brain. ✚ Strengthens the upper and lower body. ✚ Tones and strengthens the abdominal muscles. ✚ Focuses attention and develops stamina.	▲ Not recommended with a history of cardiac problems or uncontrolled blood pressure. ▲ Avoid with structural injury or pain, especially wrists and shoulders. ▲ Not recommended with abdominal or lower back issues. ✳ COUNTERPOSE ✳Pavan Muktasana	✪ Use wedges under the wrists to alleviate pain. ✪ Place support under the thighs or keep the knees on the floor.

OPTIONAL PROPS: ✓ Yoga wedges ✓ One or two blocks placed under the hips for better support

What is Kundalini?
What is Kundalini actually? You experience it when the energy at the glandular system combines with the nervous system to create such a sensitivity that the brain in its totality receives signals and integrates them. Normally you use a small portion of the brain's potential. A new clarity accompanies your perception, thought and intuition.
When Kundalini awakens, a person understands the effect and impact of an action at the beginning of a sequence of action and reaction. He has the choice to take the action or not to take the action. In other words, the person becomes totally and wholly aware. That is why it is called "the yoga of awareness." As all rivers end up in the same ocean, all yoga ends up by raising the Kundalini in man. What is the Kundalini?
The creative potential of the man." – Yogi Bhajan

KUNDALINI literally means "the curl of the lock of hair of the beloved."
It is a metaphor describing the flow of energy and consciousness that already exists within each one of us.

It is often symbolized by a snake or a pair of snakes. These snakes represent the rising of the Kundalini energy through the two nerve channels that intertwine around the central nerve of the spinal column. These two nerve channels act as main conductors.

One is called the Ida and the other is called the Pingala. Each of them makes 2-1/2 turns around the central column at the base of the spine. The Kundalini energy that they carry feeds the entire nervous system.

IDA – This nerve channel ends at the left nostril, brings in the cooling, soothing, mind-expanding energy of the moon.

PINGALA – This nerve channel ends at the right nostril and brings in the stimulating, energizing energy of the sun.

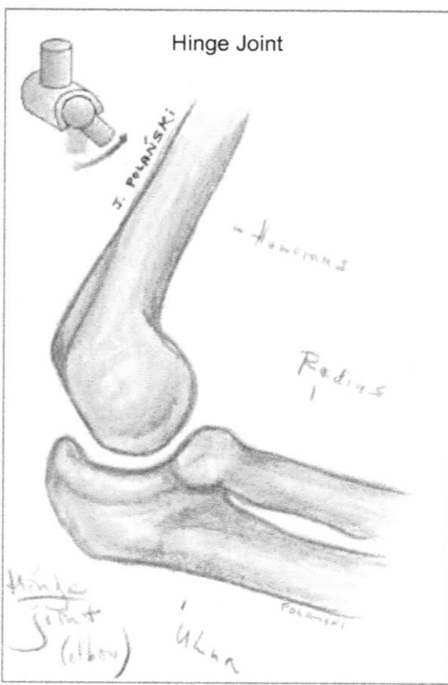

Although we all have Kundalini energy flowing in us, there is also a vast reservoir of "dormant" Kundalini energy under the fourth vertebra of the spinal column.

Through the practice of Kundalini Yoga, we stimulate and release this unused Kundalini energy, and allow it (it is never forced) to rise up the central column of the spine until it reaches the top of the skull, activating the secretion of the pineal gland. This brings about a major change of consciousness.
(Kundalini Yoga: The Flow of Eternal Power p. 48-49)

We highly recommend that you hold this mudra for at least 5 minutes in a seated meditation. Perform it at least 13 different times. Mudras may also be utilized while holding a yoga pose. Remember, mudras tend to be subtle and are very powerful in their own way.

7♣

7♣

After holding this mudra for 5 minutes, place an X in the box below. After 13 sessions, please journal your experience.

Nagabandha
[naga-band-ahm]

A Nagabandha is a iconic frieze of Nagas, quasi-divine beings, half-serpent, half-man. Guards of mineral wealth within the earth, the Nagas are powerful and wise, but also quick, courageous and at times violent. This mudra signifies those traits.

X	Mudra experience:

Urdvha Mukha Svanasana

[Upward-Facing Dog Pose]

(OORD-vah MOO-kah shvon-AHS-anna)

1 Lie in a prone position with the forehead touching the floor and the toes extended out behind.

2 Place the palms on the floor next to the shoulders, drawing the elbows close to the body.

3 Engage the legs and press into the tops of the feet.

4 Engage the core and slightly drop the tailbone.

5 Inhale, slowly lifting the chest forward and upward to raise the head and shoulders off the mat. Drop the shoulders away from the ears.

6 Arch the back increasing the space between each vertebra.

7 The head arches as a natural extension of the spine.

8 Extend out through the crown of the head and the tips of the toes.

9 Gently lift the pelvis away from the floor. If possible, also lift the upper thighs, pressing into the tops of the feet.

10 Press into the hands to come into the fullest expression of the pose.

11 Be aware of the breath.

12 Exhale to slowly release the posture, elongating the spine as the forehead comes to the floor.

✚ BENEFITS	▲ PRECAUTIONS	✪ MODIFICATIONS
✚ Opens the chest and increases lung capacity. ✚ Tones and strengthens the spinal and abdominal muscles. ✚ Promotes spinal flexibility. ✚ Alleviates menstrual disorders. ✚ Upper body strengthener. ✚ Tones kidneys, lungs, ovaries and uterus. ✚ Strengthens arms/shoulders and upper back. ✚ Increases upper-body circulation/respiration. ✚ Opens heart, strengthens legs and low back.	▲ Chronic low back pain/inflammation/surgery ▲ Shoulder pain, wrist sensitivity (carpal tunnel) ▲ Recent abdominal surgery, ankle stiffness ▲ Not recommended with a history of cardiac problems or uncontrolled blood pressure ✳ COUNTERPOSE ✳ Yoga mudra	✪ Place blanket under the tops of thighs. ✪ Use padding or wedges beneath wrists. ✪ Practice without lifting too high. ✪ Practice as part of repetitive flow vinyasa. ✪ Keep the forearms on the floor with the elbows directly under the shoulders.

OPTIONAL PROPS: ✓ Yoga wedges ✓ Blanket

No.4 Tao Te Ching
The Tao is like an empty container:
it can never be emptied and can never be filled.
Infinitely deep, it is the source of all things.
It dulls the sharp, unties the knotted,
shades the lighted, and unites all of creation with dust.

It is hidden but always present.
I don't know who gave birth to it.
It is older than the concept of God.

Muscles of the Neck

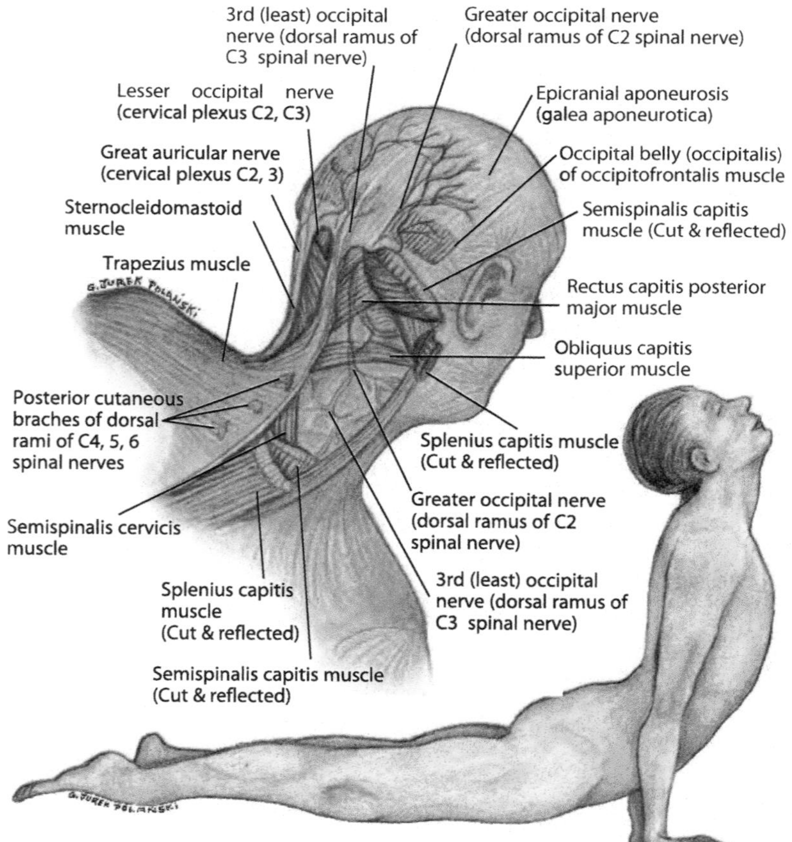

We highly recommend that you hold this mudra for at least 5 minutes in a seated meditation. Perform it at least 13 different times. Mudras may also be utilized while holding a yoga pose. Remember, mudras tend to be subtle and are very powerful in their own way.

After holding this mudra for 5 minutes, place an X in the box below. After 13 sessions, please journal your experience.

Simhamukha
[sim-hamu-kam]

The "lion-face" mudra or Simhamukha embodies warinesss and vigilance. It can represent fragrance, the testing of new ground, even salvation. It further denotes an elephant, homa or yagna, and preparations of medicine by physicians.

X	Mudra experience:

Paripurna Navasana

[Full Boat Pose]

(par-ee-POOR-nah nah-VAHS-anna)

1. From seated position with legs extended in front, bend both knees and hold the back of the thighs with the hands.
2. Allow the sit bones to roll forward and shift the weight backwards toward the sacrum. Be sure and try to balance equally on all 3 points: sit bones and sacrum.
3. Continue keeping the spine in a neutral position by aligning the crown of the head over the shoulders, the shoulders over the pelvis, and the tailbone slightly tucked under.
4. Lift and gently extend both legs, pressing out evenly through the feet.
5. Let go of the back of the thighs, facilitate abdominal engagement by pressing slightly down with both arms while lifting the chest.
6. Release the hands from the thighs and extend the arms out parallel the floor.
7. Inhale again, lengthen the spine.
8. Lift the chest, while keeping the shoulders relaxed.
9. To release the pose, exhale the legs and arms to the floor.

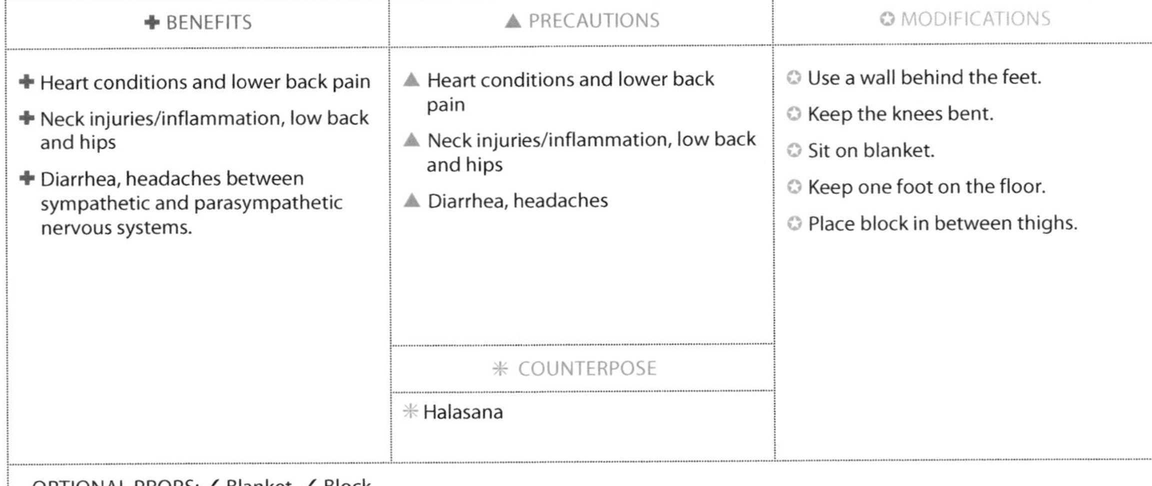

✚ BENEFITS	▲ PRECAUTIONS	✪ MODIFICATIONS
✚ Heart conditions and lower back pain ✚ Neck injuries/inflammation, low back and hips ✚ Diarrhea, headaches between sympathetic and parasympathetic nervous systems.	▲ Heart conditions and lower back pain ▲ Neck injuries/inflammation, low back and hips ▲ Diarrhea, headaches ✳ COUNTERPOSE ✳ Halasana	✪ Use a wall behind the feet. ✪ Keep the knees bent. ✪ Sit on blanket. ✪ Keep one foot on the floor. ✪ Place block in between thighs.

OPTIONAL PROPS: ✓ Blanket ✓ Block

Pranayama = breath control
Prana = the fundamental life force/energy
Yama = to channel/control

Pranayama is the conscious use of breathing as a tool to cultivate pranic energy inside the body. Prana is the essence of life in its subtlest form. Prana is found in all things, but human kind's ability to control this flow provides an immeasurable tool for transcendence.
The various pranayma techniques are used to channel subtle energy into the body or one might also say to bring energy into the subtle channels of the body.
Yama in vedic literature and iconography is also the god of death, so if prana is the essence of life, the experience of breathing is the midground between life and death as we know it. Another explanation from the Sanskrit is that "ayama" (which means to expand following "prana" suggests that the goal is to expand the body with vital force.

Benefits to the Internal Organs

The movement of the diaphragm places an increased pressure on the internal organs. This has the following effects on the digestive, immune, nervous, and cardiovascular/ respiratory systems:

1. Increases digestive homeostasis by facilitating peristalsis (normally incited by parasympathetic and sympathetic nervous system control), which is the wavelike movement of contractions of the intestines. Peristalsis works like a gentle pump for vascularizing the abdominal organs. Also impacts the liver and helps with the removal of waste products. Acts on the kidneys by creating a massaging effect with the diaphragm. One role that the kidneys play is in controlling blood pressure.

2. The spleen, which is involved in the immune system function, is massaged and better able to perform its job of filtering blood, and storing lymphatic tissue and white blood cells.

3. The movement of the diaphragm supports the movement of lymphatic fluid from the lower body to the thorax where it is reabsorbed into the circulatory system. This aids in the production of immune system agents.

4. Regulates the flow of blood to the brain, which can stimulate both hemispheres of the brain creating balance between the sympathetic and parasympathetic nervous systems.

5. Stimulates the olfactory bulb which rests near the emotional center of the brain, and can have a quieting effect. Pranayama is effective for clearing the mind and concentrating attention mentally.

6. The full use of the lungs can prevent toxic buildup of waste materials in the bloodstream. Pranayama techniques affect the heart rate. Slow, even breathing can reduce the heart rate, and breath cessation can also in some cases slow heart rate. This effect reduces the workload on the heart and makes its actions more efficient.

7. Many pranayama techniques can increase the flow of blood to the base of the lungs to remove fluids that build up there. The base of the lungs— where more alveoli are found due to gravity— does not naturally absorb as much oxygen because bloof gases are more easily drawn into the upper portion of the bronchial tract. Many pranayamas can increase the amount of oxygen transferred into the alveoli, by extending the length of breath into the lower lobe of the lungs.

8. Pranayama affects the residual amount (functional residual capacity) of oxygen which remains in the lungs, more often than not making room for more air uptake by the alveoli.

We highly recommend that you hold this mudra for at least 5 minutes in a seated meditation. Perform it at least 13 different times. Mudras may also be utilized while holding a yoga pose. Remember, mudras tend to be subtle and are very powerful in their own way.

9♣

Summer 9

After holding this mudra for 5 minutes, place an X in the box below. After 13 sessions, please journal your experience.

Tripataka
[t r i-pah-tahk-ahm]

Tripataka symbolizes a three-part streamer, and can represent both a beckoning and a dismissal. As a dance gesture, it denotes a crown, a tree, a lamp, a fire, an arrow, and a bird.

X	Mudra experience:

Bharadvajasana

[Bharadvaja's Twist Pose]

(bah-ROD-va-JAHS-anna)

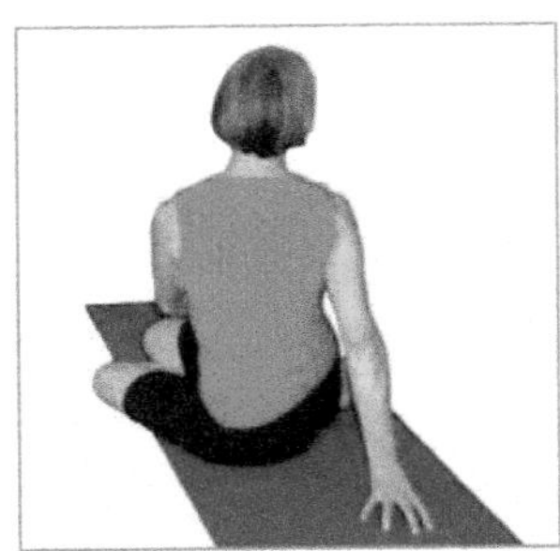

1. Sit on the floor with both legs extended out to the front of the mat.
2. Inhale, and take both legs and slide them over to the left side of the mat as pictured above.
3. Be sure to place the lower shin bone (just above the ankle) in the notch of the arch of the left foot.
4. While supporting the body with the left hand and arm, place the right hand to the outside of the left upper shin bone (just below the knee). Without letting the front of the ribs protrude forward, be sure to get safe lengthening throughout the column of the spine.
5. While keeping the hips grounded, begin to minimize any excess lack in the lower back. (If your lower back is too stiff or relaxed, do not try to work and twist yourself any further into the pose.)
6. Keeping the ear lobes level, turn the head toward the left shoulder.
8. Repeat on the opposite side.

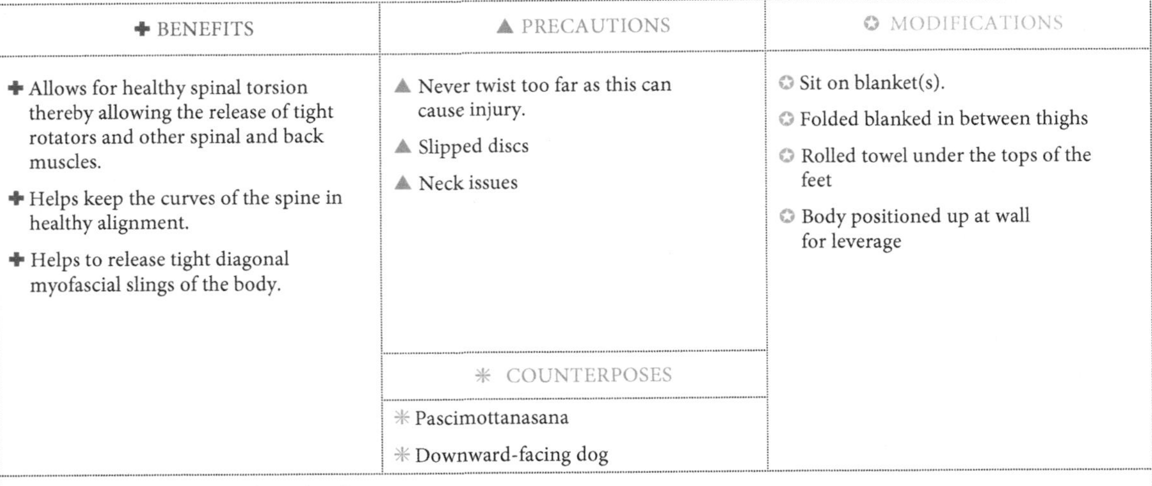

✚ BENEFITS	▲ PRECAUTIONS	✪ MODIFICATIONS
✚ Allows for healthy spinal torsion thereby allowing the release of tight rotators and other spinal and back muscles. ✚ Helps keep the curves of the spine in healthy alignment. ✚ Helps to release tight diagonal myofascial slings of the body.	▲ Never twist too far as this can cause injury. ▲ Slipped discs ▲ Neck issues ✳ COUNTERPOSES ✳ Pascimottanasana ✳ Downward-facing dog	✪ Sit on blanket(s). ✪ Folded blanked in between thighs ✪ Rolled towel under the tops of the feet ✪ Body positioned up at wall for leverage

OPTIONAL PROPS: ✓ Blanket ✓ Wall

Vertebral Column (Spine)

The spine is a flexible column of 24 vertebrae that are grouped into 3 regions based on their structure and function. From top to bottom, they are called the cervical, thoracic, lumbar, and pelvic regions. The cervical region of the spine is designed for mobility, the thorax (including the ribs) has limited mobility and is designed to protect the lungs and heart, while the lumbar region together with the pelvis is designed for some mobility and transferring loads through the trunk to the lower extremities and transferring force from the lower extremities to the upper extremities.

i. Cervicals – 7
ii. Thoracics – 12 (each has a pair of ribs attached to it)
iii. Lumbars – 5
iv. Sacrum – embryologically 5 vertebrae that fuse into 1 bone by adulthood
v. Coccyx – embryologically 3-5 vertebrae that fuse into 1bone by adulthood
vi. Total – 26 (adult), 32-34 (embryologically)

The Spine in Torsion

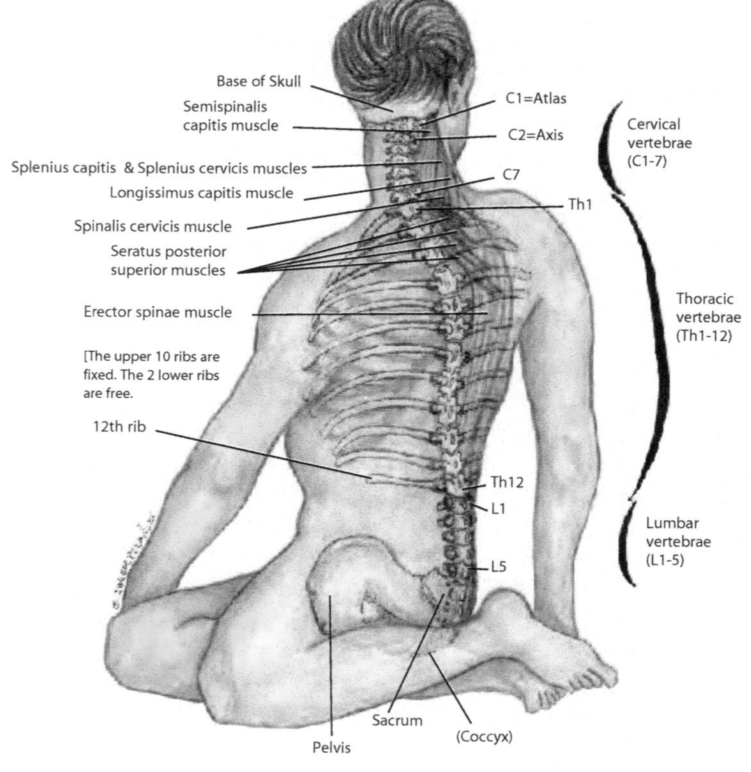

THE SPINE IN TORSION
(Bharadvajasana)

We highly recommend that you hold this mudra for at least 5 minutes in a seated meditation. Perform it at least 13 different times. Mudras may also be utilized while holding a yoga pose. Remember, mudras tend to be subtle and are very powerful in their own way.

10♣

Summer 10♣

After holding this mudra for 5 minutes, place an X in the box below. After 13 sessions, please journal your experience.

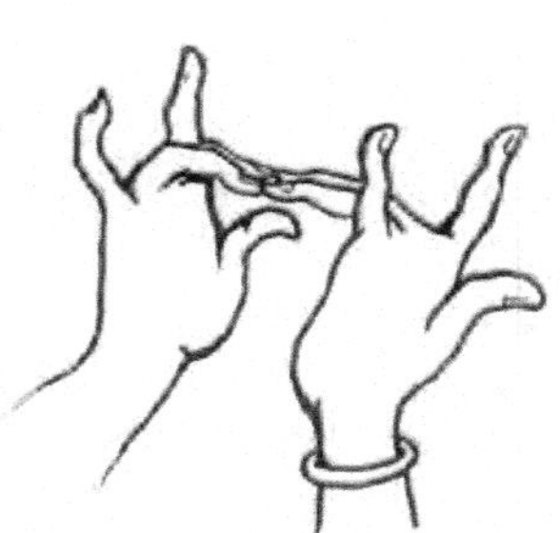

Khatva
[Kat-vah-tam]

The Khatva mudra denotes "bedstead," a litter, and thus response and security.

X	Mudra experience:

Yoga Mudra

[The Great Yoga Seal Pose]

(yoga muu-drah)

1. From the table posture, exhale, releasing the hips back toward the ankles.
2. Extend the abdomen and chest over the thighs, touching the forehead to the mat.
3. Inhale. Lengthen the entire spine by contracting the buttocks back and down while extending the crown of the head forward.
4. Exhale. Draw the shoulder blades together and interlock the fingers behind the back. Draw the arms back and down.
5. Inhale, lifting the sternum.
6. Exhale, slowing bending forward, hinging at the hips.
7. Lift through the arms as the spine extends over the thighs.
8. Rest the forehead on the mat.
9. Continue to straighten the arms, allowing them to lift up over the head.
10. Relax and breathe into the asana.
11. To release, inhale, bringing the arms back down, to help raise the head and neck to vertical position.

The word "yoga" has many meanings. For the purposes of this pose, we will translate it as "union." A mudra is a seal, symbol, or gesture. This pose can be called the seal, symbol, or gesture of union. In many systems, a form of this pose is used at the end of a practice to "seal" the fruits within the student. In this pose, which is initiated by the belly, the emotional center, the chest, the center of compassion, opens and the third eye is stimulated. These are the 3 main receptive centers in the body, or chakras. Yoga mudra stimulates digestion, absorption, and elimination, opens the shoulders and the tops of the feet, increases circulation to the eyes, ears, nasal passages and thyroid gland, and relaxes the mind.

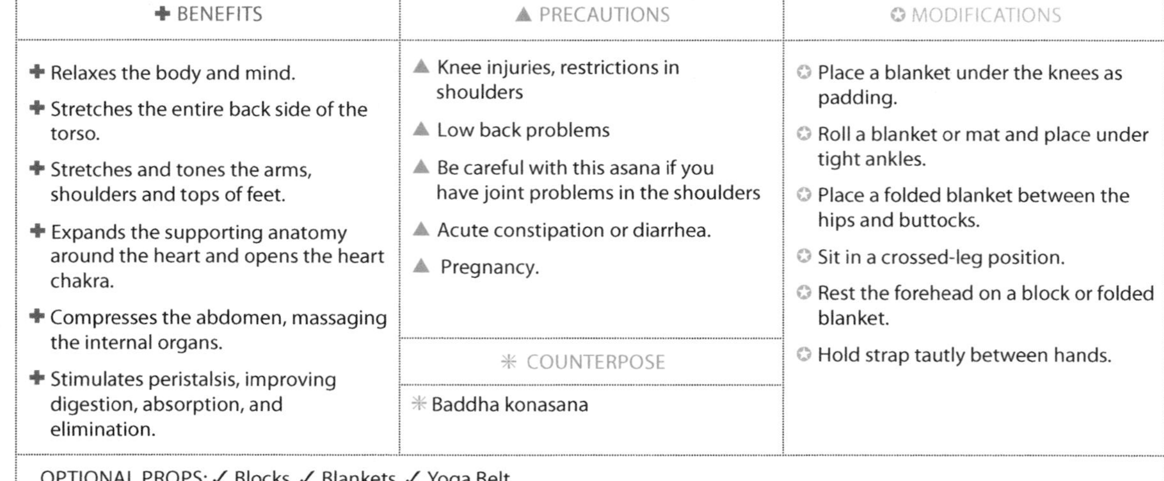

✚ BENEFITS	▲ PRECAUTIONS	✪ MODIFICATIONS
✚ Relaxes the body and mind. ✚ Stretches the entire back side of the torso. ✚ Stretches and tones the arms, shoulders and tops of feet. ✚ Expands the supporting anatomy around the heart and opens the heart chakra. ✚ Compresses the abdomen, massaging the internal organs. ✚ Stimulates peristalsis, improving digestion, absorption, and elimination.	▲ Knee injuries, restrictions in shoulders ▲ Low back problems ▲ Be careful with this asana if you have joint problems in the shoulders ▲ Acute constipation or diarrhea. ▲ Pregnancy. ✳ COUNTERPOSE ✳ Baddha konasana	✪ Place a blanket under the knees as padding. ✪ Roll a blanket or mat and place under tight ankles. ✪ Place a folded blanket between the hips and buttocks. ✪ Sit in a crossed-leg position. ✪ Rest the forehead on a block or folded blanket. ✪ Hold strap tautly between hands.

OPTIONAL PROPS: ✓ Blocks ✓ Blankets ✓ Yoga Belt

The 6 Darshans (philosophical schools of yogic thought)

1) Samkhya (codified by the sage Kapila commentary provided by Ishvara Krishna).

2) Yoga (codified by the sage Patanjali commentary provided by Vyasa)

3) Vedanta (based on the Braha Sutras of Badarayana)

4) Mimamsa (based on the Mimamsa Sutras of Jaimini)

5) Nyaya (based on multiple texts but founded by Akshapada Gautama)

6) Vaisheshika (based on the Vaisheshika sutras of Kanada)

Vectors of Nutation

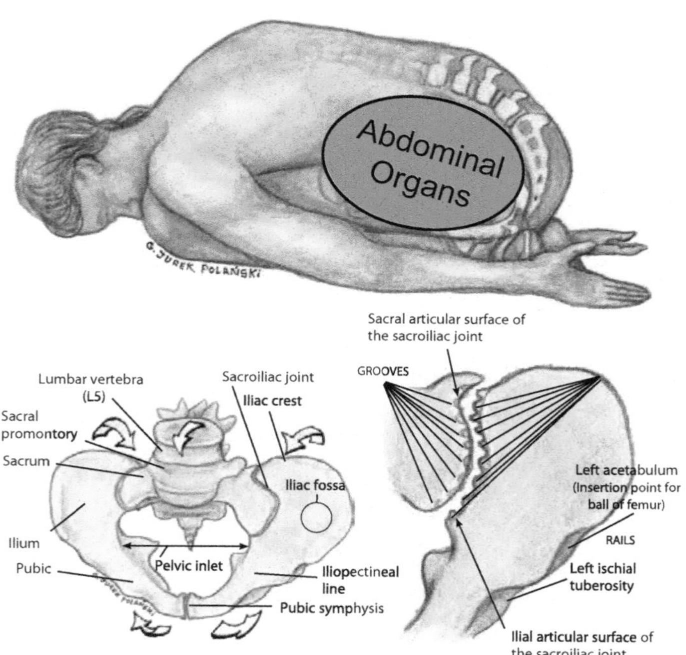

We highly recommend that you hold this mudra for at least 5 minutes in a seated meditation. Perform it at least 13 different times. Mudras may also be utilized while holding a yoga pose. Remember, mudras tend to be subtle and are very powerful in their own way.

After holding this mudra for 5 minutes, place an X in the box below. After 13 sessions, please journal your experience.

Sakata

[shak-ah-tam]

The Sakata or "wagon" mudra derives from the conventional images of the gestures of Raksasas or demons.

X	Mudra experience:

Summer

Supta Matseyendrasana

[Lord of the Fish Pose]

(SOUP-tah MOT-see-en-DRAHS-anna)

1. Come into supine Tadasana.
2. Bend the legs at the knees and separate feet hip distance—ground the feet.
3. Lift up the hips and move them over to the right about t2 inches—set them back down again on the floor.
4. Exhale, draw the right knee into the chest and extend the left leg on the floor.
5. Drop the right knee over the left side of the body.
6. Take the right arm to the floor on the right side of the body—slightly bent at elbow and lined up with shoulder.
7. Keeping the neck aligned with the spinal column turn the head to the right, looking just over the shoulder.
8. Be soft in the pose and allow your knee and shoulder to rest completely.
9. Repeat on opposite side.

✚ BENEFITS	▲ PRECAUTIONS	✪ MODIFICATIONS
✚ Helps to relieve a tight spine. ✚ Helps to release tight hip adductors. ✚ Improves digestion. ✚ Helps to release tight glutes. ✚ Helps to release mild sciatica.	▲ Any back problems such as herniation, sublaxation or hypertonicity of spinal muscles ▲ Any recent surgeries ✳ COUNTERPOSE ✳ Dandasana	✪ Use a folded blanket under the shoulders and torso for stability and comfort. ✪ Position a block under the legs so that the legs can rest on the block(s). ✪ Place a folded blanket in between the thighs for a more neutral feeling in the S.I. joint

OPTIONAL PROPS: ✓ Blanket ✓ Blocks

Matseyendrasana

...matseyendrasana increases the appetite by fanning the gastric fire [pitta], and destroys physical ailments. Kundalini is awakened and the moon made steady.

For the first time the text mentions kundalini, a latent force of highest potential, said to lie in three and one-half coils, like the snake churning in the ocean of milk, sleeping at the lowest center (muladhara chakra at the foot of the "tree of life," the spinal column.

...the "mountain in the center of the world" has the earth at its foot and the sky at its peak. Between earth and sky are the sun (the center of the planetary system and the moon. In the center of the triangle formed by the navel and the two nipples is the "sun" (solar plexus}; at the upper end of the spinal column, at the medulla oblongata, sits the "moon."
"sun" and "moon" are not chakras but are spheres that stand directly under the influence of two chakras, lying respectively just above and just below.[1]

Supta Matseyendrasana is translated as reclining lord of the fishes pose. It has quite a story behind it. Matsya was a fish who overheard Siva teaching the secrets of yoga to Parvati, his consort. In putting this wisdom into practice, Matsya experienced a state of Samadhi, losing all sense of his fish nature, and experiencing himself as pure consciousness. Siva felt this, and gradually transformed Matsya into a human being, naming him Matseyendra, lord of the fishes. Matseyendra then came onto the shore and listened to the continuing discourse of Siva and Parvati. Through the course of his education, and the various stages of transformation between fish and man, he floated in the water, and lay and sat upon the ground, in spinal twists, which enabled him to free his mind from any discomfort or distraction from his physical body. This story reveals the foundations of yoga as a process of transformation. All variations of matseyendrasana free the spine, the nervous system, and thus the mind, of stiffness, blockage, and pain, allowing us to take in the fruits of practice. In supta matseyendrasana, the ground helps to protect and align the spine, making it an appropriate beginning twist.

We highly recommend that you hold this mudra for at least 5 minutes in a seated meditation. Perform it at least 13 different times. Mudras may also be utilized while holding a yoga pose. Remember, mudras tend to be subtle and are very powerful in their own way.

Q♣

Summer Q♣

After holding this mudra for 5 minutes, place an X in the box below. After 13 sessions, please journal your experience.

Puspaputa

[push-papu-tam]

The Puspaputa or "flower casket." denotes to take water or fruits, rice, a cluster of flowers, or flower offering. It can signify both begging or an offering to the deities, and to perform arati.

X	Mudra experience:

1 Hatha Yoga Praddapika, translated by Hans-Ulrich Reiker, pgs 49-50

K♣

Summer

Dandayamana Ardha Chandrasana

[Balancing Half-Moon Pose]

(Dan-dah-MY-ah ARE-dah chan-DRA-ahs-ana)

1 Place a block about fourteen (14) inches out in front (and about two inches to the right of the inseem) of your left foot as above

2 From tadasna, lengthen the entire spine by engaging the core and activating the glutes.

3 Place the right hand to the right hip for greater stability.

4 Inhale. Exhale slightly bend forward from the hips so that as you fold you lower the torso and hand to the block on the floor out in front of you.

5 Once balanced and in good form, fully engage the standing leg (which has a slight bend).

6 Once stable, begin to turn the right hip and leg up toward the sky so that the right hip is now stacked just above the lower left hip.

7 Be sure to lengthen out through the entire spinal column including extensioning through the neck.

8 Keep your gaze down toward the floor or looking straight ahead as shown in the picture above.

9 To release the pose, simply look down toward the floor and lower the leg and torso back into tadasana.

10 Repeat on the opposite side.

✚ BENEFITS	▲ PRECAUTIONS	✪ MODIFICATIONS
✚ Strengthens the standing leg. ✚ Great hip opener ✚ Great for focus and concentration ✚ Increases circulation of the body.	▲ Hyperflexion of the knees ▲ Pronated or supinated feet ▲ Hip issues ✳ COUNTERPOSE ✳ Uttanasana	✪ Left forearm to the seat of a chair. ✪ Place the back leg up on a wall. ✪ Lean the entire body up against a wall for greater support. ✪ Try doing the pose while laying down on the floor (prone).

OPTIONAL PROPS: ✓ Chair ✓ Blocks ✓ Wall

Pearls of Wisdom

In Sanskrit, Ardha means "half" and Chandra means "moon." The moon has extensive references in Vedic literature, one of which is expressed in the word "hatha"—referring to sun, ha, and moon, tha. Each pose in hatha yoga is designed to bring together the polarities within the practitioner. Lunar qualities include receptivity, grounding, connection to the earth, absorption of light, and surrender to the cycles of life. In standing Ardha Chandrasana, we use the grounding of the hips and legs and the subsequent connection to the earth to draw the energy upward, freeing the upper body to extend into space. As the moon waxes and wanes, it reflects the cycles of our lives. A half moon is half in darkness and half in the sun's reflected light. As one side of the body draws itself to its shadow, the other opens to the experience of light, thus teaching the practitioner to honor the experience of polarity and the necessity of change-- again "working a miricle as one"

Gliding Joint

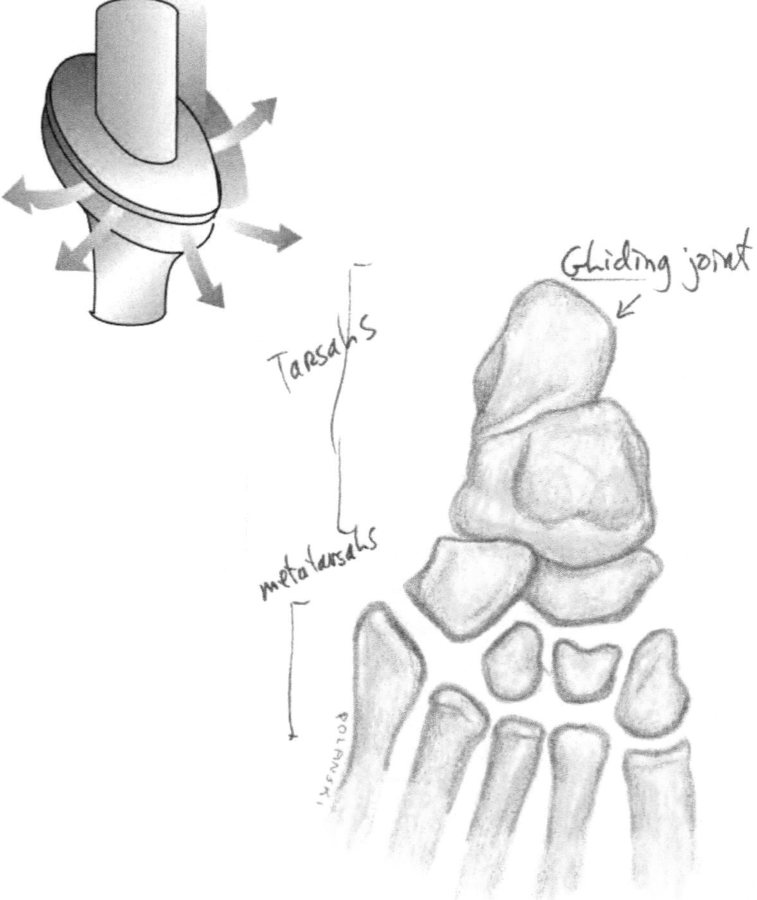

We highly recommend that you hold this mudra for at least 5 minutes in a seated meditation. Perform it at least 13 different times. Mudras may also be utilized while holding a yoga pose. Remember, mudras tend to be subtle and are very powerful in their own way.

K♣

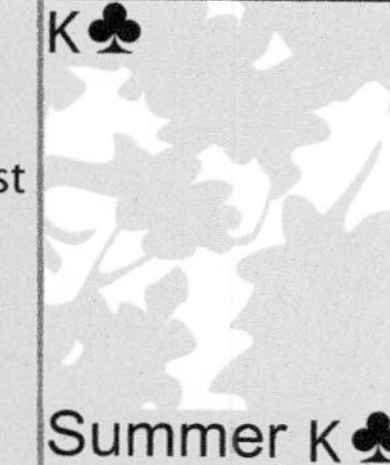

Summer K♣

After holding this mudra for 5 minutes, place an X in the box below. After 13 sessions, please journal your experience.

Arala

[ara-lam]

The Arala mudra is like the Pataka, but here the forefinger is bent. It denotes courage in men and self-admiration in women. It can also signify a storm.

X	Mudra experience:

Fall

Garbhasana

[Child's Pose]

(gar-bahs-AHS-anna)

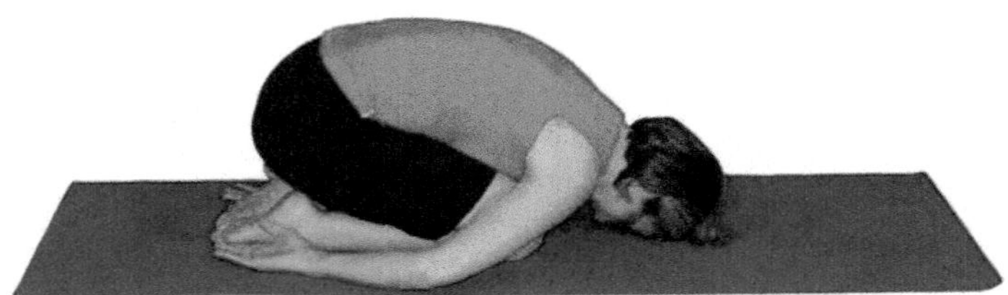

1. From the table posture, bring the big toes together.
2. Exhale and extend the abdomen and chest over the thighs, touching the forehead to the mat.
3. Inhale, filling the back with the breath.
4. Exhale releasing the hips back toward the ankles.
5. Lengthen the entire spine by contracting the buttocks back and down while extending crown of the head forward.
6. Rest the arms along the sides of the body, hands extending toward the ankles with the palms up.
7. Release the shoulders.
8. Bring awareness to the breath.

Garbha means embryo in Sanskrit. The pose of the fetus, as it is translated; or the pose of the child, as it is often referred to, creates a safe space in which to rest, regenerate, and connect to our primal origins. Garbhasana is one of the most important restorative poses, as it relaxes the whole body and calms and quiets the nervous system, mind, and emotions.
(As in all forward bends, the back body is lengthened; however, in child's pose, the positioning of the legs creates a gentle compression massage for the internal organs, helping to remove congestion from the liver, gallbladder, spleen and pancreas, and improving the digestion, absorption and elimination of the gastrointestinal tract.) There is considerable evidence connecting the functioning of the enteric nervous system—which resides in the gut, often referred to as the "second brain"—to having established a complete relationship to gravity in our formative years. In this pose, we can give in to gravity, allowing it to hold us. For all of these reasons, garbhasana is helpful with menstrual pain, fatigue, headaches, and shortness of breath.

✚ BENEFITS	▲ PRECAUTIONS	✪ MODIFICATIONS
✚ Improves one's sense of balance and alignment. ✚ Proper alignment helps prevent joint injury. ✚ Develops a sense of groundedness. ✚ Uplifts the rib cage allowing more room for respiration and creates space for improved functioning of the internal organs. ✚ Helps circulation of the body.	▲ Diarrhea ▲ Arthritis of the knees ▲ Pregnancy ▲ Knee or ankle injury **✳ COUNTERPOSES** ✳ Savasana ✳ Dandasana	✪ Use a small bolster under the torso or under the knees and upper shin bones. ✪ Place 2 blocks (parallel to each other) under the shin bones— close to the knees to create a smart center of gravity. ✪ Place the hands at low back or out in front of body on the floor— be sure not to compress the neck.

OPTIONAL PROPS: ✓ Blanket ✓ Blocks

Yoga and Healing: Respiratory System

Asthma:

Gentle practice with short holds
Practice chest opening— use pranayama bolster
Nadi Shodna is excellent - suggest twice daily
Ujjayi and Kappalubhati breathing while in posture
Pigeon (Kapotasana) and Cobra (Bhujangasana)
Relaxation is key

Emphysema:

Practice slow regular breathing
- -Start shallow
- -Practice abdominal breathing

Gentle slow postures
No holding breath
No vigorous postures

Yoga and Healing: Digestive System

Inversions, twists and forward bends

Reposition organs and encourage peristalsis
Wring out toxins
Replenish fresh blood supply

Diarrhea

Avoid belly down poses
Practice slow Ujjayi breathe

Constipation - do forward bends

Poor digestion
- -Belly down postures
- -Kapalabhati

Gallbladder and Liver

Half moon pose (Ardha Chandrasana)

Ulcers, irritable bowel, Crohn's disease

Avoid Kapalabhati and stomach pumping
Practice Ujjayi
Relaxation is key

Incontinence

Practice Mula Bandha

We highly recommend that you hold this mudra for at least 5 minutes in a seated meditation. Perform it at least 13 different times. Mudras may also be utilized while holding a yoga pose. Remember, mudras tend to be subtle and are very powerful in their own way.

Fall A♦

After holding this mudra for 5 minutes, place an X in the box below. After 13 sessions, please journal your experience.

Catura
[chatu-ram]

The Catura mudra denotes aesthetic emotion, musk, a little sorrow, a glance, breaking to pieces, sweetness, taking small steps, playful discourse, affection, hope and grace. It is further used to express pouring oil ghee in the sacrificial fire and youth.

X	Mudra experience:

Virasana

[Hero Pose]

(vir-AH-sah-nah)

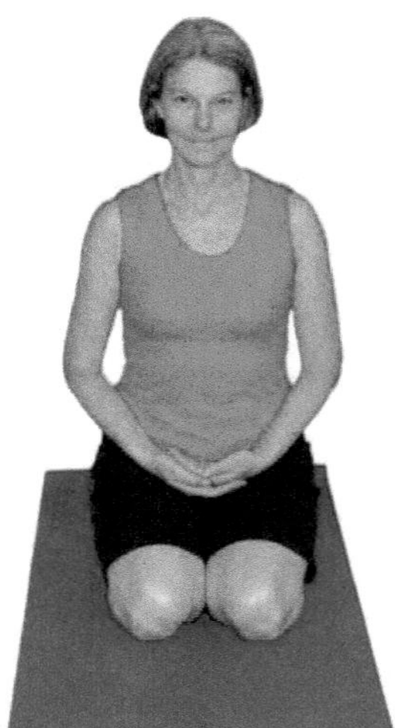

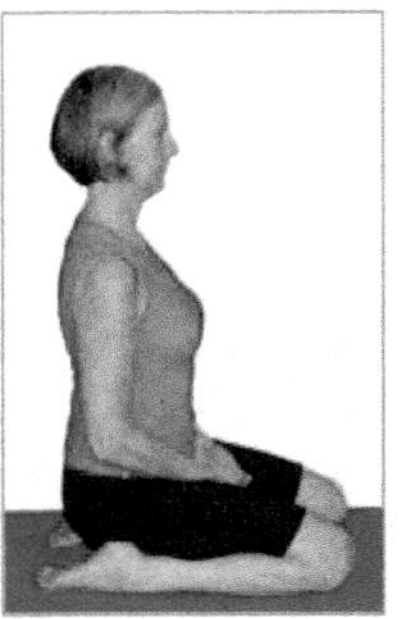

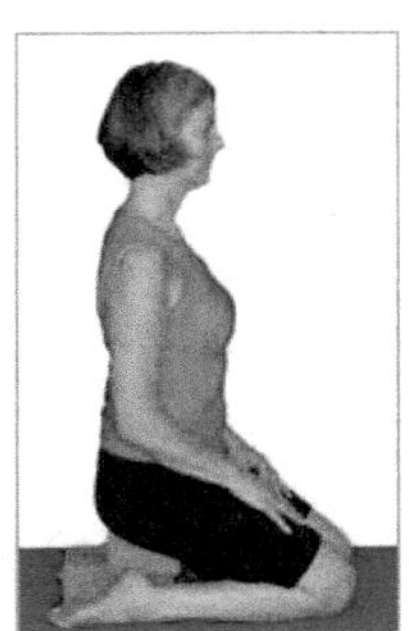

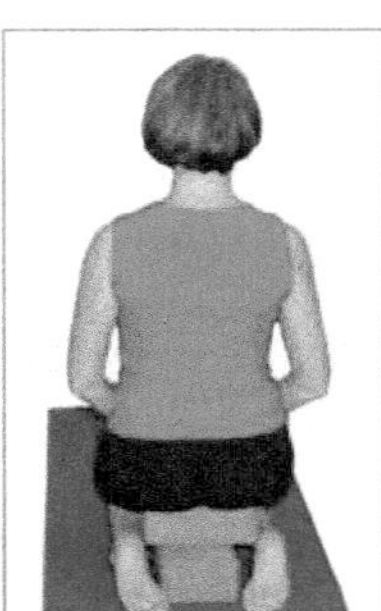

1 Position your body in tabletop pose. Place the wrists under shoulders and knees under the hips.

2 Place a yoga block in between the feet (optional) and slowly lower the hips down toward the block or to the feet. Be sure you are comfortable as possible as pictured above.

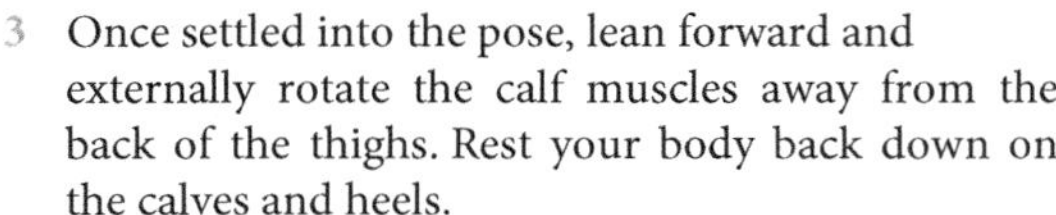

3 Once settled into the pose, lean forward and externally rotate the calf muscles away from the back of the thighs. Rest your body back down on the calves and heels.

4 Be sure to keep knees pressed together and watch to not increase the lordosis of the lower back or neck.

5 If this pose is not easily accessible, simply place a folded blanket under the block or sit bones.

6 Be sure to keep the torso vertical.

✚ BENEFITS	▲ PRECAUTIONS	✪ MODIFICATIONS
✚ Tones and rejuvinates knees. ✚ Helps to reset lateral hip rotators. ✚ Helps to regulate menstural cycle. ✚ Tones kidneys and abdominal organs. ✚ Strengthens the arches of the feet. ✚ Helpful for high blood pressure.	▲ Sciatica ▲ Weak or injured knees, ankles or feet ▲ Headache or diarrhea ✳ COUNTERPOSES ✳ Dandasana ✳ Tadasana	✪ Blocks or folded blankets under sitz bones. ✪ Small rolled hand towels under the tops of the feet for foot support.

OPTIONAL PROPS: ✓ Blocks, ✓ Blankets, ✓ Bolster

Yoga and Healing: Endocrine System

Hypothyroid
- Yoga is efficient treatment
- Shoulder stand to balance thyroid

Hyperthyroid
- No overexertion
- Keep head in line with spine or tucked into chest

Diabetes
- Rejuvenate the pancreas: Cobra (Bhujangasana) Boat (Navasana) Camel (Ustrasana) and Bridge (Setu Bandhasana)
- Relaxation is crucial

Yoga and Healing: Cardiovascular System

Cardiac conditions:
- Avoid: Hot, vigorous, intense practice and intense inversions
- Do not hold breath
- Do not hold postures for an extended time
- Do not overexert oneself
- Improving circulation through Yoga improves heart efficiency

Hypertension: Regulated by medication, or glaucoma and Detached retina

Hold the following for 15 seconds or less:
- •Half shoulder stand (Ardha Sarvanasana)
- •Downward Facing Dog (Adho Mukha Svanasana)
- •Standing Yoga Mudra
- •Camel (Ustrasana)
- •Fish (Matsyasana)
- •Bridge (Setu Bandhasana)

Arteriosclerosis:
- Yoga generally relaxes vessels for better circulation
- Phlebitis and varicose veins
- Short holding of postures
- Legs up the wall
- Practice forward bends
- Stimulates "relaxation response" to lower blood pressure and heart rate

We highly recommend that you hold this mudra for at least 5 minutes in a seated meditation. Perform it at least 13 different times. Mudras may also be utilized while holding a yoga pose. Remember, mudras tend to be subtle and are very powerful in their own way.

Fall 2♦

After holding this mudra for 5 minutes, place an X in the box below. After 13 sessions, please journal your experience.

Sivalinga
[shiva-ling-ahm]

Sivalinga references the phallus of Shiva. The male linga denotes consciousness; the female yoni generative power, a mother earth. Linga (male) concealed partly within yoni (female) symbolizes divinity veiled by unknowing; the exposed part of linga denotes divinity unveiled.

X	Mudra experience:

Fall

Salambhasana

[Locust Pose]

(sha-la-BAHS-anna)

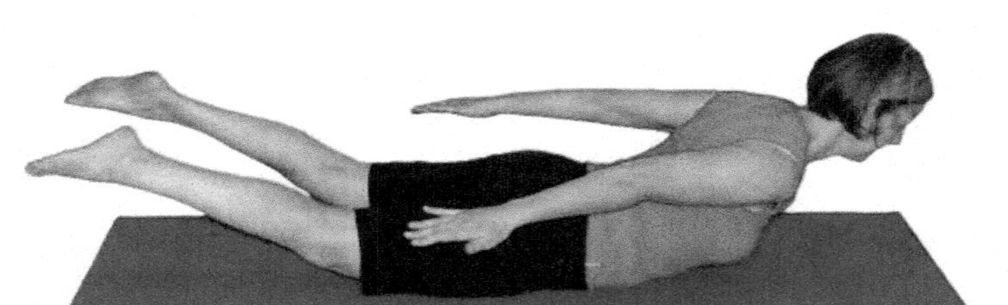

1. Begin in prone position, arms beside body, palms down and pressing slightly into the floor.
2. Inhale, extend one or both legs 4 to 6 inches up off the floor.
3. Inhale, lift the upper body slightly to counter balance the legs. (Hold the pose for 6-12 breaths or 12-30 seconds with no discomfort to the lower back)
4. Square the hips so that both maintain contact with the mat.
5. Exhale, slowly lower legs and relax with head facing to one side.
6. Repeat a second or third time, whichever is right for you.

✚ BENEFITS	▲ PRECAUTIONS	✪ MODIFICATIONS
✚ Strengthens the low back.	▲ Pregnancy	✪ Do half locust version (lift one leg only).
✚ Tones abdomen, uterus, gonads.	▲ Low back conditions	✪ Perform only the extension component without lifting arms or legs.
✚ Stimulates adrenals, pancreas, thyroid.	▲ Abdominal conditions—hernia, diarrhea, etc.	✪ Raise each leg only a minimal amount.
✚ Tones and massages the abdominal organs.		✪ Place the hands or fists under the thighs.
✚ Alleviates menstrual disorders.		
	✳ COUNTERPOSE	
	✳ Janu Sirsasana	

OPTIONAL PROPS: ✓ place neatly folded blanket on floor, under hips

No.13 Tao Te Ching
Success is as dangerous as failure,
and we are often our own worst enemy.

What does it mean that success is as dangerous as failure?
He who is superior is also someone's subordinate. Receiving favor and losing it both cause for alarm.
That is what is meant by success is as dangerous as failure.
What does it mean that we are often our own worst enemy?
The reason I have an enemy is because I have a "self."
If I no longer had a "self," I would no longer have an enemy.

Love the whole world as if it were your self;
then you will truly care for all things.

Yoga and Healing: Nervous System

Parkinson's, Epilepsy, MS

Emphasis grounding and being in the body
Gentle practice, short holding and slow steady breathe
Shoulder stand soothes nerves and calms fear and anxiety Practice assisted balancing postures

M.S. Relaxation and stretching helps the myelin sheath to rejuvenate itself

Anxiety

Slow deep breathing reverses 'flight or fight' response
Slow steady postures
Tadasana, Half Moon (Ardha Chandrasana)

Sphinx

Tone the adrenals
Cobra (Bhujangasana) Bridge (Setu Bandhasana)

Depression

Reinforcement and encouragement

We highly recommend that you hold this mudra for at least 5 minutes in a seated meditation. Perform it at least 13 different times. Mudras may also be utilized while holding a yoga pose. Remember, mudras tend to be subtle and are very powerful in their own way.

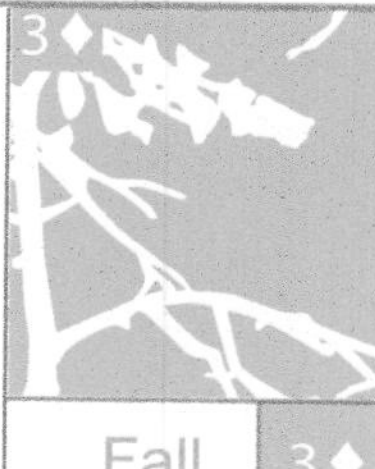

Fall 3♦

After holding this mudra for 5 minutes, place an X in the box below. After 13 sessions, please journal your experience.

Sarpasirsa
[sarpa-sir-sham]

Sarpasirsa is the "snake-head" mudra. This wavering gesture can equally evoke a sprinkling of water to the gods, the movement of an elephant's ears, the arms of wrestlers, or a poised serpent.

X	Mudra experience:

Setu Bhandasana

[Bridge Pose]

(SET-too BAHN-dahs-anna)

Fall

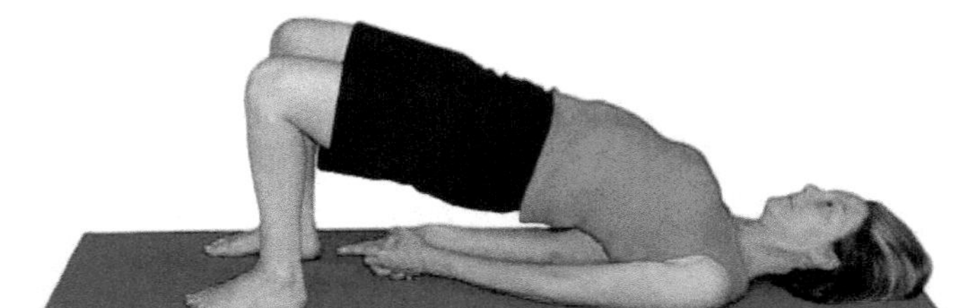

Setu means "bridge" bandha means "lock." A bridge is a transition across a divide, a unified piece. As the body takes the shape of a bridge, it becomes the union point for the experience of transition, opening us to the potential of possibility. Setu bhandasana stretches and strengthens the spine, tones the abdominals and the kidneys, strengthens the arms and shoulders, opens the chest and heart, regulates the thyroid and the adrenals, oxygenates the brain, increases circulation in the arteries, and relieves strain in the neck and shoulders.

1 Come into supine Tadasana. Bend both knees bringing the feet rather close to the buttocks about hip distance apart.

2 Extend the arms along side the body with palms down. Bring the scapulas slightly together. Press down into the arms.

3 Inhale. Engage the core and lift the pelvis up towards the ceiling. Keep the legs internally rotated and press down into the feet.

4 Engage the muscles of the buttocks and continue to lift the spine.

5 Interlace fingers.

6 Fully open the chest.

7 Maintain the natural curvature of the neck.

8 Breathe into the posture.

9 To come out of the pose, exhale while slowly releasing the scapulas and lower the spine one vertebrae at a time.

✚ BENEFITS	▲ PRECAUTIONS	✪ MODIFICATIONS
✚ Strengthens arms and shoulders. ✚ Strengthens back and stimulates abdominal and improves digestion. ✚ Helps improve respiration and thyroid function. ✚ Tones the kidneys. ✚ Tones abdominal muscles and organs. ✚ Regulates functioning of the thyroid and adrenal glands. ✚ Oxygenates the brain.	▲ Cervical spine injuries and low back ▲ Shoulder pain and elbows ▲ Advanced pregnancy **✳ COUNTERPOSE** ✳ Child's pose	✪ Support pelvis with block/bolster beneath the sacrum.

OPTIONAL PROPS: ✓ Place folded blanket under the shoulders

Yoga and Healing: Skeletalmuscular System

Generally: Stretching allows muscles to relax, thus receiving increased blood flow and oxygen. It helps to release lactic acid.

Stiffness:
- Movement is treatment
- Use warm-ups and basic postures

Overflexible- tendons and ligaments too loose, therefore weak:
- Strengthen joints: Elbow, knee, and back

Inflammatory diseases: Fibromylagia, arthritis, etc.:
- Increased blood flow relaxes area
- Gentle yoga and stretching
- Avoid excessive pressure on joints

Osteoporosis:
- Created by lack of movement against gravity, which diminishes bone growth and decreases circulation yoga, walking.

Lower back pain:
- Knees to chest (Apanasana)
- Relieves vertebral compression or misalignment

Carpal tunnel:
- Wear wristbands
- Use fists when doing Cobra (Bhujangasana), inclined plane, etc.
- Build up wrists by squeezing a hand spring or hand ball.

Ball and Socket Joint

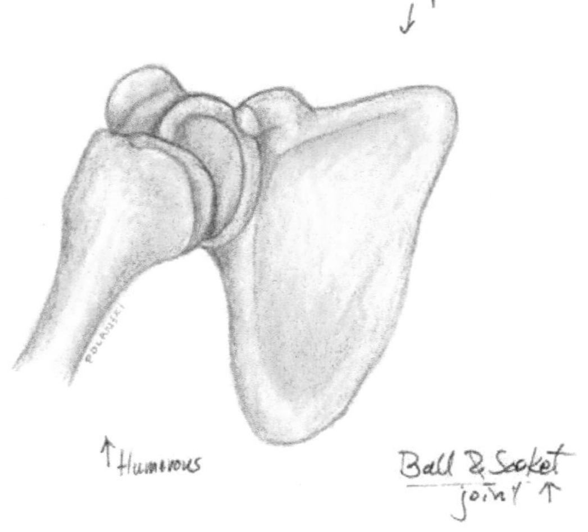

We highly recommend that you hold this mudra for at least 5 minutes in a seated meditation. Perform it at least 13 different times. Mudras may also be utilized while holding a yoga pose. Remember, mudras tend to be subtle and are very powerful in their own way.

Fall 4♦

After holding this mudra for 5 minutes, place an X in the box below. After 13 sessions, please journal your experience.

Kapitta

[kapi-tam]

Kapittha, the "wood-apple" mudra represents a holding of flowers during flirtation.

X	Mudra experience:

Fall

Halasana

[Plough Pose]

(hah-LAHS-anna)

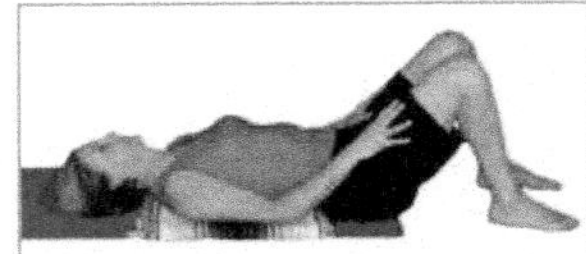

1 Place 2 or 3 folded blankets on the floor with the folds at one end.

2 Lie in a supine position with the shoulders firmly on the blankets at the folded end, the head resting on the mat to maintain the natural curve of the neck.

3 Bend the knees and place the feet flat on the floor.

4 Draw the shoulder blades gently together.

5 Bring the arms to the outside of the hips and press the forearms into the blankets

6 Exhale, engaging the core and drawing the knees up toward the chest. Inhale.

7 Exhale. Lift the pelvis away from the floor. Place the hands on the small of the back, fingertips pointing toward the buttocks.

8 Inhale. Extend the legs out over head and down to a 45° angle.

9 Exhale, lowering the toes to the floor above the head. Keep the legs as straight as possible and press the heels away.

10 Soften the throat and face.

11 Breathe easily.

12 As in the shoulder stand, it is important to protect the natural cervical curve in the neck in this asana.

✚ BENEFITS	▲ PRECAUTIONS	✪ MODIFICATIONS
✚ Calms the mind and nervous system. ✚ Increases abdominal/digestive fires. ✚ Useful with menopause/stress/fatigue reduction. ✚ Stimulates and tones the abdominal and reproductive organs by reversing their position in the body. ✚ Relieves menopausal symptoms. ✚ Tones the buttocks and legs. ✚ Strengthens the shoulders and neck.	▲ Menstruation ▲ Structural pain or injury, especially the neck or shoulders ▲ H.P.P. breathing disorders ▲ Detached retina or other eye problems. ▲ Headache ▲ Uncontrolled hypertension ▲ Acute constipation or diarrhea ✳ COUNTERPOSE ✳ Ustrasana	✪ Keep legs parallel to the floor. ✪ Blanket folded and under shoulder girdle. ✪ Bring feet to chair seat or block. ✪ Use a belt above the elbows to prevent the arms from splaying.

OPTIONAL PROPS: ✓ Yoga belt ✓Blanket ✓ Chair or block

Yoga and Healing: Immune System

Stimulate thymus: Pigeon (Kapotasana) and Fish (Matsyasana)
Supine postures with elevated pelvis encourage:

Breathing and relaxation

- Being present in the body
- Being sensitive to their energy levels
- Increase circulation of blood and lymphatic systems

Fatigue

- Fewer poses held for shorter time
- More supportive, stationary, restorative poses

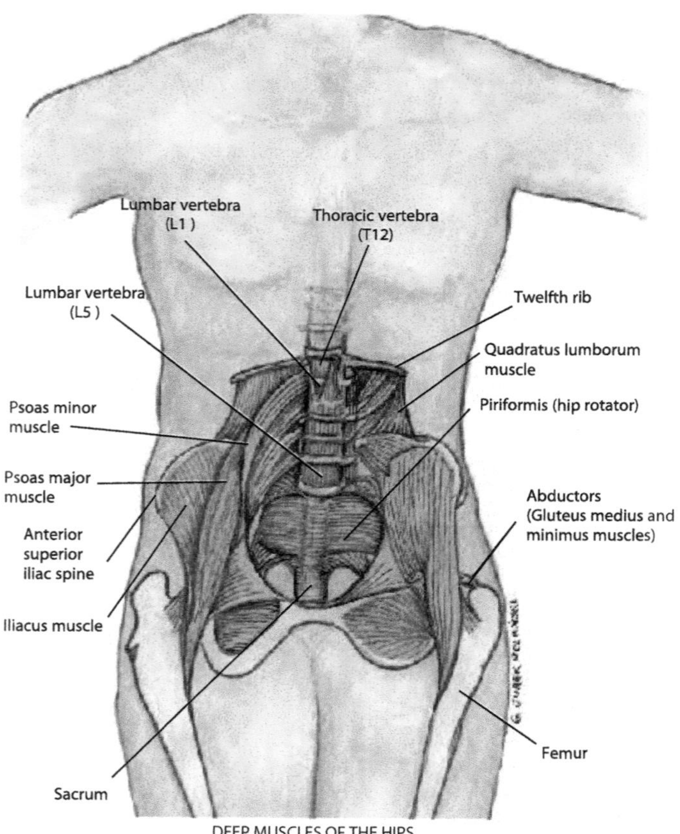

DEEP MUSCLES OF THE HIPS
(Vavishthasana)

We highly recommend that you hold this mudra for at least 5 minutes in a seated meditation. Perform it at least 13 different times. Mudras may also be utilized while holding a yoga pose. Remember, mudras tend to be subtle and are very powerful in their own way.

Fall 5♦

After holding this mudra for 5 minutes, place an X in the box below. After 13 sessions, please journal your experience.

Mahasir
[mah-ah-sram]

The Mahasir or "large head mudra" orchestrates the paths of energies, induces relaxation and ease, and as well cleanses the frontal sinesis.

X	Mudra experience:

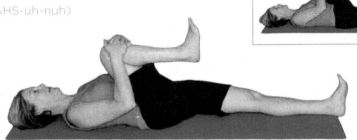

Fall

Pawan Muktasana

[Wind-Relieving Pose]

(PUH-vuhn mukt-AAHS-uh-nuh)

Introduction

In Sanskrit, pawan means “wind” and mukta means “free” or “release.” True to its name, pawan muktasana helps to free the body of excess wind, whether in the form of intestinal gas or mental distraction. By creating space in the lower back and posterior hip, the body can ground itself physically and energetically. The internal organs are massaged and refreshed, and digestion and elimination are stimulated. Remember to always begin with the right knee to the chest. This follows the movement of the digestive tract, massaging the ascending colon first, then the descending colon with the left thigh.

1. Come into supine Tadasana.
2. Bend the right knee and draw it toward the chest on the exhale. Interlock the fingers across the shin.
3. Extend the left leg out though the heel and engage the thigh muscles into the bone. Keep the pelvis and left leg softly grounded into the mat. Keep the toes and knee facing up to the ceiling.
4. Release the shoulders down and away from the ears.
5. Maintain the natural curvature of the neck.
6. On the inhale, extend the abdomen into the right thigh.
7. On the exhale, draw the right knee closer to the body.
8. Continue for several breaths and repeat on the opposite side.

✚ BENEFITS	▲ PRECAUTIONS	✪ MODIFICATIONS
✚ Tones and flushes abdominal organs.	▲ Advanced pregnancy	✪ Clasp the thigh under the knee to avoid knee pain.
✚ Improves digestion and elimination.	▲ Structural injury or pain especially knee	✪ Bend extended leg to alleviate low back pain.
✚ Regulates reproductive functions.	▲ Abdominal pain or injury	✪ Extended leg at wall or slightly bent.
✚ Releases lower back strain.	▲ Acute constipation or diarrhea	✪ Blanket folded and under shoulder girdle.
✚ Flexes the knee and hip joints and opens up the psoas.		

✳ COUNTERPOSE
✳ Virabhadrasana

OPTIONAL PROPS: ✓ Blanket

Yoga and Healing: Reproductive System

Males:

- Prostrate tone, bladder control, and sexual stamina
  - Practice Mula Bandha, pelvic tilts,
  - Bridge (Setu Bandhasana)

Female

- Displaced or prolapsed uterus
  - Avoid Baddhakonasana
- Practice Half Shoulder stand (Ardha Sarvangasana)
- Endometriosis
  - Practice squatting postures
- Menstruation
  - Practice prone postures, Child's Pose (Garbhasana), Yoga Mudra, Squatting (Utkatasana)
  - Practice Joint Freeing Series to eliminate excess energy and fluids

Pregnancy

Strengthen pelvis floor, genital area and anal sphincter with bandhas. Open hips with Warrior I (Virabhadrasana I) Extended Triangle. Stretch inner thigh adductors with Spread Leg Stretch (Upavistha. Konasana)
Stretch groin with Forward Bends and Frog (Mandukasana)

Bones & Ligaments of the SI Joint

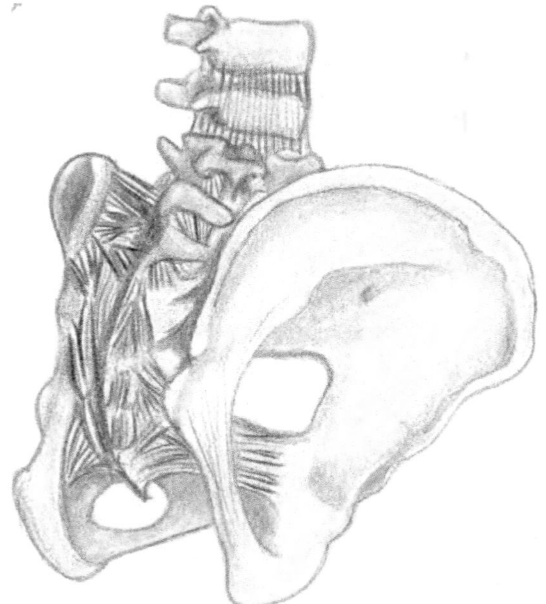

We highly recommend that you hold this mudra for at least 5 minutes in a seated meditation. Perform it at least 13 different times. Mudras may also be utilized while holding a yoga pose. Remember, mudras tend to be subtle and are very powerful in their own way.

Fall 6♦

After holding this mudra for 5 minutes, place an X in the box below. After 13 sessions, please journal your experience.

Mukalam
[muh-ka-lam]

Mukulam represents the bud of the water lily, and symbolizes any flower bud, lovers touching breasts, eating, worship given to the gods, and ultimately the god of love.

X	Mudra experience:

Viparita Karani

[Inverted Lake Pose]

(vip-par-ee-tah car-AHN-ee)

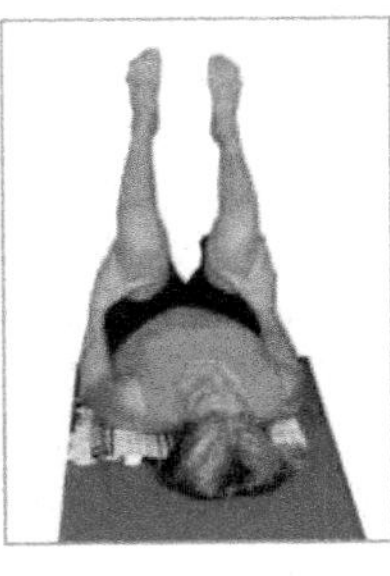

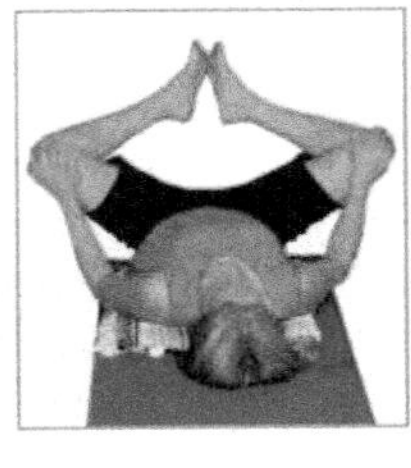

1 Lie on the left shoulder and hip with both buttock muscles at the wall.

2 Inhale swinging the legs up the wall to a fully extended position. The heels reach upward directly above the hips.

3 The arms are at a comfortable distance from each side with the palms facing up.

4 Exhale pressing the small of the back into the mat while extending out through the crown of the head.

5 Inhale raising the arms up with finger tips pointed toward the ceiling, palms facing one another. The outer shoulders press into the mat.

6 Close the eyes.

7 Exhale slowly, lowering the hands overhead, extending through the inside of each arm and out the fingertips.

8 Hold the posture and focus on the breath.

9 Inhale, raising the arms towards the ceiling.

10 Exhale, bringing the hands to the abdomen.

11 Slowly bring the knees to the chest and roll to the right.

Also known as Urdhva Prasarita Padasana. Picture the energy rising up the inside of the legs. This is a restorative pose, especially for the low back.

✚ BENEFITS

- ✚ Rejuvenates tired legs.
- ✚ Protects the back while engaging the arms and legs.
- ✚ Opens the ribs and intercostal muscles.
- ✚ Tones the kidneys.
- ✚ Strengthens the abdominal muscles.
- ✚ Stretches the hamstring muscles.
- ✚ Calms the mind and restores the body.

▲ PRECAUTIONS

- ▲ Glaucoma or other eye pressure/problems
- ▲ Serious neck or low back problems
- ▲ Shoulder pain or injury

✳ COUNTERPOSE

- ✳ Upavishta konasana

✪ MODIFICATIONS

- ✪ Bend knees slightly if necessary.
- ✪ Allow the hands and arms to remain by the side of the torso on the mat.
- ✪ Place a folded blanket under the hips, except during menstruation.
- ✪ Cushion the pelvis with a bolster or blanket.

OPTIONAL PROPS: ✓ Bolster ✓ Blanket

No. 46 Tao Te Ching
When the world follows the Tao,
horses run free to fertilize the fields.
When the world does not follow the Tao,
war horses are bred outside the cities.

There is no greater transgression
than condoning people's selfish desires,
no greater disaster than being discontent,
and no greater retribution than for greed.

Whoever knows contentment will be at peace forever.

Muscles of the Respiratory

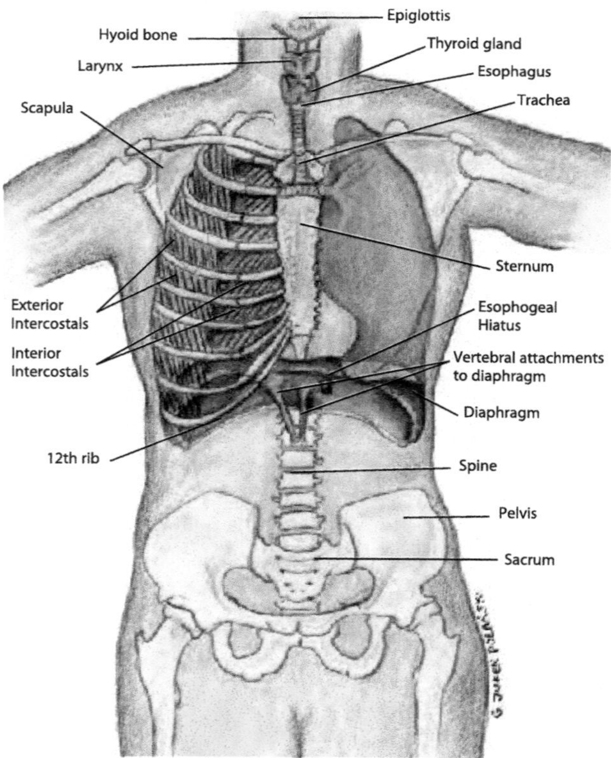

RESPIRATORY ENSEMBLE

We highly recommend that you hold this mudra for at least 5 minutes in a seated meditation. Perform it at least 13 different times. Mudras may also be utilized while holding a yoga pose. Remember, mudras tend to be subtle and are very powerful in their own way.

Fall 7♦

Sukatunda
[shu-kath-un-dam]

Sukatunda or "parrot's beak mudra" denotes a peck, an axe, a spear-throw, shooting an arrow, as well as a lover's jealousy or anger, a challenge.

After holding this mudra for 5 minutes, place an X in the box below. After 13 sessions, please journal your experience.

X Mudra experience:

Sarvangasana

[Shoulder Stand Pose]

(SAHR-vahn-GAH-sah-nah)

1 Place 2 or 3 folded blankets on the floor with the folds at one end.

2 Lie in a supine position with the tops of the shoulders firmly on the blankets at the folded end, and the head resting on the mat.

3 Maintain the natural curve of the neck.

4 Bend the knees and place the feet flat on the floor.

5 Draw the shoulder blades gently together.

6 Bring the arms to the outside of the hips and press the forearms into the blankets.

7 Inhale, engaging the core and drawing the knees up toward the chest.

8 Lift the pelvis away from the floor. Cradle the hips with the hands, fingertips pointing toward the buttocks.

9 Extend the legs at a 45° angle over the head.

10 Press out through the heels.

11 Soften the throat and face.

12 Breathe easily.

13 To release the pose, move the scapulas away from each other. Bring the knees to the chest.

14 Exhale, slowly rolling down one vertebra at a time. The shoulder stand is known as the mother pose of all the asanas, or the mystical asana, because of its many great benefits.

✚ BENEFITS

- ✚ Calming to the mind, stimulates thyroid, parathyroid and pituitary glands to better regulate metabolism.
- ✚ Strengthens shoulders and neck and tones legs and buttocks.
- ✚ Helpful for menopause symptoms.
- ✚ Improves venous circulation in the legs and torso. Alleviates varicose veins.
- ✚ Stimulates and tones the abdominal and reproductive organs by reversing their position in the body.
- ✚ Helps to treat hemorrhoids.

▲ PRECAUTIONS

- ▲ Diarrhea
- ▲ Headaches
- ▲ Neck or shoulder injuries
- ▲ Menstruation or pregnancy (without regular practice)
- ▲ Structural pain or injury, especially the neck or shoulders
- ▲ Detached retina or other eye problems
- ▲ Uncontrolled hypertension or heart disease

✳ COUNTERPOSE

- ✳ Ustrasana

✪ MODIFICATIONS

- ✪ Use wall to assist in entry/exit.
- ✪ Use chair to support hips.
- ✪ Use a belt above the elbows to prevent the arms from splaying.

OPTIONAL PROPS: ✓ Yoga belt ✓ Chair

Pearls of Wisdom

No. 34 Tao Te Ching
The great Tao flows unobstructed in every direction.
All things rely on it to conceive and be born,
and it does not deny even the smallest of creation.
When it has accomplished great wonders,
it does not claim them for itself.
It nourishes infinite worlds,
yet it doesn't seek to master the smallest creature.
Since it is without wants and desires,
it can be considered humble.
All of creation seeks it for refuge
yet it does not seek to master or control.
Because it does not seek greatness;
it is able to accomplish truly great things.

Shoulder Cuff Assembly

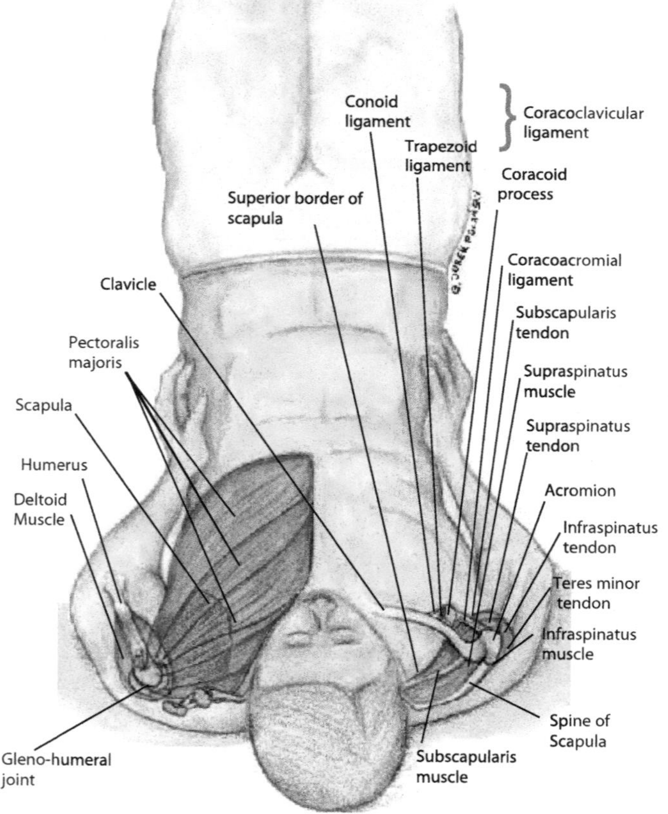

(sarvangasana)

We highly recommend that you hold this mudra for at least 5 minutes in a seated meditation. Perform it at least 13 different times. Mudras may also be utilized while holding a yoga pose. Remember, mudras tend to be subtle and are very powerful in their own way.

After holding this mudra for 5 minutes, place an X in the box below. After 13 sessions, please journal your experience.

Kurma

[kur-mahm]

The Kurma (Karma) mudra denotes the "cosmic tortoise," whose lower shell is the earth, and whose upper shell is the heavens. It symbolizes the perfected man: disciplined and deliberate, restrained and at peace.

X Mudra experience:

9♦

Fall

Vashistasana

[Side Plank Pose]

(vah-sish-TAHS-ana)

Fig. 2

Fig. 1

1 From Dandasana, place the left foot up and over the side of the right leg (closer to the thigh).

2 Place the right hand (palm down and fingers pointing away from hips) on the floor about nine inches away from the right side of the body.

3 Place the left hand to the top of the left knee and lift the hips up from the floor-- your left hand should help assist in a smooth liftoff.

4 Once the hips are stable, take the left arm up toward the sky and then bring your gaze the hand or the thumb.

5 Once your body is stable and suspended in midair (as pictured in Figure 1), simply set and stack your left leg over the right leg. If that proves to be too much, simply place top leg by bending it at 90° in front of the lower leg as is shown in Figure 2.

6 Repeat on the opposite side.

✚ BENEFITS	▲ PRECAUTIONS	✪ MODIFICATIONS
✚ Great for osteoperosis. ✚ Great muscle toner for the wrists, arms, shoulders and core. ✚ Helps to reunite the upper, mid and lower kinetic chains of the body. ✚ Improves respiration and circulation of the body.	▲ Shoulder injury ▲ Wrist or carpel tunnel syndrome ✳ COUNTERPOSE ✳ Janu sirsasana	✪ Place 2 or 3 blocks under hips for support. ✪ Place one block in between thighs. ✪ Have the feet up against wall for greater support and stability.

OPTIONAL PROPS: ✓ Blocks ✓ Wall

Pearls of Wisdom

No.14 Tao Te Ching
Look for it, and it can't be seen.
Listen for it, and it can't be heard.
Grasp for it, and it can't be caught.
These three cannot be further described,
so we treat them as The One.

Its highest is not bright.
Its depths are not dark.
Unending, unnameable, it returns to nothingness.
Formless forms, and imageless images,
subtle, beyond all understanding.

Approach it and you will not see a beginning; follow it and there will be no end.
When we grasp the Tao of the ancient ones, we can use it to direct our life today.
To know the ancient origin of Tao:
this is the beginning of wisdom.

Saddle Joint of Wrist

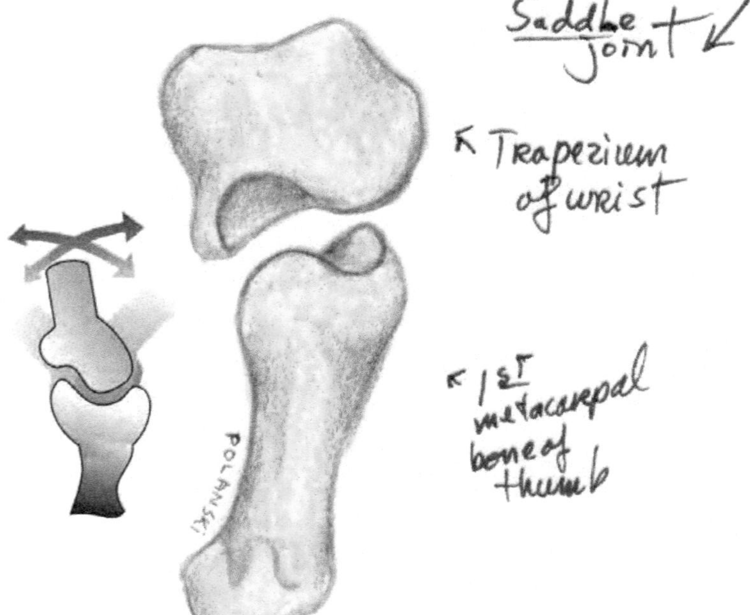

We highly recommend that you hold this mudra for at least 5 minutes in a seated meditation. Perform it at least 13 different times. Mudras may also be utilized while holding a yoga pose. Remember, mudras tend to be subtle and are very powerful in their own way.

Fall 9♦

Samputa
[sampu-tam]

Samputa is a "casket" mudra, and it denotes the concealment of things. Also, a great mudra for the joining of mantras.

After holding this mudra for 5 minutes, place an X in the box below. After 13 sessions, please journal your experience.

X	Mudra experience:

Urdvha Dhanurasana

[Upward-Facing Bow Pose]

(OORD-vah don-your-AHS-anna)

Fall

1 While laying down on the floor, place your hands in front of the shoulders with the fingers pointing toward feet.

2 Retract the feet back towards the hips, while keeping the feet 12 to 14 inches apart.

3 Firmly engage the hands, arms feet and legs so that your hips can be lifted up off the floor and perhaps resting on top of the head (be sure to not compress the neck while doing so).

4 Once ready, simply use all your available strength by pressing the hands and feet into the floor so that your body, head and hips lift higher in space.

5 While holding this pose be sure that the heels and elbows do not sneak out away from each other.

6 Keep the thighs internally rotating, while at the same time, externally rotating the calf muscles.

7 When ready to release the pose, simply lower to the top of the head, pause and then lift the head slightly to lower the entire body to the floor.

✚ BENEFITS	▲ PRECAUTIONS	✪ MODIFICATIONS
✚ Healthy blood flow. ✚ Tones the spinal column. ✚ Stimulates the glands of the body.	▲ Sciatica ▲ Carpel tunnel syndrome ▲ Hypertension ▲ Diarrhea ✳ COUNTERPOSE ✳ Uttanasana	✪ Place 2 blocks at wall for hand placement. ✪ Place block between thighs. ✪ As a warm-up to this pose, first hold bridge pose.

OPTIONAL PROPS: ✓ Blocks, chairs or wall

Mantras

Pearls of Wisdom

Mantra can be divided into two words. "Man "means mind and "tra" means to tune the vibration. Mantra is a sound current that tunes and controls mental vibration *(Kundalini Yoga: The Flow of Eternal Power, p. 35)*.

All sound, of course, is vibration. The ears create sound from this vibration, but even without ears, there is still vibration. Every moment of the day, everywhere we are, the energy vibrations that can create sound travel through us, vibrating every cell in our bodies. Even in the vacuum of space, sound waves vibrate to the outer recesses of the universe, toward infinity.
In the human body, the vibratory waves that can cause sound have their most pronounced effect upon our two most sensitive systems:

1. The Neurological System
2. The Endocrine System

These include the brain, and the Pituitary (master gland of the endocrine system) and Hypothalamus glands. The vibrations that we create ourselves, through our own speech, have the most direct, powerful effects. Vibrating the pituitary increases its output of secretions, and this in turn optimizes the function of the entire endocrine system.

The vibratory effects of chanting have several important physical actions.

1. They improve immune function, via the hypothalamic-pituitary axis.
2. They increase brain hemispheric balance.
3. They send ethereal energy through the nadis.
4. They help quiet the inner dialogue.
5. They help potentiate the proper replication of DNA.

Positive medical results that have been achieved by chanting include:

1. Lowered heart rate
2. Lowered blood pressure
3. Reduction of stress hormone
4. Improved output of melatonin
5. Increased lymphatic circulation
6. Enhanced release of endorphins
7. Increased immune system function

Dr. Robert Gass shows us that sound has an effect upon animals and even plants. Playing certain music to plants can dramatically increase their up-take of nutrients. Since plants don't have ears, it is the vibration of the sound that they respond to. *(Meditation as Medicine, pgs.100-120)*

Specific Mantras also influence the nadis and chakras by vibrating the upper palate of the mouth which has 84 meridian points connected to the body's ethereal energy system. Some of these points carry energy directly to the hypothalamus and pituitary.
(Meditation as Medicine, p. 29)

Please note: We strongly encourage you to refer to page 92 where question 68 takes you through a universal mantra practice known as "Om Namha Shivaha."

We highly recommend that you hold this mudra for at least 5 minutes in a seated meditation. Perform it at least 13 different times. Mudras may also be utilized while holding a yoga pose. Remember, mudras tend to be subtle and are very powerful in their own way.

Fall 10♦

After holding this mudra for 5 minutes, place an X in the box below. After 13 sessions, please journal your experience.

Mayura
[mayu-ram]

The Mayura or "peacock's neck" mudra alludes to immortality since the peacock arose from feathers shed by the grand Garuda bird. The peacock traditionally slays serpents, the symbols of cyclical time. This gesture embraces omen, the wiping away of tears, a creeper, to remove knots from the hair, to praise, to apply tilakam, and adherence to fundamental truth.

X	Mudra experience:

Adho Mukha Vrksasana

[Hand Stand Pose]

(ah-doh moo-kah vriks-SHAHS-anna)

Fall

1 Place your hands on the floor about 6 inches from the wall and just beneath the shoulders.

2 Allow your stronger leg to be behind you to help push and lift you up off the floor and up to the wall.

3 The leg closest to your hands should be bent enough to easily follow the other leg up against the wall upon the jump

4 Not too forcefully, push off with the back leg and allow your other leg, waist, torso and shoulders to follow suit up against the front of the wall.

5 Continue pushing out from the hands and arms by pressing into the floor. Allow the armpits to feel like they're actively stretching away from all points.

6 Stretch and push out from the feet as if you were lifting the ceiling up from the center of the room.

7 Keep the thighs rotating internally.

8 Allow the head and neck to be somewhat soft by letting the head feel as if it were hanging like a piece of fruit on a tree. Gaze is at the floor (if possible).

9 Keep your body very active, but be sure to keep the facial muscles soft and released.

✚ BENEFITS	▲ PRECAUTIONS	✪ MODIFICATIONS
✚ Strengthens the shoulders and arms. ✚ Alleviates insomnia. ✚ Builds stamina	▲ Wrist issues ▲ Hypertension ▲ Menstruation	✪ Kneeling on the floor, back the backside of your body up to a wall. The bottom of the feet should be placed up against the wall so that as your arms extend your torso upright off the floor your feet begin to walk up higher on the wall.
	✳ COUNTERPOSE	
	✳ Dandasana	

OPTIONAL PROPS: ✓ Bolster upright at wall for the back of the head to rest against

No. 28 Tao Te Ching
Know the masculine,
but keep to the feminine:
and become a watershed to the world.
If you embrace the world,
the Tao will never leave you
and you become as a little child.

Know the white,
yet keep to the black:
be a model for the world.
If you are a model for the world,
the Tao inside you will strengthen
and you will return whole to your eternal beginning.

Know the honorable,
but do not shun the disgraced:
embracing the world as it is.
If you embrace the world with compassion,
then your virtue will return you to the uncarved block.

The block of wood is carved into utensils
by carving void into the wood.
The Master uses the utensils, yet prefers to keep to the block
because of its limitless possibilities.
Great works do not involve discarding substance.

Pivot Joint of the Atlas - Axis

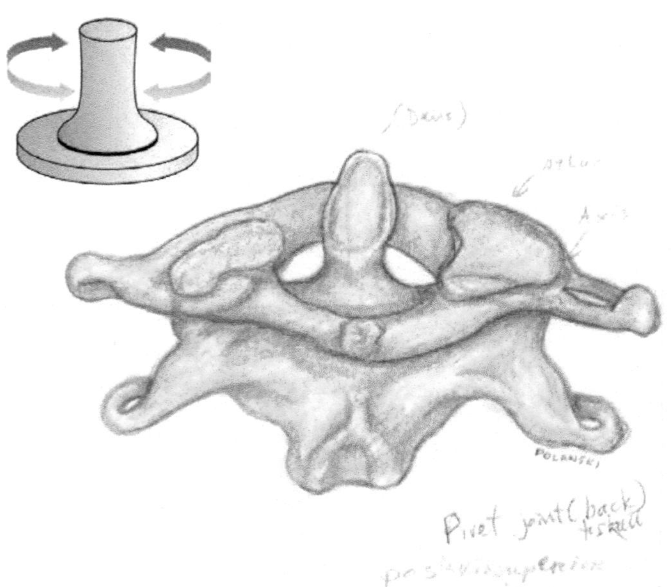

We highly recommend that you hold this mudra for at least 5 minutes in a seated meditation. Perform it at least 13 different times. Mudras may also be utilized while holding a yoga pose. Remember, mudras tend to be subtle and are very powerful in their own way.

J♦

Fall J♦

After holding this mudra for 5 minutes, place an X in the box below. After 13 sessions, please journal your experience.

Samkha
[sam-khah-yam]

Samkha signifies the conch shell.

X	Mudra experience:

Salamba Sirsasana

[Head Stand Pose]

(sah-LOM-bah shear-SHAHS-anna)

Fall

Fig. 1

Fig. 2

Fig. 4

Fig. 3

1 While in Table position, bring your elbows to the floor, interlace your fingers and then place the palms of your hands to the back of the skull as shown in Figure 1.

2 Once the fingers and hands are firmly in place cradle the head so that it does not move.

3 Be sure the crown of the head is firmly placed on the mat so that the elbows can move in toward each other. Elbows should be no further out than the shoulders.

4 Inhale. Exhale and begin to walk your feet in toward the elbows so that you can now straighten out the legs as shown in Figure 2.

5 Either stay in this position so that your back can work to become more vertical and that the hips are stacked above the shoulders as in Figure 2.

6 Once perfecting the form, begin to pull the legs and feet up off the floor toward the mid body so that you are carefully balanced as pictured in Figure 3.

7 From Figure 3, begin to straighten out the legs so that your body is now vertically straight as shown in Figure 4. Please note: This pose should never be executed if the neck is unstable and not fully supported by the arms and elbows.

✚ BENEFITS

- ✚ Calms the mind and nervous system.
- ✚ Increases abdominal/digestive fires.
- ✚ Useful with menopause/stress/fatigue reduction.
- ✚ Stimulates and tones the abdominal and reproductive organs by reversing their position in the body.
- ✚ Relieves menopausal symptoms.
- ✚ Tones the buttocks and legs.
- ✚ Strengthens the shoulders and neck.

▲ PRECAUTIONS

- ▲ Menstruation
- ▲ Structural pain or injury, especially the neck or shoulder
- ▲ H.P.P. breathing disorders
- ▲ Detached retina or other eye problems
- ▲ Headache
- ▲ Uncontrolled hypertension
- ▲ Acute constipation or diarrhea

✳ COUNTERPOSE

- ✳ Child's pose

✪ MODIFICATIONS

- ✪ Keep legs parallel to the floor.
- ✪ Use bolster beneath shoulders.
- ✪ Bring feet to chair seat or block.
- ✪ Use a belt above the elbows to prevent the arms from splaying.

OPTIONAL PROPS: ✓ Chair ✓ Block ✓ Yoga belt ✓ Wall

Pearls of Wisdom

No. 36 Tao Te Ching
If you want something to return to the source,
you must first allow it to spread out.
If you want something to weaken,
you must first allow it to become strong.
If you want something to be removed,
you must first allow it to flourish.
If you want to possess something,
you must first give it away.

This is called the subtle understanding
of how things are meant to be.

The soft and pliable overcomes the hard and inflexible.

Just as fish remain hidden in deep waters,
it is best to keep weapons out of sight.

Muscles of the Neck

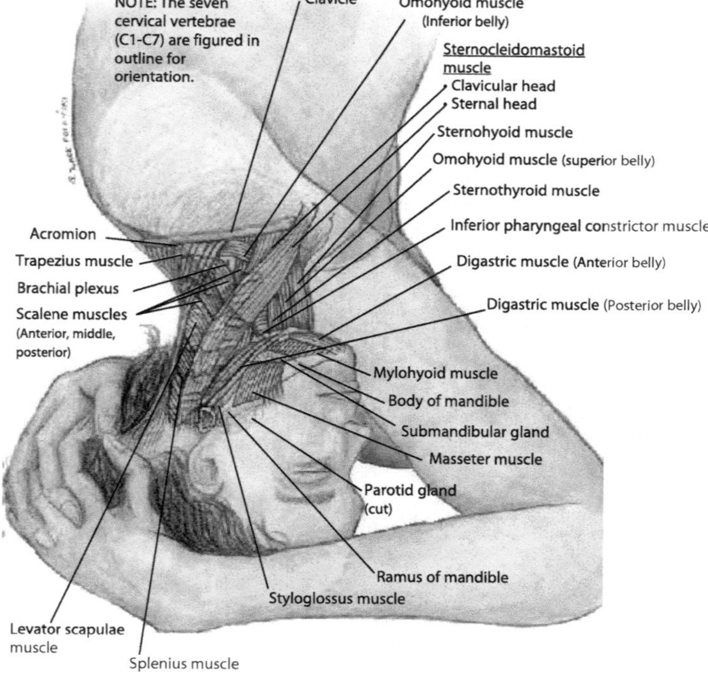

We highly recommend that you hold this mudra for at least 5 minutes in a seated meditation. Perform it at least 13 different times. Mudras may also be utilized while holding a yoga pose. Remember, mudras tend to be subtle and are very powerful in their own way.

Fall Q♦

After holding this mudra for 5 minutes, place an X in the box below. After 13 sessions, please journal your experience.

Kartarisvastika
[Kar-t ar-ish-vah-stee-kham]

Kartarisvastika is the mudra of "crossed arrow shafts." It symbolizes trees, their boughs, and hilltops as well.

X Mudra experience:

Shavasana

[Corpse Pose]

(shah-VAHS-anna)

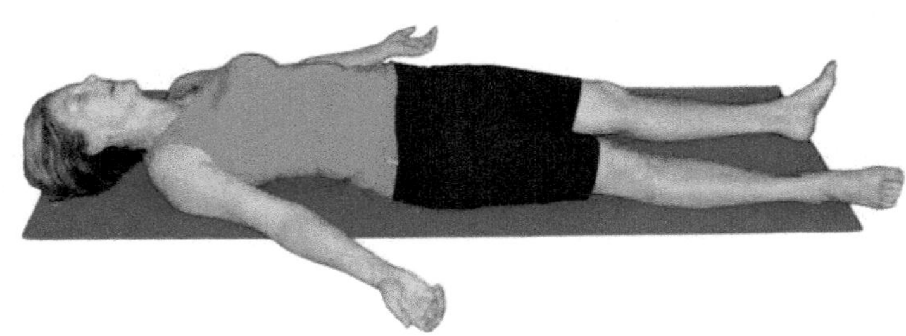

1 Come into supine Tadasana.

2 Separate the legs hip distance apart and allow the feet to fall to either side.

3 Rest the arms palms up at a 45° angle from the body

4 Bring the shoulder blades slightly together and move them down toward the waist.

5 Allow for the natural curve in the neck.

6 Scan the body for any tension and melt into the mat.

7 Breathe softly. Close the eyes.

8 Quiet the mind.

9 To come out of the posture, exhale and gently roll to the right side, and then support the head with the right arm. Inhale and slowly push off with the hands coming up to a seated position.

✚ BENEFITS

- ✚ Relaxes the entire body.
- ✚ Relieves stress.
- ✚ Helps to lower high blood pressure.
- ✚ Quiets the mind.
- ✚ Balances the emotions.
- ✚ Provides the occasion for healing to take place.

▲ PRECAUTIONS

- ▲ If pregnant or have a respiratory ailment, place a bolster under the head and chest
- ▲ Kyphosis whereas the cervical spine (neck) is causing it to become lordotic

✳ COUNTERPOSE

- ✳ Sukhasana

✪ MODIFICATIONS

- ✪ Place rolled blanket under the knees to alleviate back pain.
- ✪ Support the neck with a folded blanket under the head.
- ✪ Use an eye pillow to keep out excessive light.
- ✪ Cover the body with a blanket to conserve warmth.

OPTIONAL PROPS: ✓ Blankets ✓ Eye pillow

Pearls of Wisdom

No.43 Tao Te Ching
That which offers no resistance,
overcomes the hardest substances.
That which offers no resistance
can enter where there is no space.

Few in the world can comprehend the
teaching without words,
or understand the value of non-action.

Bones of the Hand

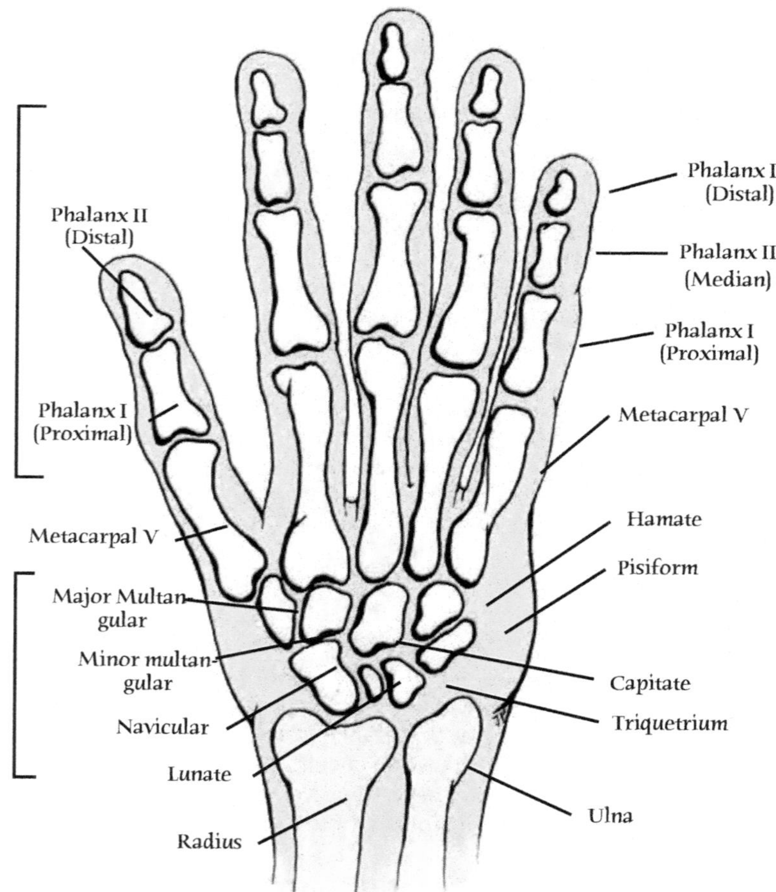

The fingers each are composed of three bones – the numbered phalanxes. The thumb is composed of two bones. There are eight bones in the wrist.

We highly recommend that you hold this mudra for at least 5 minutes in a seated meditation. Perform it at least 13 different times. Mudras may also be utilized while holding a yoga pose. Remember, mudras tend to be subtle and are very powerful in their own way.

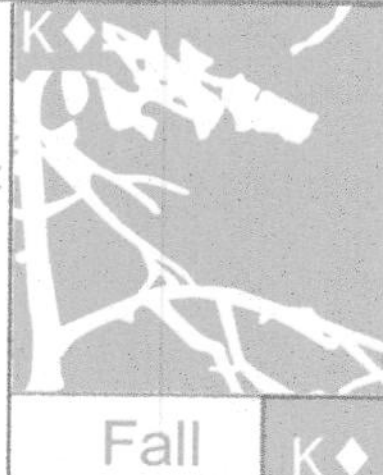

Fall K♦

After holding this mudra for 5 minutes, place an X in the box below. After 13 sessions, please journal your experience.

Alapadma
[alapad-mam]

The Alapadma mudra has several name variants: Alapadya, Alapallava, or Utpalapadma. It symbolizes the fully open lotus. This gesture can signal beauty, a hair knot, the full moon, a hill, or a mountain, a mirror, and both inquiry ("who are you?") or beholding of oneself.

X Mudra experience:

Introduction to the Master Emotions Index (MEI) Chart and Personal Emotions Imprint Map (PEIM)

"The best and most beautiful things in the world cannot be seen or even touched. They must be felt with the heart"
- Helen Keller

Let's talk about how to derive the greatest benefit from utilizing the MEI to build out your PEIM wheel. On page 288 and 289 you will find flowcharts and spreadsheets instructing you on how to effectively construct your very first PEIM. This chart shows you how to transfer all of the "Scale of Intensities" from each Chart of Emotions (COE) to the 4 MEI spreadsheets. Once finished transferring these points, the second step prompts you to tally the said values (of all the 17 different emotions) of the MEI downward to determine the "Sub Totals." Once finished, the third step teaches you how to transfer the said "Sub Totals" of the MEI into what is called the Cumulative Emotions Index (CEI) which is located on page 294. This spreadsheet reflects all the *global* values or "Points" from having answered any or all of the workbook questions and journal entries. The CEI has the option to impart 5 different PEIM "Trial rounds". And why would you want to have the option of constructing 5 different rounds? Well, let's say, hypothetically, that you have worked a quarter way through this book . . . and you were thinking to yourself . . . "I'd love to get an overall picture as to what my "preliminary" PEIM looks like?" ... But that you're also thinking ... "in order to do so, I must first have fully completed all or at least most of the workbook questions and journal entries"— well, this is not the case. Remember, at any given point in throughout this book, you may add any new points from the COE to the MEI to the PEIM wheel. This very process helps to provide a more updated, yet picturesque view of your PEIM wheel. That said, this book contains two distinct kinds of PEIM wheels: the first one is called a 'Preliminary" PEIM and it is the first stage of crafting your PEIM wheel. It is based on "tenths" and its values range from 10 to 100. However, the second PEIM wheel is "Continuing", it is the second stage wheel and allows you to continually populate or build out. . . that is to say, until you've completed your Part 1 of the book. And, unlike the Preliminary PEIM, this one is based on "hundredths": whose values range from 100 to 1000. These two PEIM charts may be found on pages 296 and 297 respectively.

To be clear, you will first begin to populate your preliminary PEIM, and then once any given house reaches 100 points you will simply begin to use the "Continuing" PEIM Wheel. Each wheel succinctly juxtaposes one emotion to the other. For example, page 4 contains a random PEIM wheel, and this example attempts to illustrate how your (or any other person's) chart might look like. It is important to keep in mind that your PEIM wheel is based solely upon the information you had entered as it pertains to the 102 workbook questions and journal entries—Know why it is that you would chose a workbook question over a journal entry to populate its correlate COE.

ALFW is extremely rich in what it has to offer. And, as expressed so many other times in throughout this book, emotions (metaphorically speaking) evoke color, they give flavor and expression to the beautiful life we chose to lead. That said, our emotions have a profound affect on other people's lives: people with whom we belong and chose to be in community. So, why not use the PEIM wheel? Why not (based on your life's timeline) get a glimpse into your emotional intelligence and awareness? When you do so, interesting things seem to unfold: Light bulbs go off . . . and now you're able to see so many of the aspects of your life— all in a different ray of light. Yet, another opportunistic window into the world of cultivating extraordinary awareness. Sometimes the hardest things to see from within ourselves are more obvious to others. Thus, we need to value alternate points of view, other ways of looking at the how the *stories of our life* give grist and rise the movement that it so does. So with this information in mind, it is important to reiterate the fact that one of the main goals of ALFW is to share a new set of tools: one's with which to help balance the many misperceived and perhaps out-of-balance emotions. For example, if you turn to the PEIM wheel on page 4 you will see that the house of joy far exceeds that of anger— well, this is probably a very healthy thing, both emotionally and intellectually—for all of us and especially when in groups with others. Conversely, should we shift our awareness to the emotion of anger and see that it has an overall sum total of 40 points, well, that may be enough to raise an eyebrow and perhaps suggest further examination? Where emotional well-being is concerned, it is important to have a healthy rapport not just with your self, but with all the other people around you: one person affects the other, it is called emotional contagion. It's really that simple!

Emotions as They Often Relate to the 7 Major Chakras

There is a lot of research of late which suggests that because we are individually, yet endlessly in contact with most all of the gross and subtle details of "who we are" and "what's going on in our life" . . . we cannot see ourselves as the "bigger picture." This "not-being-able-to-see-ourselves-fully" undermines our power, it holds us back from being able to fully unearth our full potential from within." However, these endless details present one very large problem: they often lead our minds and bodies astray and feeling as if "we" were stuck in the muck of mud! This is one of the most compelling reasons as to why ALFW, yoga, pranayama and meditation prove to be so highly effective— each lends a hand in helping us to peel the layers get unstuck!

Just below is a wheel suggesting how it is our emotions and feelings attach and relate to one of the 7 chakras of the body. These chakras invisibly align themselves along the axis of our spine and has a clockwise rotational spin, and sometimes when our bodies are out of balance the spin is reversed couterclockwise. Each chakra belongs to one of the seven glands of the human body. All seven have an electromagnetic-like frequency or vibration that works in tangent with the rest of the body— and, as has been postulated by numerous people, the universe too. Each chakra is supplied with just the right amount of energy so as to neither "short-circuit" nor "overload" from either too little, too much a voltage. There is an old saying from India: "Prana follows thought." If this maxim has any validity (and I firmly believe it does), well then its very prana (from which we uniquely exist) takes its form within the domain of our mind, body and spirit. So please remember, refer back to this page as you work through this book. Look over all the categorized words and perhaps contemplate which emotion or feeling is most related to which chakra. The chart below suggests just that: a reminder as to how the energy of emotions and feelings aligns itself along the axis of our chakra system.

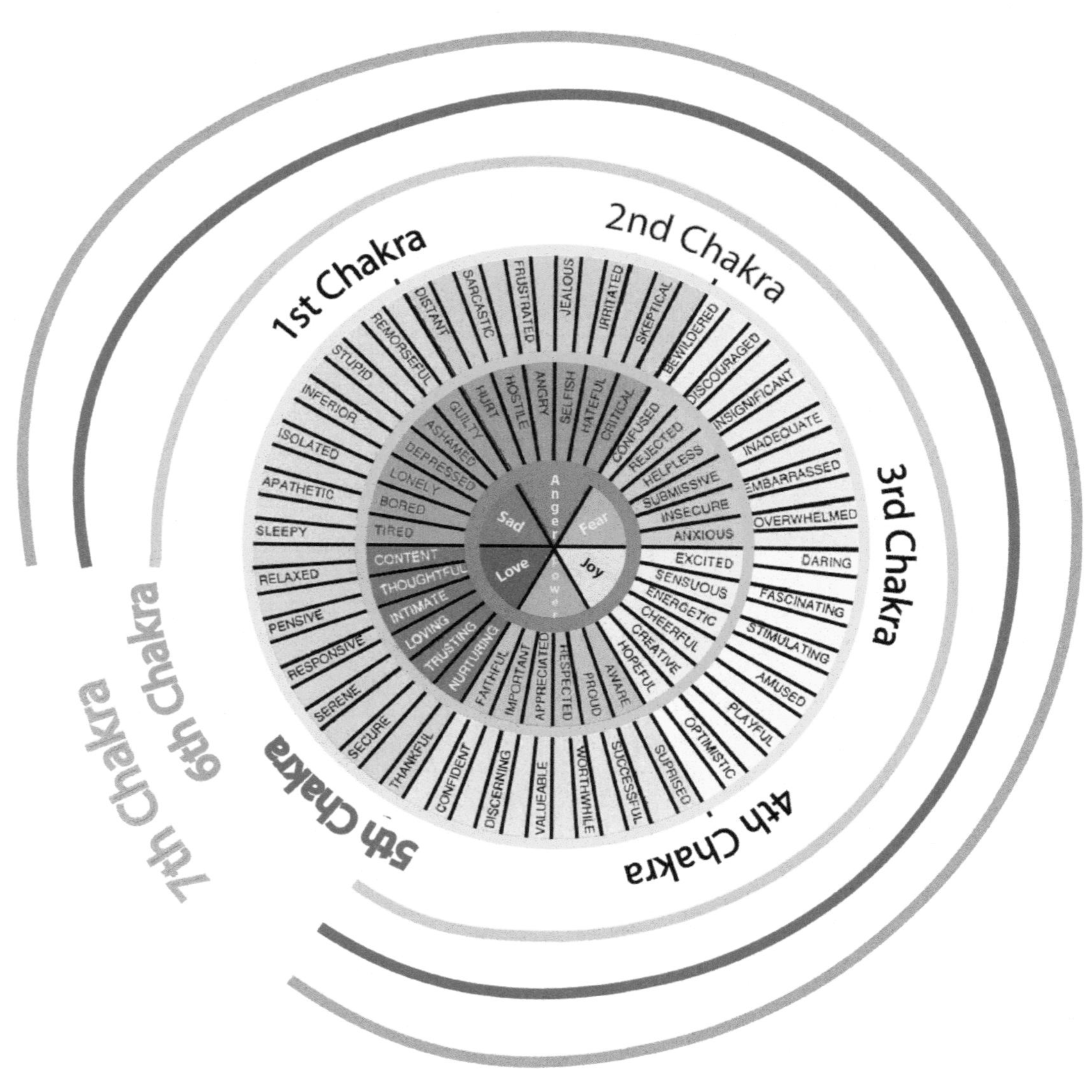

Chart of Emotions as it Relates to the MEI for the Cumulative Emotions Index

Step 1: Read, interact and respond to any workbook questions and journal entry. Decide (and then check mark) whether you will be using the workbook question or journal entry to populate the COE. Once decided, simply circle any and all applicable emotions that may have surfaced while you were working through that entry. When finished, proceed to checkmark applicable tense of time e.g., past, present and future as it relates to each emotion.

Step 2: Once all emotions and responses have been circled, simply assign a scale of intensity (from 1 to 10) as to how strong each and every emotion may have been experienced.

Step 3: Transfer all scaled intensities (from each circled emotion) of the COE to its correlating Master Emotions Index (MEI) on which is located on pages 290 - 293.

Step 4: Once finished entering information from that seasons MEI, simply add each row (of each emotion) downward toward the bottom line. These are your sum value totals.

Step 5: Transfer all values of each of the four seasons to the Cumulative Emotions Index (CEI) on page 294.

Chart of Emotions (COE) Question #1 Winter

Having procured and made the choice to work with *A Light From Within*: How do you feel?

This illustration shows how to record all the emotional responses from your Workbook questions and Journal entries.

Some questions generate more responses than others— just be sure to choose the closest emotion as it relates to your work at hand. Also remember to rate the "scale of intensity" (from 1 to 10) of each emotion so that it can be transferred to the "Master Emotions Index (MEI)" to populate the PEIM. Please see process the example just below.

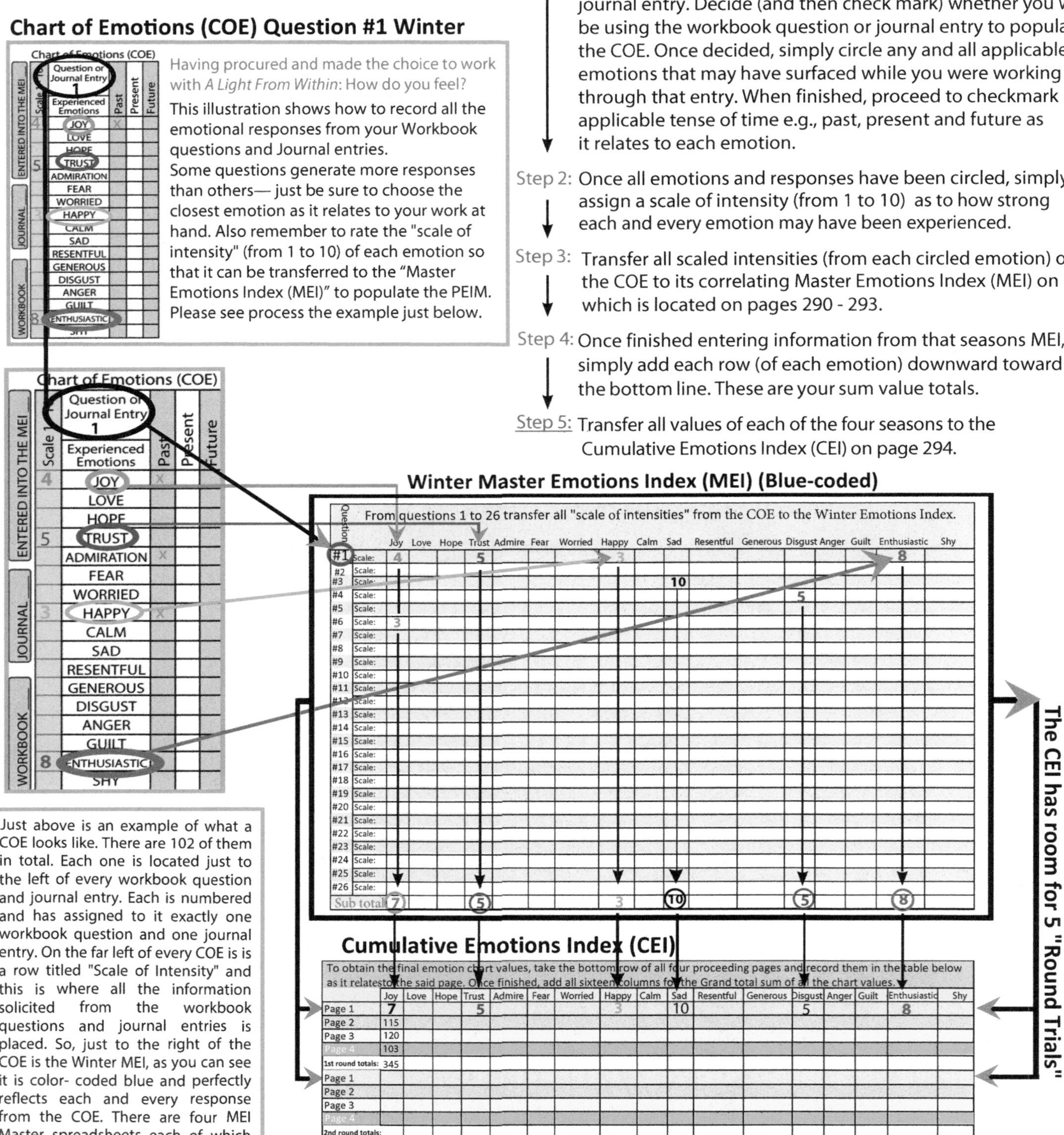

	Joy	Love	Hope	Trust	Admire	Fear	Worried	Happy	Calm	Sad	Resentful	Generous	Disgust	Anger	Guilt	Enthusiastic	Shy
Page 1	7			5				3		10			5			8	
Page 2	115																
Page 3	120																
Page 4	103																
1st round totals:	345																
Page 1																	
Page 2																	
Page 3																	
Page 4																	
2nd round totals:																	

Just above is an example of what a COE looks like. There are 102 of them in total. Each one is located just to the left of every workbook question and journal entry. Each is numbered and has assigned to it exactly one workbook question and one journal entry. On the far left of every COE is is a row titled "Scale of Intensity" and this is where all the information solicited from the workbook questions and journal entries is placed. So, just to the right of the COE is the Winter MEI, as you can see it is color- coded blue and perfectly reflects each and every response from the COE. There are four MEI Master spreadsheets each of which represents one of the four seasons. So you see, all 102 workbook questions and journal entries are dispersed and equally assigned to one of the four seasons of this book.

The CEI (above) reflects all your responses from each of the four different seasons of the MEI. Every question and journal entry that you had responded to is recorded into this cumulative spreadsheet. So, let's just say, for example, that of the books 102 workbook questions and journal entries, there were 35 unique occasions in which you had selected "Joy" as being one of the governing emotions. Consequently, you assigned 10 as being the "Scale of Intensity" experienced. Well, now you can see that these 10 points multiplied by 35 "occasions" turns out to be 350 points. These points are then transferred to the CEI to then populate the PEIM on pages 295 thru 297. It's really that simple. See more detailed instructions on the next page.

How to Populate Your Personal Emotions Imprint Map (PEIM)

Master Emotions Index (MEI) to Cumulative Emotions Index (CEI) to PEIM Workflow Process

Just below are 5 spreadsheets and 1 PEIM wheel. The first 4 spreadsheets are the MEI. They communicate the "Scale of Intensity" of any of the 17 emotions as it relates to the 102 COE of Part 1 of this book. (There are about 26 workbook questions, as well 26 journal entries— each belonging to one of the the 4 color-coded seasons.) The lower (cropped) spreadsheet is called the CEI and it expresses the "grand sum totals" of all four seasons MEI "sub totals." This way, all 17 rows (of each numbered emotion) can be added downward to derive at the "Grand Sum Totals." We then take these totals and call them "points)"all of which are used to populate and color out the PEIM wheel as is shown in the example below. The red lined arrows leading out horizontally from the last row of each MEI spreadsheet is the "sub total" line And, once all 17 columns of each season has been added, simply proceed to transfer these "sub total" numbers to the CEI as is shown in the flowchart below. You may remember, there are 5 opportunities ("1st through the 5th round totals") for which each can be used to create and/or update your PEIM wheel. In other words, think of your PEIM wheel as "a work in progress" and that as you progress through the book, you'll need to update it accordingly. Remember, for more information as to how to better manage your PEIM please visit www.alightfromwithin.com

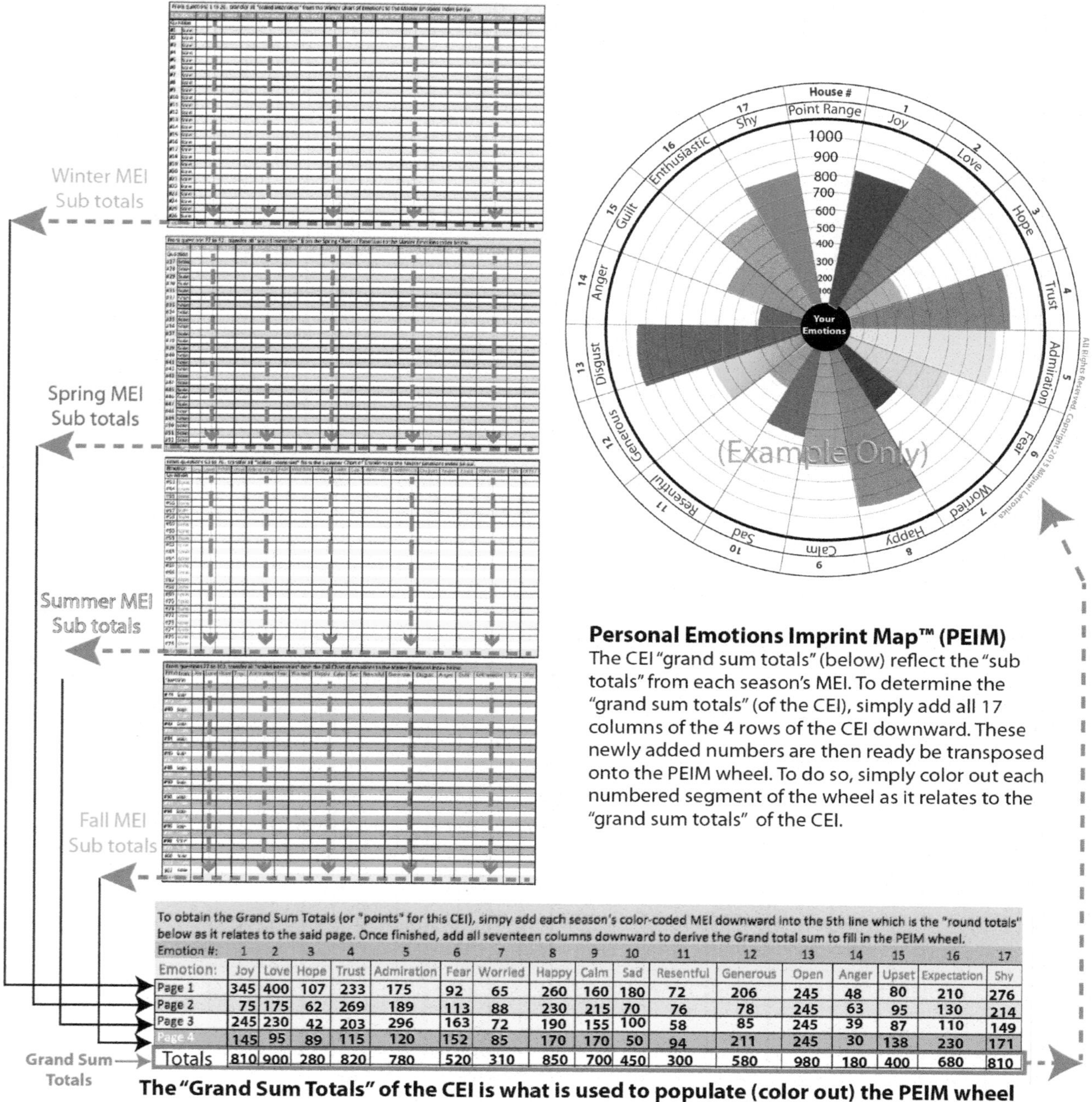

Personal Emotions Imprint Map™ (PEIM)
The CEI "grand sum totals" (below) reflect the "sub totals" from each season's MEI. To determine the "grand sum totals" (of the CEI), simply add all 17 columns of the 4 rows of the CEI downward. These newly added numbers are then ready be transposed onto the PEIM wheel. To do so, simply color out each numbered segment of the wheel as it relates to the "grand sum totals" of the CEI.

To obtain the Grand Sum Totals (or "points" for this CEI), simpy add each season's color-coded MEI downward into the 5th line which is the "round totals" below as it relates to the said page. Once finished, add all seventeen columns downward to derive the Grand total sum to fill in the PEIM wheel.

Emotion #:	1	2	3	4	5	6	7	8	9	10	11	12	13	14	15	16	17
Emotion:	Joy	Love	Hope	Trust	Admiration	Fear	Worried	Happy	Calm	Sad	Resentful	Generous	Open	Anger	Upset	Expectation	Shy
Page 1	345	400	107	233	175	92	65	260	160	180	72	206	245	48	80	210	276
Page 2	75	175	62	269	189	113	88	230	215	70	76	78	245	63	95	130	214
Page 3	245	230	42	203	296	163	72	190	155	100	58	85	245	39	87	110	149
Page 4	145	95	89	115	120	152	85	170	170	50	94	211	245	30	138	230	171
Totals	810	900	280	820	780	520	310	850	700	450	300	580	980	180	400	680	810

The "Grand Sum Totals" of the CEI is what is used to populate (color out) the PEIM wheel

Winter Master Emotions Index

Winter Questions 1 thru 26

From questions 1 to 26, transfer all "scaled intensities" from the Winter Chart of Emotions to the Master Emotions Index below.

		1	2	3	4	5	6	7	8	9	10	11	12	13	14	15	16	17
Emotion:		Joy	Love	Hope	Trust	Admiration	Fear	Worried	Happy	Calm	Sad	Resentful	Generous	Disgust	Anger	Guilt	Enthusiastic	Shy
Question																		
#1	Scale:																	
#2	Scale:																	
#3	Scale:																	
#4	Scale:																	
#5	Scale:																	
#6	Scale:																	
#7	Scale:																	
#8	Scale:																	
#9	Scale:																	
#10	Scale:																	
#11	Scale:																	
#12	Scale:																	
#13	Scale:																	
#14	Scale:																	
#15	Scale:																	
#16	Scale:																	
#17	Scale:																	
#18	Scale:																	
#19	Scale:																	
#20	Scale:																	
#21	Scale:																	
#22	Scale:																	
#23	Scale:																	
#24	Scale:																	
#25	Scale:																	
#26	Scale:																	
Sub Total																		

Spring Master Emotions Index

Spring Questions 27 - 52

From questions 27 to 52, transfer all "scaled intensities" from the Spring Chart of Emotions to the Master Emotions Index below.

		1	2	3	4	5	6	7	8	9	10	11	12	13	14	15	16	17
Emotion:		Joy	Love	Hope	Trust	Admiration	Fear	Worried	Happy	Calm	Sad	Resentful	Generous	Disgust	Anger	Guilt	Enthusiastic	Shy
Question																		
#27	Scale:																	
#28	Scale:																	
#29	Scale:																	
#30	Scale:																	
#31	Scale:																	
#32	Scale:																	
#33	Scale:																	
#34	Scale:																	
#35	Scale:																	
#36	Scale:																	
#37	Scale:																	
#38	Scale:																	
#39	Scale:																	
#40	Scale:																	
#41	Scale:																	
#42	Scale:																	
#43	Scale:																	
#44	Scale:																	
#45	Scale:																	
#46	Scale:																	
#47	Scale:																	
#48	Scale:																	
#49	Scale:																	
#50	Scale:																	
#51	Scale:																	
#52	Scale:																	
Sub Total																		

Summer Master Emotions Index

Summer Questions 53 - 76

From questions 53 to 76, transfer all "scaled intensities" from the Summer Chart of Emotions to the Master Emotions Index below.

	1	2	3	4	5	6	7	8	9	10	11	12	13	14	15	16	17
Emotion:	Joy	Love	Hope	Trust	Admiration	Fear	Worried	Happy	Calm	Sad	Resentful	Generous	Disgust	Anger	Guilt	Enthusiastic	Shy
Question																	
#53 Scale:																	
#54 Scale:																	
#55 Scale:																	
#56 Scale:																	
#57 Scale:																	
#58 Scale:																	
#59 Scale:																	
#60 Scale:																	
#61 Scale:																	
#62 Scale:																	
#63 Scale:																	
#64 Scale:																	
#65 Scale:																	
#66 Scale:																	
#67 Scale:																	
#68 Scale:																	
#69 Scale:																	
#70 Scale:																	
#71 Scale:																	
#72 Scale:																	
#73 Scale:																	
#74 Scale:																	
#75 Scale:																	
#76 Scale:																	
Sub Total																	

Fall Master Emotions Index

Fall Questions 77 - 102

From questions 77 to 102, transfer all "scaled intensities" from the Fall Chart of emotions to the Master Emotions Index below.

		1	2	3	4	5	6	7	8	9	10	11	12	13	14	15	16	17
Emotion: Question		Joy	Love	Hope	Trust	Admiration	Fear	Worried	Happy	Calm	Sad	Resentful	Generous	Disgust	Anger	Guilt	Enthusiastic	Shy
#77	Scale:																	
#78	Scale:																	
#79	Scale:																	
#80	Scale:																	
#81	Scale:																	
#82	Scale:																	
#83	Scale:																	
#84	Scale:																	
#85	Scale:																	
#86	Scale:																	
#87	Scale:																	
#88	Scale:																	
#89	Scale:																	
#90	Scale:																	
#91	Scale:																	
#92	Scale:																	
#93	Scale:																	
#94	Scale:																	
#95	Scale:																	
#96	Scale:																	
#97	Scale:																	
#98	Scale:																	
#99	Scale:																	
100	Scale:																	
101	Scale:																	
102	Scale:																	
Sub Total:																		

Cumulative Emotions Index (CEI)

Questions From all Four Seasons

Trial:	House:	1	2	3	4	5	6	7	8	9	10	11	12	13	14	15	16	17	Season
	Emotion:	Joy	Love	Hope	Trust	Admiration	Fear	Worried	Happy	Calm	Sad	Resentful	Generous	Disgust	Anger	Guilt	Enthusiastic	Shy	
1st Round	Page 289																		Winter
	Page 290																		Spring
	Page 291																		Summer
	Page 292																		Fall
	1st round totals:																		
2nd Round	Page 289																		Winter
	Page 290																		Spring
	Page 291																		Summer
	Page 292																		Fall
	2nd round totals:																		
3rd Round	Page 289																		Winter
	Page 290																		Spring
	Page 291																		Summer
	Page 292																		Fall
	3rd round totals:																		
4th Round	Page 289																		Winter
	Page 290																		Spring
	Page 291																		Summer
	Page 292																		Fall
	4th round totals:																		
5th Round	Page 289																		Winter
	Page 290																		Spring
	Page 291																		Summer
	Page 292																		Fall
	5th round totals:																		

Place all color-coded sub totals of each seasons MEI into the CEI above. Please note: there are exactly five trial rounds or opportunities with which to recalculate and/or update your "Preliminary" or "Continuing" PEIM wheel. Once finished populating all four rows of each season, simply add all 17 columns downward: These are your "Grand sum totals" or "Points" for which you must populate by coloring in all 17 segments of your Personal Emotions Imprint Map.

Before Even Beginning to Work With This Book, Where do You Think You're at on the PEIM Wheel of Emotions?

The PEIM wheel below is self-rating and is designed for you to hand color. Each house represents the overall strength of each emotion. The wheel is rated from 100 to 1000. Thus, helping you to plot the characteristics and contrasts of your primary and secondary, positive and negative emotions. This PEIM below has nothing to do with the workbook questions and journal entry exercises; rather it is intended to be a *picture-in-time*: A purview as to where you think you're at emotionally. So, before even beginning to work with this book— please complete it. Then, later on, you will have an opportunity to compare it to the "Continuing PEIM" which is located on page 297. Sometimes we believe ourselves to accurately know how emotionally well-balanced we are, but then, especially after working with *A Light From Within,* we see ourselves as being very different from what we had initially thought. Every person seems to make their own intuitive sense as to what their PEIM wheel means to them. Because feelings are subjective, they often act as a predictor to the ebb and flow of life. The PEIM is a birds-eye-view reflection of your life. And just like the weather-- it changes!

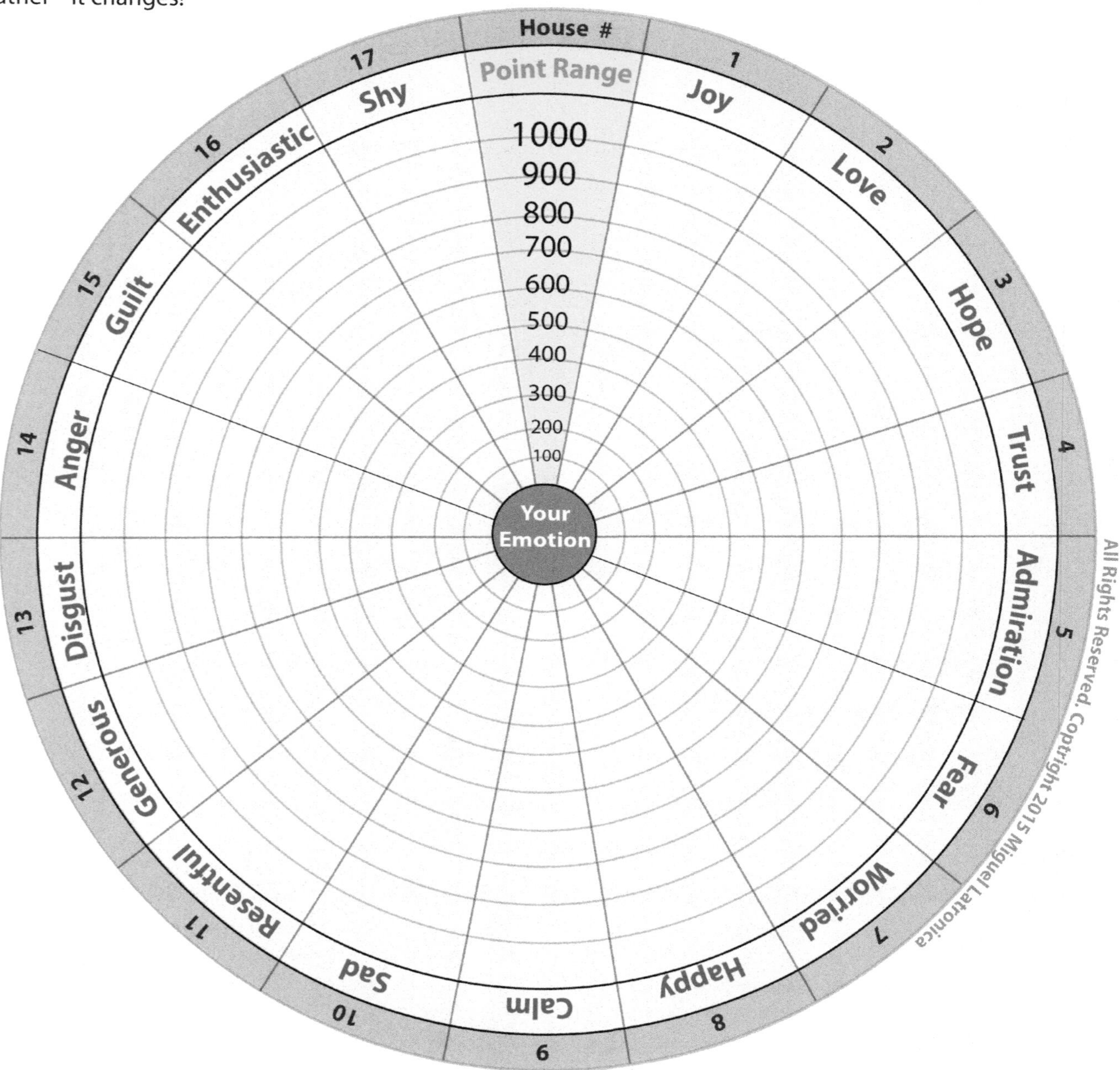

The PEIM wheel above has nothing to do with the workbook exercises. Therefore, it should be filled in by coloring out (with crayons or colored pencils) each of the 17 segments: before even beginning to work with the workbook questions and journal entry exercises from Part One of this book.

Preliminary Personal Emotions Imprint Map (in tenths)

This PEIM is based on tenths, and it is based on the first third of this book. The concluding PEIM (next page) is to be started once this "preliminary" wheel has been fully colored out.

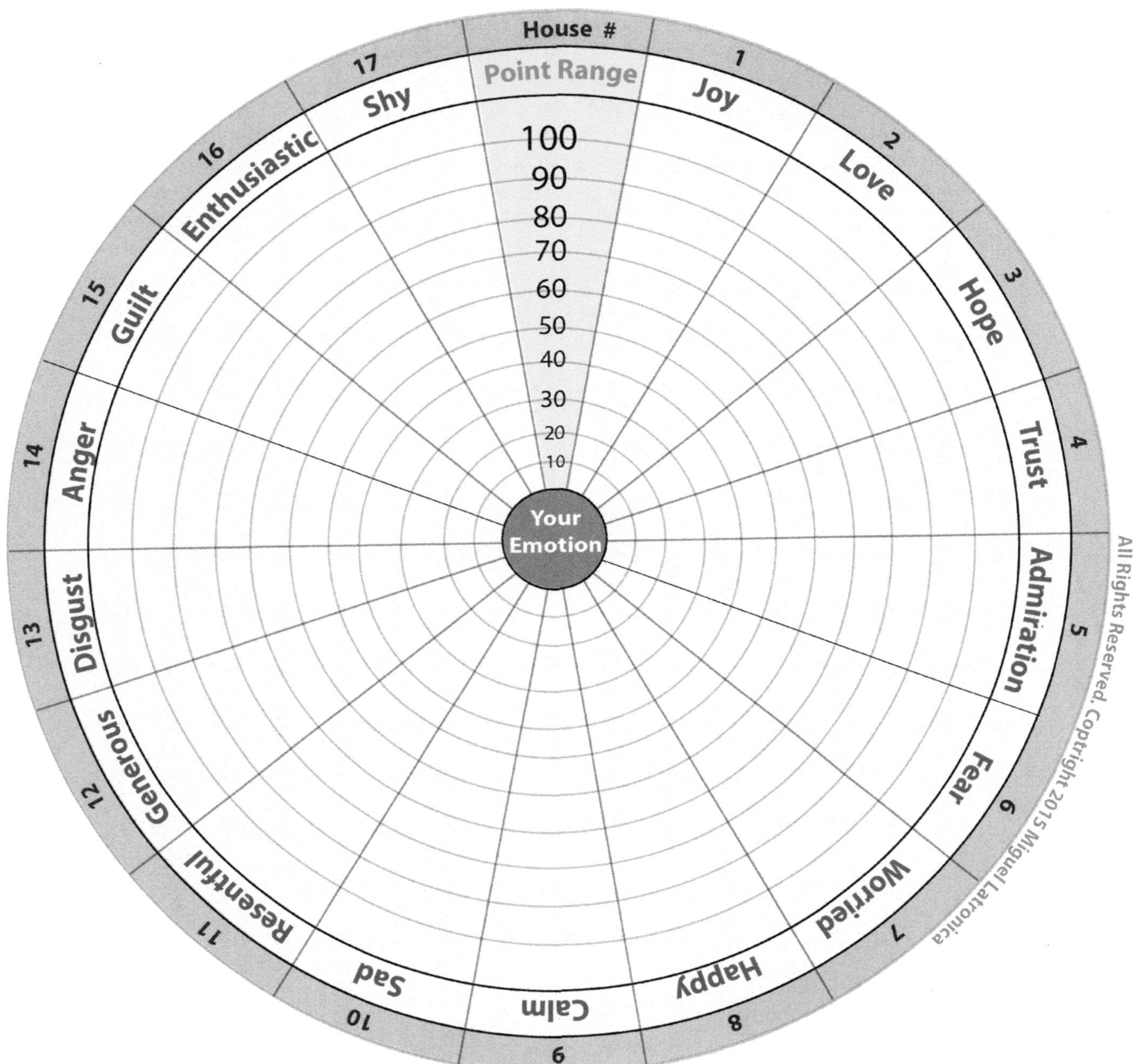

Preliminary Personal Emotions Imprint Map (PEIM)— Based on tenths

In the above PEIM wheel there are 17 fields that contain the various emotions used and referenced in throughout ALFW. The very top of the chart determines how far out from the center of the wheel that you should color or gray-out as it pertains to the grand totals of the CEI on page 294. To complete your PEIM, please use any of the "round totals" from the CEI and transfer them to their respective, numbered house as is pictured above. For example, the 1st house above is the House of Joy and it correlates with the first column (Joy) in the CEI. So, accordingly, color out each house above so that is congruent and matches all the "Grand Sum Totals" on the CEI. Please see page 288-289 for further instructions on personalizing your PEIM.

Concluding Personal Emotions Imprint Map (in hundredths)

This PEIM is based on hundredths. It should be used once you have completed or reached the 100 point limit from any of the 17 emotions from the PEIM on the previous page.

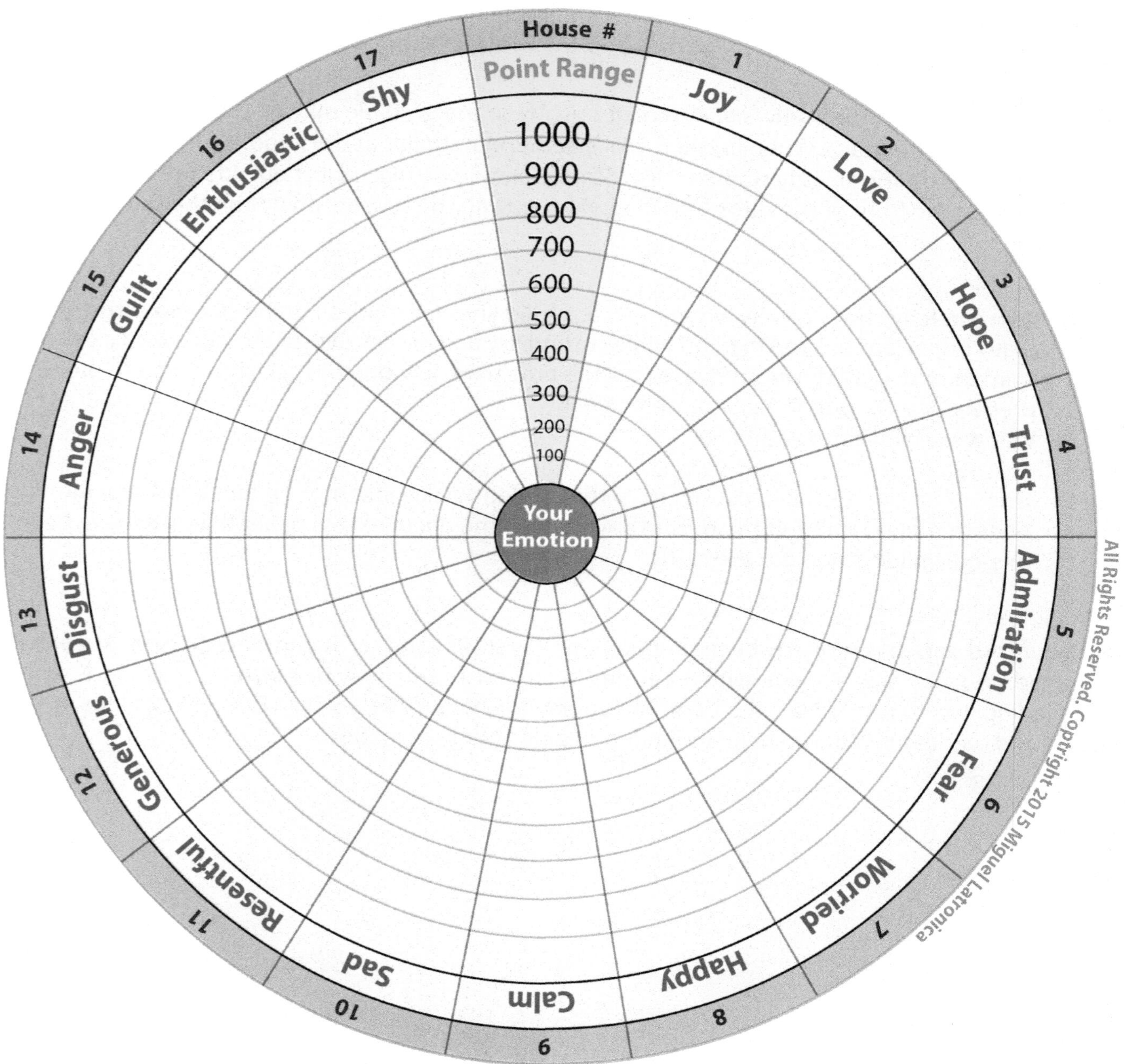

Concluding Personal Emotions Imprint Map (PEIM)— Based on hundredths

In the above PEIM wheel there are 17 fields that contain the various emotions used and referenced in throughout ALFW. The very top of the chart determines how far out from the center of the wheel that you should color or *gray-out* as it pertains to the grand totals of the CEI on page 294. To complete your PEIM, please use any of the "round totals" from the CEI and transfer them to their respective, numbered house as is pictured above. For example, the 1st house above is the House of Joy and it correlates with the first column (Joy) in the CEI. So, accordingly, color out each house above so that is congruent and matches all the "Grand Sum Totals" on the CEI. Please see page 288-289 for further instructions on personalizing your PEIM.

Directions for cutting out the 52 card deck

Step 1- With a pair of scissors, very carefully cut out pages 297 through 310. It is important to use only the first 2 inches (near the tips of the scissors) as this will help you to cut more closely along the inside edge of the book.

Step 2- Once all 8 physical pages have been cut and separated from the book, simply place the front sides of of the cards (Yoga Bent Method™) so that they are facing up toward the sky.

Step 3- Align and stack the corners of all 8 pages neatly so that a staple may be put into place at all four corners of the stack. When finished, place additional staples at the middle edge of each of the four sides of the already stapled stack. Staples should be placed just outside the solid black lines on the front of the cards—so that when cutting the scissors do not hit the staples.

Step 4- Very carefully cut as closely along the black solid lines (all 4 sides) of the stacked cards. One really important to keep in mind while cutting: try and not let the sheets of stacked cards shift from their stapled position. Please take the time to review our video. It shows you to properly prepare and cut out all 52 cards of the deck.
Visit www.alightfromwithin.net

Step 5- Once all cards have been cut out from the stapled stack, look through them and separate the ones that may need trimming. Trim away any of the uncut excess paper that may have been missed while cutting out the cards.

Once your card deck has properly been prepared, simply shuffle the cards and start playing. As earlier mentioned, you may play alone or with others: most any card game may be played. The cards are a fun and engaging way to learn about the book and yourself. What's more, you can develop all kinds of personalized games as well. You're really limited to only your imagination!

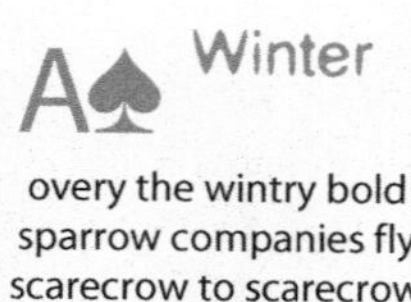
Winter

overy the wintry bold
sparrow companies fly
scarecrow to scarecrow
–Sazanami

Trisula

God's supply is in abundance now that you accept His gifts.

Tadasana
[Mountain Pose]

2♠ Winter

my very bone-ends made
contact with the icy quilts
of deep december
–Busun

Sikhara

I have the strength of ten because my heart is filled with the light of truth.

Virabhadrasana II
Warrior 2 Pose]

3♠ Winter

in my dark winter
lying ill... at last i ask
how fares my
neighbor
–Basho

Candrakala

Be a living temple in which God dwells.

Virabhadrasana I
Warrior I Pose]

Winter

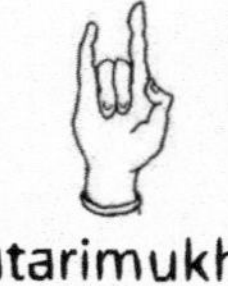

a thousand roof-tops a
thousand market voices...
winter-morning mist
–Busun

Katarimukha

You are that which you seek

Virabhadrasana III
Warrior III Pose]

5♠ Winter

first snow last night... there
across the morning bay
sudden mountain-white
–Shiki

Pataka

You must see the best in others before you see the good in yourself.

Utkatasana
[Chair Pose]

Winter

there in the winter color
of the water moves
transluscent fish
–Raizen

Ardha Chandra

There is no destiny but what you yourself make. All is well because you think it is.

Tadasana Urdhva Hastasana [Half Moon Pose

7♠ Winter

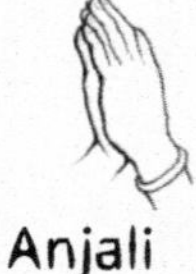

see the red berries... fallen
like little footprints
on the garden snow
–Shiki

Anjali

Great things were never achieved in a day. Their creation was formed by constant toil and thought.

Vrkshasana
[Tree Pose]

7♠

8♠ Winter

midnight wanderer walking
through the snowy street...
echoing dog-bark
–Shiki

Suci

Hate is poison, slowly seeping into the heart, bringing a cruel death in its wake.

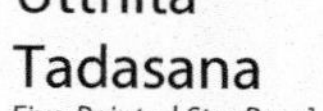

Utthita Tadasana
Five-Pointed Star Pose]

9♠ Winter

blinding wild snow
blows, whirls and drifts
about me... in this world
alone
-Chora

Tamracuda

Love all alike, free from attachment.

Utthita Parsvakonasana
Extended Side Angle Pose]

Winter
Spring
Summer
Fall
Yoga Bent Method®

Winter
Spring
Summer
Fall
Yoga Bent Method®

Winter
Spring
Summer
Fall
Yoga Bent Method®

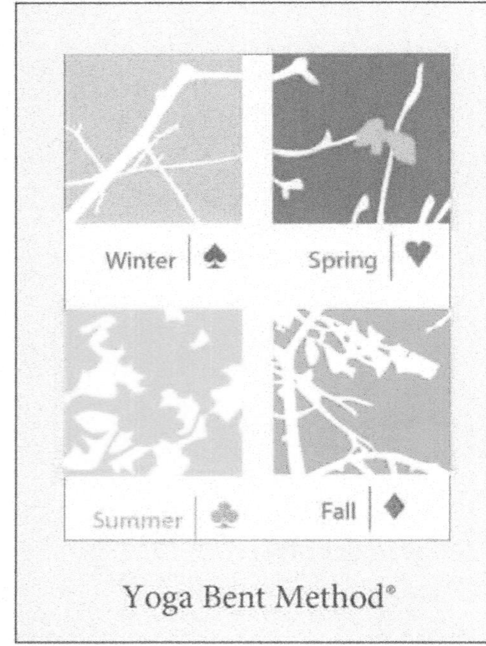
Winter
Spring
Summer
Fall
Yoga Bent Method®

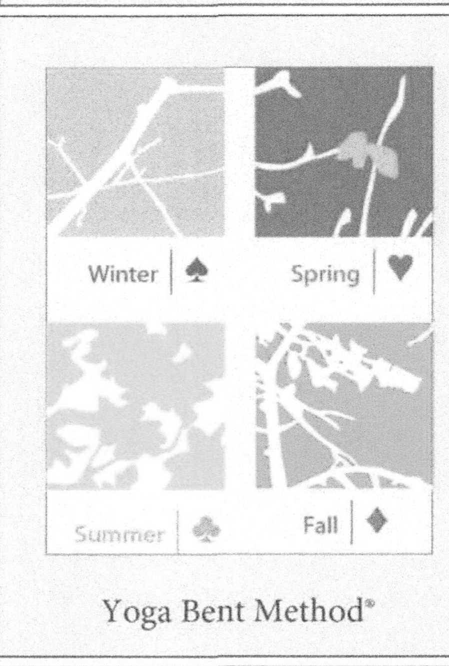
Winter
Spring
Summer
Fall
Yoga Bent Method®

Winter
Spring
Summer
Fall
Yoga Bent Method®

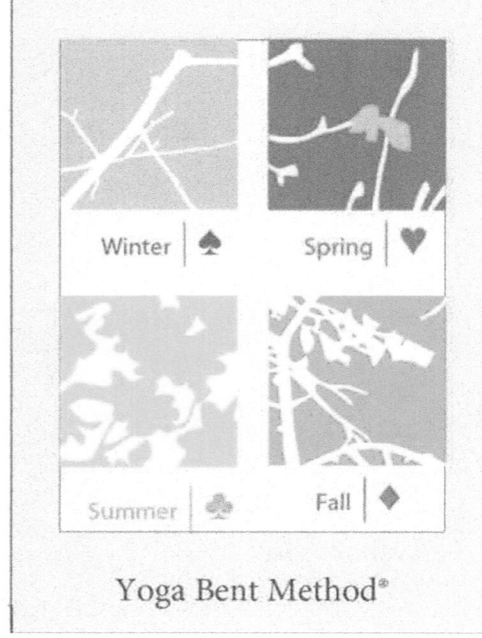
Winter
Spring
Summer
Fall
Yoga Bent Method®

Winter
Spring
Summer
Fall
Yoga Bent Method®

Winter
Spring
Summer
Fall
Yoga Bent Method®

10♠ Winter

from my tiny roof
smooth...soft... still-white
snow melts in melody
-Issa

Guruda

My body is the outer layer of my mind.

Garudasana

[Eagle Pose]

 Winter

look at that stray cat
sleeping...snug under the
eaves in the whistling snow
-Taigi

Mrgasirsa

All craving and seeking for love in a form is the inner urge to find God.

Uttanasana

[Standing Forward Fold Pose]

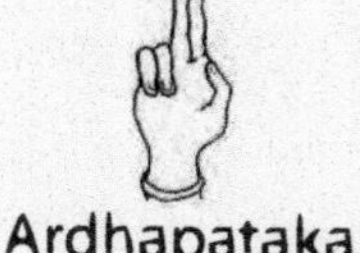

solitary crow...
companioning
my progress over
snowy fields
-Senna

Ardhapataka

Be like a river of supply starting and ending in the same place. From the ocean of life you take, and the ocean of life you give.

Utthita Trikonasana

[Triangle Pose]

 Winter

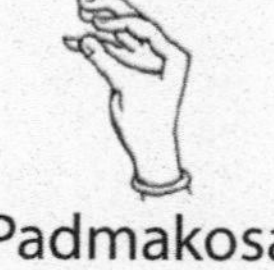

poet nightingale... will i
hear your later verses
in the vale of death
–Anon

Padmakosa

Your tomorrow is the creation of today.

Parivrtti Trikonasana

Revolved Triangle Pose]

Winter
Spring
Summer
Fall
Yoga Bent Method®

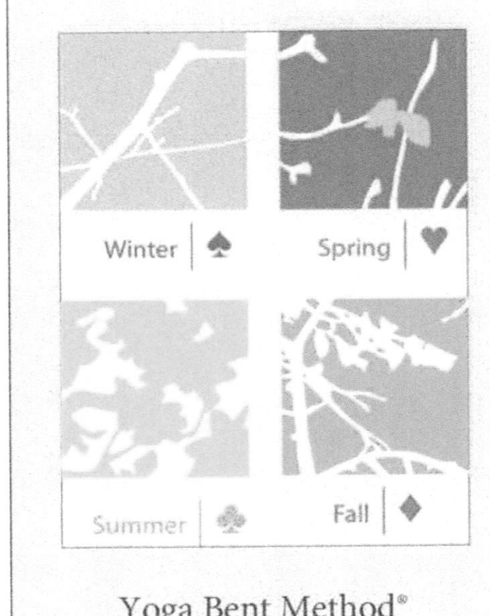
Winter
Spring
Summer
Fall
Yoga Bent Method®

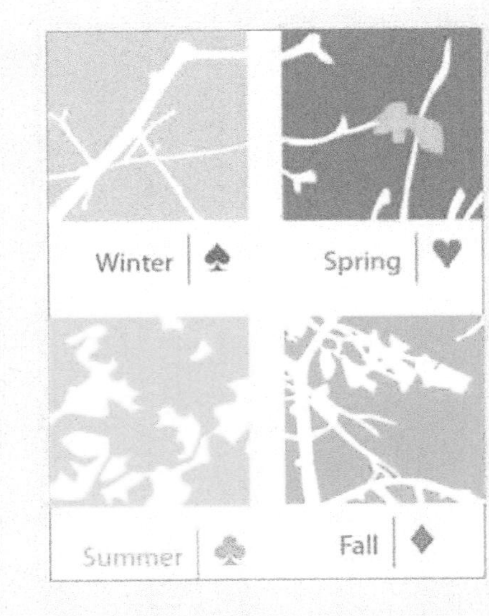
Winter
Spring
Summer
Fall
Yoga Bent Method®

Winter
Spring
Summer
Fall
Yoga Bent Method®

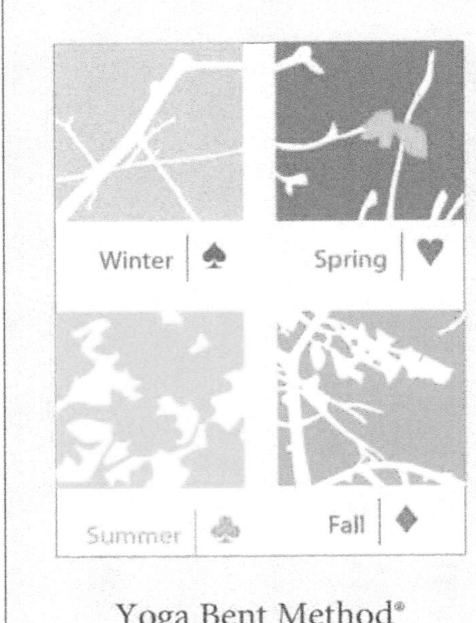
Winter
Spring
Summer
Fall
Yoga Bent Method®

Winter
Spring
Summer
Fall
Yoga Bent Method®

Winter
Spring
Summer
Fall
Yoga Bent Method®

Winter
Spring
Summer
Fall
Yoga Bent Method®

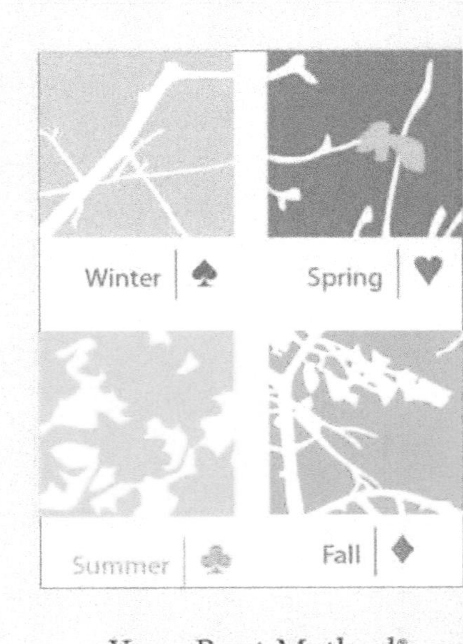
Winter
Spring
Summer
Fall
Yoga Bent Method®

A ♥ Spring
rain-obliterated...
the river, some roofs,
a bridge without a shore
–Basho
Kangulagula
It is through the invisible
vibration of love that
trust in myself and others.
Bhjangasana
(Cobra Pose)
A ♥

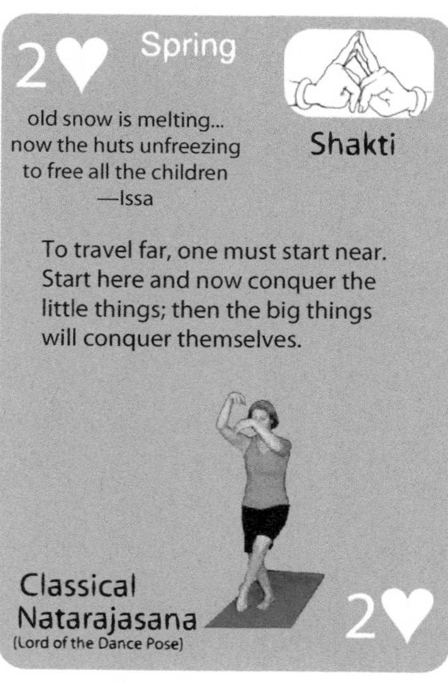
2 ♥ Spring
old snow is melting...
now the huts unfreezing
to free all the children
—Issa
Shakti
To travel far, one must start near.
Start here and now conquer the
little things; then the big things
will conquer themselves.
Classical
Natarajasana
(Lord of the Dance Pose)
2 ♥

3 ♥ Spring
now wild geese
return... what
draws them crying
all the long dark
night
–Roka
Katakavardhana
Love is the vibration of
all unselfish joy— the
perfect oneness with
vibrant life.
Dandasana
(Staff Pose)
3 ♥

4 ♥ Spring
cold morning rainfall...
mingling all their gleaming
horns oxen at the fence
–Ranko
Svastika
Strength comes from purity of the heart.
Parsvattonasana
(Intense Side Stretch Pose)
4 ♥

5 ♥ Spring
hazy ponded moon and
pale night sky are broken...
bungling black frog...
–Busun
Sandamsa
Love and the world is yours.
Ardha Salabhasana
(Grasshopper/Locust Pose)
5 ♥

6 ♥ Spring
an april shower ... see that
thirsty mouse lapping
river sumida
-Issa
Musti
Open wide the portals of the heart and
let the sunlight warm it and burn out all
toxins.
Prasarita
Padottanasana
(Wide-Angle Standing Forward Bend)
6 ♥

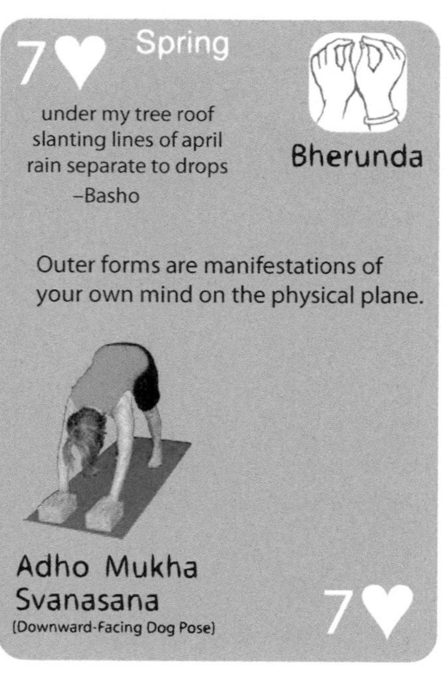
7 ♥ Spring
under my tree roof
slanting lines of april
rain separate to drops
–Basho
Bherunda
Outer forms are manifestations of
your own mind on the physical plane.
Adho Mukha
Svanasana
(Downward-Facing Dog Pose)
7 ♥

8 ♥ Spring
bird droppings pattern
the purples and the
yellows of my iris petals
–Busun
Matsya
When desire ceases bliss follows.
Matsyasana
(Fish Pose)
8 ♥

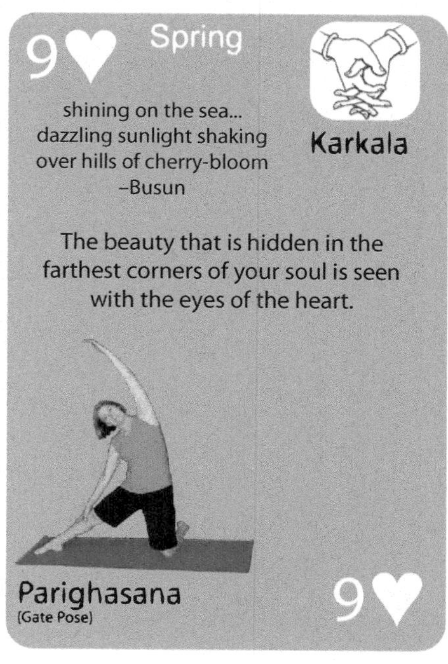
9 ♥ Spring
shining on the sea...
dazzling sunlight shaking
over hills of cherry-bloom
–Busun
Karkala
The beauty that is hidden in the
farthest corners of your soul is seen
with the eyes of the heart.
Parighasana
(Gate Pose)
9 ♥

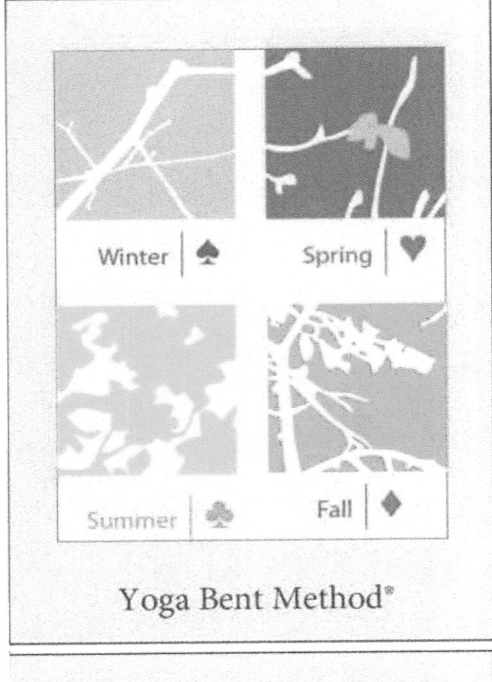
Winter ♠
Spring ♥
Summer ♣
Fall ♦
Yoga Bent Method®

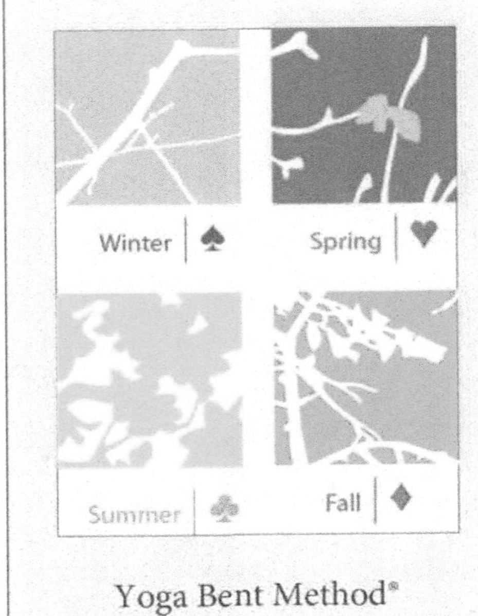
Winter ♠
Spring ♥
Summer ♣
Fall ♦
Yoga Bent Method®

Winter ♠
Spring ♥
Summer ♣
Fall ♦
Yoga Bent Method®

Winter ♠
Spring ♥
Summer ♣
Fall ♦
Yoga Bent Method®

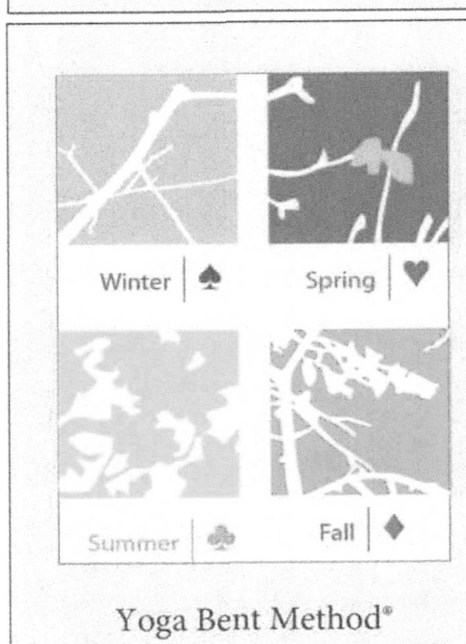
Winter ♠
Spring ♥
Summer ♣
Fall ♦
Yoga Bent Method®

Winter ♠
Spring ♥
Summer ♣
Fall ♦
Yoga Bent Method®

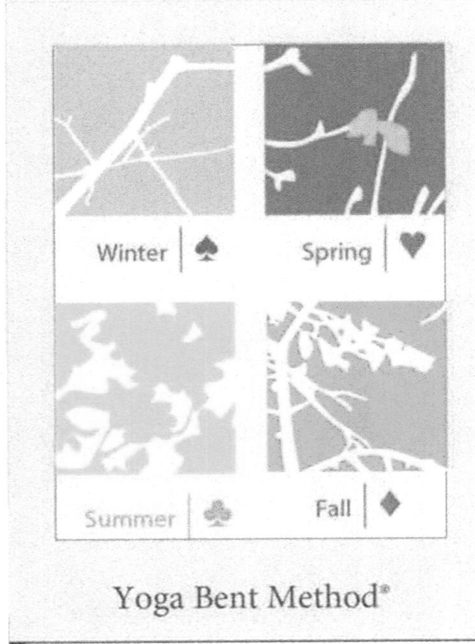
Winter ♠
Spring ♥
Summer ♣
Fall ♦
Yoga Bent Method®

Winter ♠
Spring ♥
Summer ♣
Fall ♦
Yoga Bent Method®

Winter ♠
Spring ♥
Summer ♣
Fall ♦
Yoga Bent Method®

10♥
Pasa
moonlight stillness lights
the petals falling... falling...
on the silenced lute
–Shiki
Activity is God in action.
Pashimottanasana
[Intense West Stretch Pose]
10♥

J♥
Hakini
come now, play with me...
fatherless motherless
dear little sparrow-child
-Issa
See the best in yourself
and others will follow suit.
Baddha Konasana
[Bound Angle Pose]
J♥

Q♥
Hamsasya
no bold rain-cloud for
a hundred miles around...
dares brave the peonies
-Busun
Watch all thy words. They are
the creator, the preserver and
the destroyer of thy destiny.
Sukhasana
[Easy Sitting Pose]
Q♥

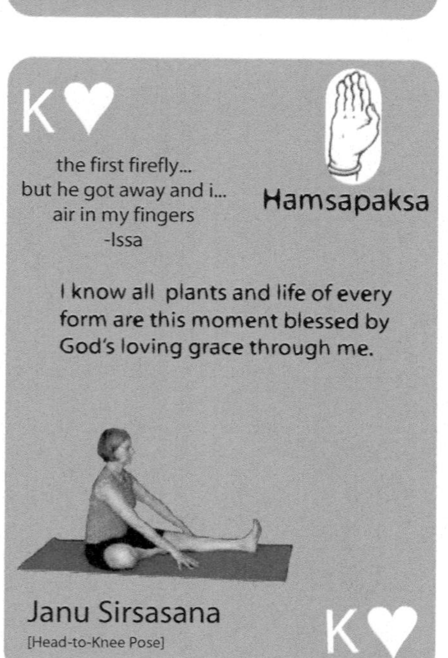
K♥
Hamsapaksa
the first firefly...
but he got away and i...
air in my fingers
-Issa
I know all plants and life of every
form are this moment blessed by
God's loving grace through me.
Janu Sirsasana
[Head-to-Knee Pose]
K♥

Yoga Bent Method®

Yoga Bent Method®

Yoga Bent Method®

Yoga Bent Method®

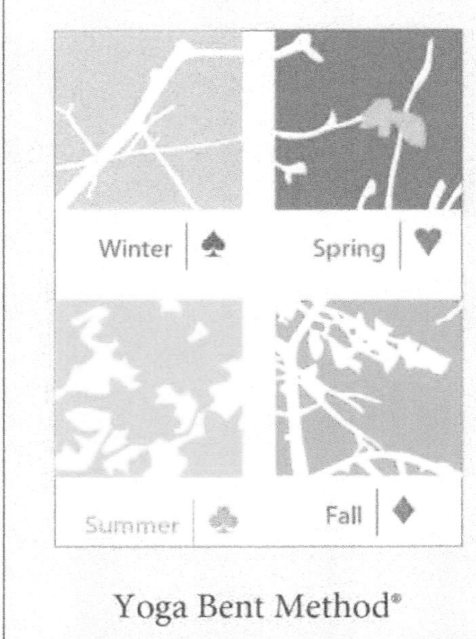

Yoga Bent Method®

Yoga Bent Method®

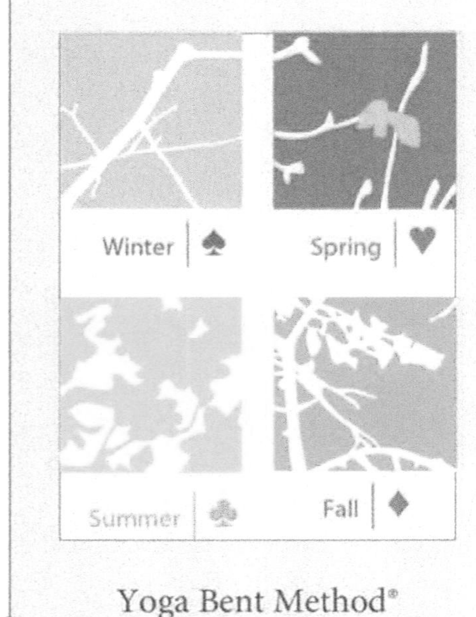

Yoga Bent Method®

Yoga Bent Method®

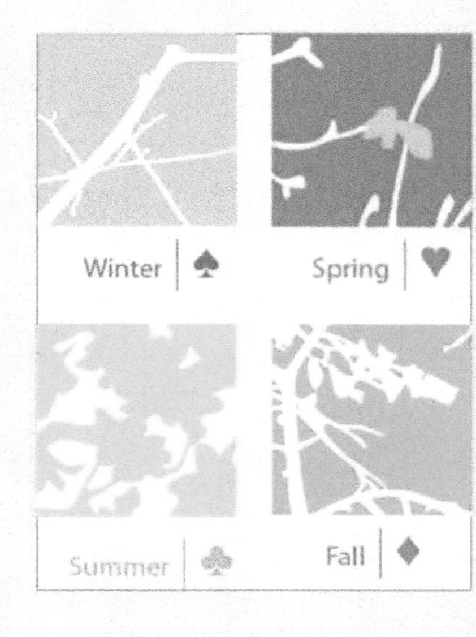

Yoga Bent Method®

A♥ Summer
with that new clothing
alas...spring
has been buried
in that wooden chest
–Saikaku
Kilaka
All is good; there is no evil in
God's loving eyes.
Marichyasana I
(Ray of Light Pose)
A♥

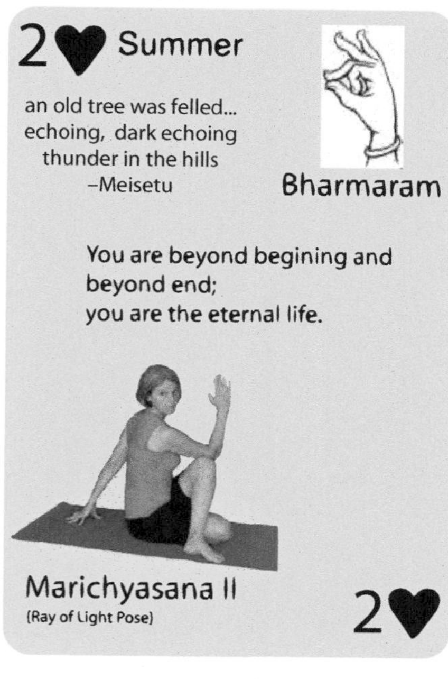
2♥ Summer
an old tree was felled...
echoing, dark echoing
thunder in the hills
–Meisetu
Bharmaram
You are beyond begining and
beyond end;
you are the eternal life.
Marichyasana II
(Ray of Light Pose)
2♥

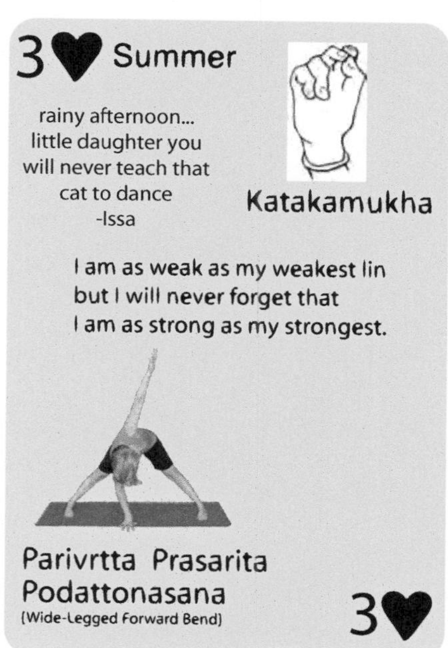
3♥ Summer
rainy afternoon...
little daughter you
will never teach that
cat to dance
-Issa
Katakamukha
I am as weak as my weakest lin
but I will never forget that
I am as strong as my strongest.
Parivrtta Prasarita
Podattonasana
(Wide-Legged Forward Bend)
3♥

4♥ Summer
squads of frogs jumped
in when they heard the
plaunk-plash of a single frog
–Wakyu
Ganesha
Where ever there is God, there is
beauty, and God is everywhere.
Gumakhasana
(Cow Face Pose)
4♥

5♥ Summer
moon-in-the-water turned
a white sumersault...yes
and went floating off
–Ryota
Makara
See beauty in seeming uglines
Ustrasana
(Camel Pose)
5♥

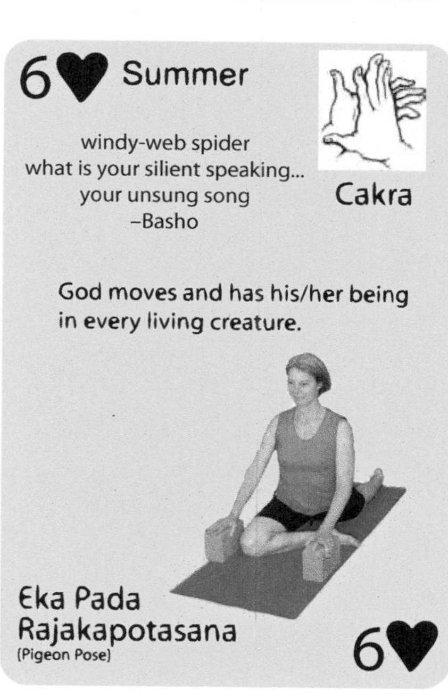
6♥ Summer
windy-web spider
what is your silient speaking...
your unsung song
–Basho
Cakra
God moves and has his/her being
in every living creature.
Eka Pada
Rajakapotasana
(Pigeon Pose)
6♥

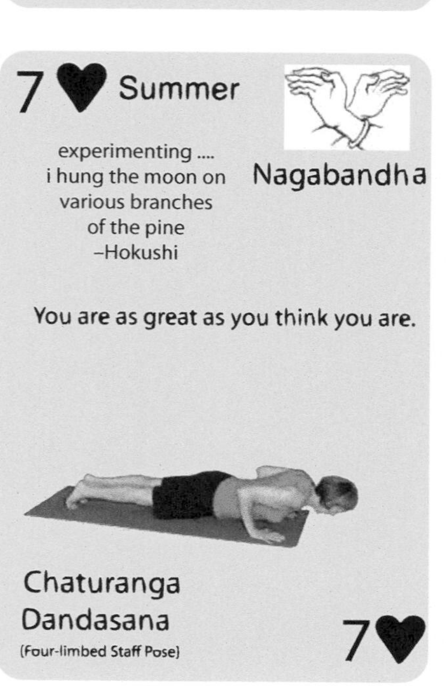
7♥ Summer
experimenting ....
i hung the moon on
various branches
of the pine
–Hokushi
Nagabandha
You are as great as you think you are.
Chaturanga
Dandasana
(Four-limbed Staff Pose)
7♥

8♥ Summer
on his garden path this
sparrow scatters pebbles...
man forgotten
-Shoha
Simhamukha
God is the one and only that has the right to
judge right or wrong. He and He alone can
see the great plan.
Urdvha Mukha
Svanasana
(Upward-Facing Dog Pose)
8♥

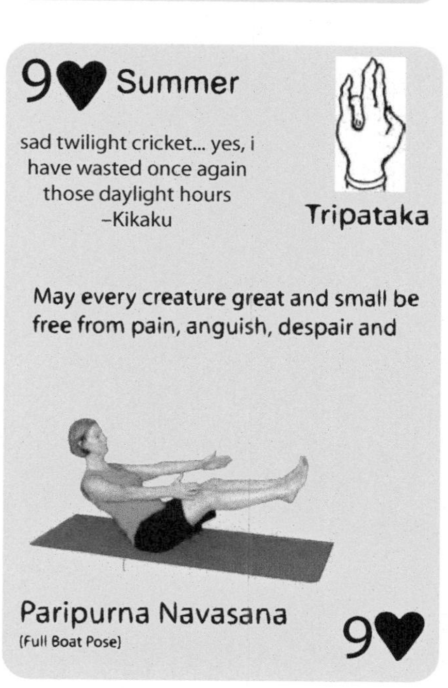
9♥ Summer
sad twilight cricket... yes, i
have wasted once again
those daylight hours
–Kikaku
Tripataka
May every creature great and small be
free from pain, anguish, despair and
Paripurna Navasana
(Full Boat Pose)
9♥

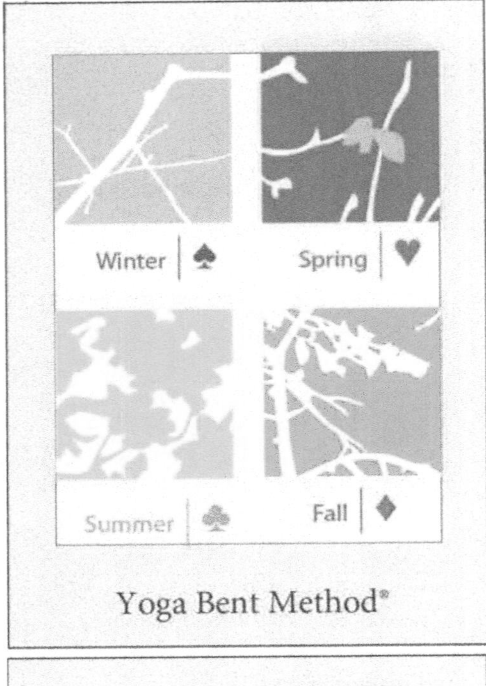

Yoga Bent Method®

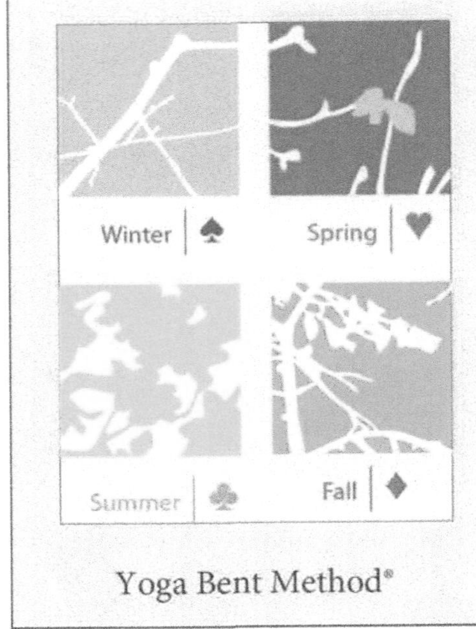

Yoga Bent Method®

Yoga Bent Method®

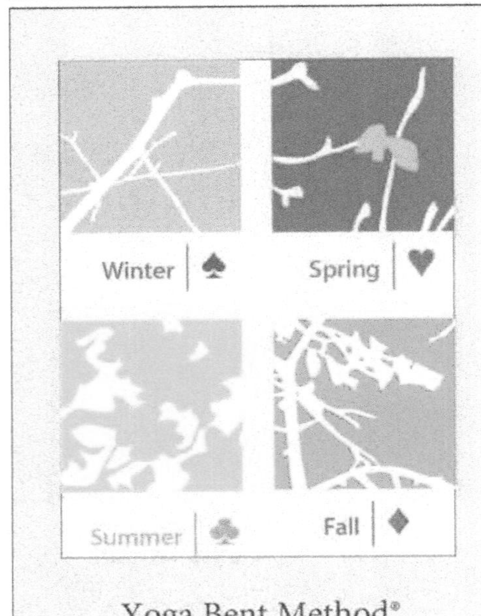

Yoga Bent Method®

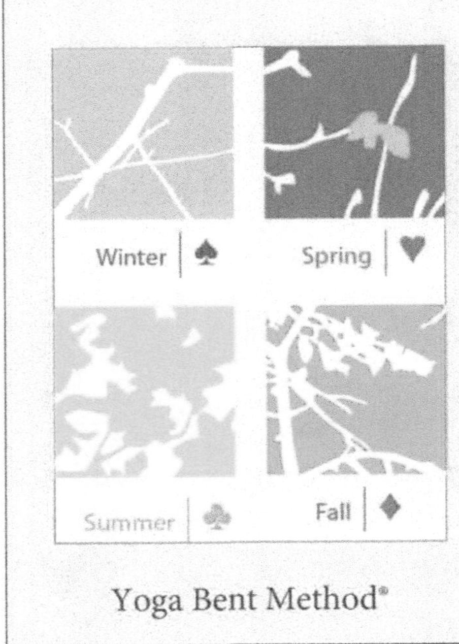

Yoga Bent Method®

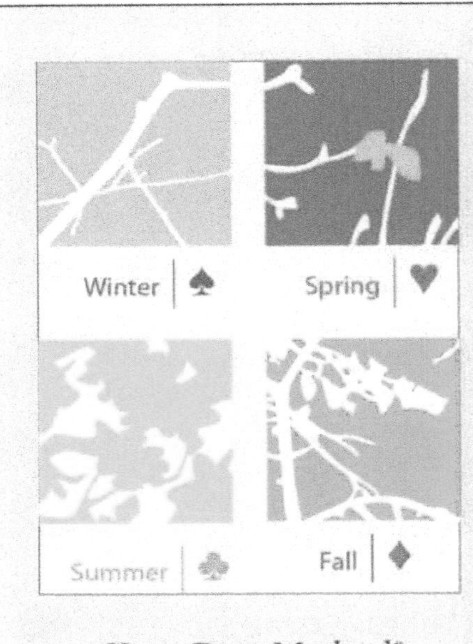

Yoga Bent Method®

Yoga Bent Method®

Yoga Bent Method®

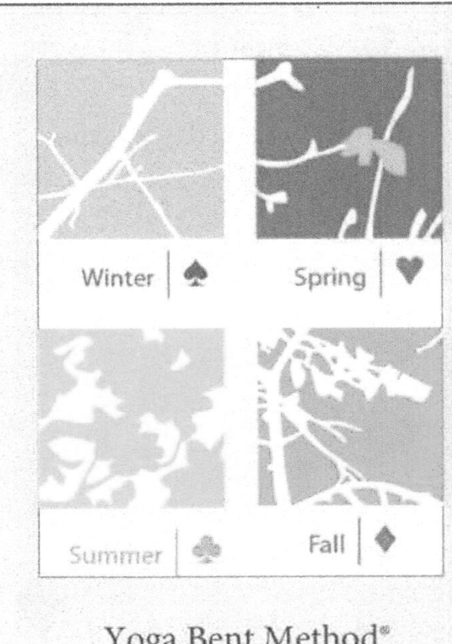

Yoga Bent Method®

10♥ Summer
Khatva
the night was hot...
stripped to the waist the
snail enjoyed the
moonlight
-Issa
The only truly wise person is one who
feels him or herself one with Nature
Bharadvajasana
[Bharadvaja's Twist Pose]
10♥

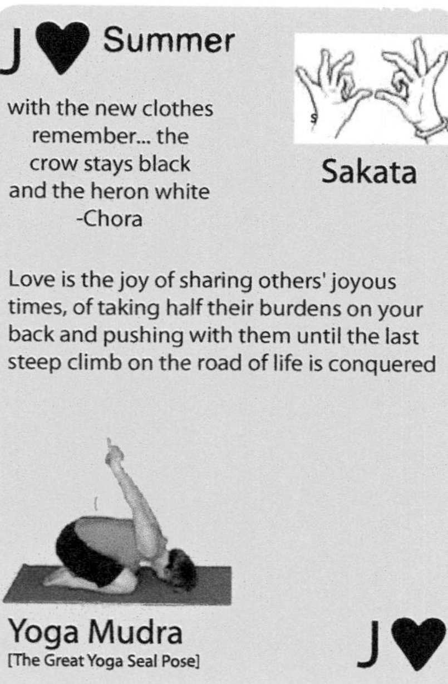
J♥ Summer
Sakata
with the new clothes
remember... the
crow stays black
and the heron white
-Chora
Love is the joy of sharing others' joyous
times, of taking half their burdens on your
back and pushing with them until the last
steep climb on the road of life is conquered
Yoga Mudra
[The Great Yoga Seal Pose]
J♥

Q♥ Summer
Puspaputa
a summer shower... along
all the street, servants
slapping shut shutters
–Shiki
Vibrations of nature are the very
keystone of my heart-felt being
Supta
Matseyendrasana
[Lord of the Fish Pose]
Q♥

K♥ Summer
Arala
suddenly you light and as
suddenly go dark...
fellow firefly
–Chine
Don't stop the source of supply by
hoarding and thoughts of greed.
Dandyamana Ardha
Chandrasana
[Balancing Half Moon Pose]
K♥

Yoga Bent Method®

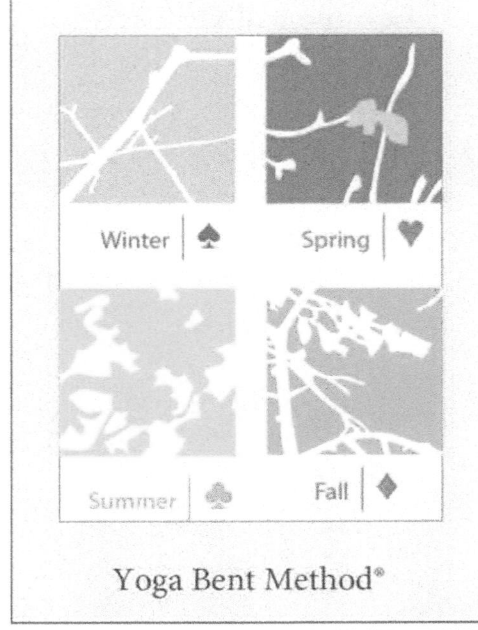

Yoga Bent Method®

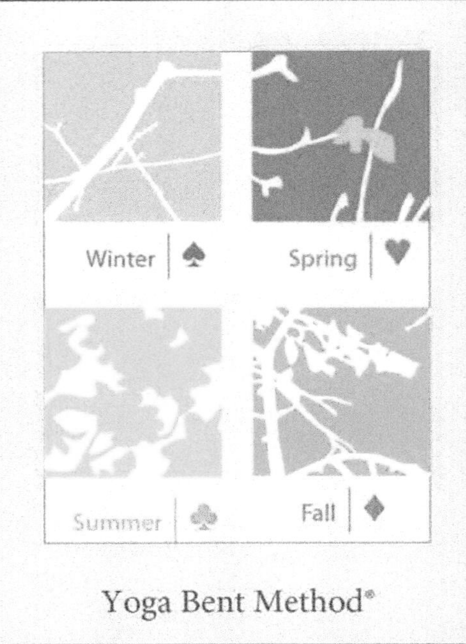

Yoga Bent Method®

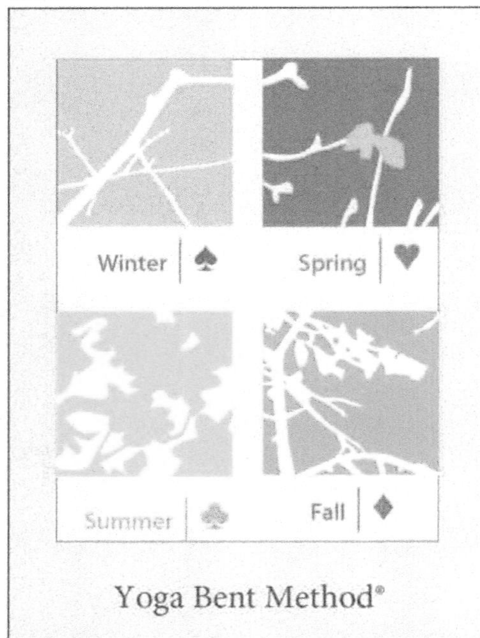

Yoga Bent Method®

Yoga Bent Method®

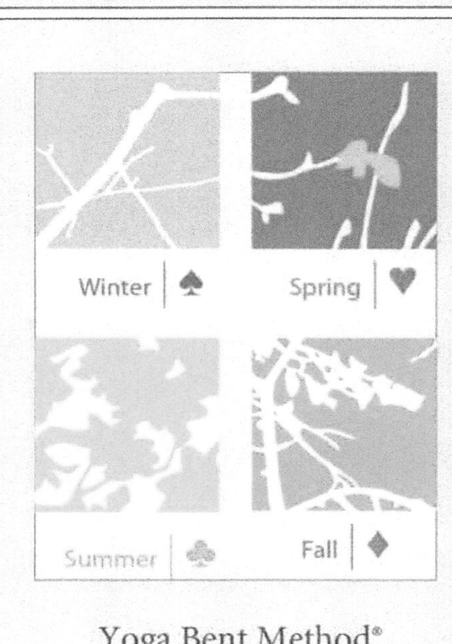

Yoga Bent Method®

Yoga Bent Method®

Yoga Bent Method®

Yoga Bent Method®

A ♦ Fall
again coolness comes... silver undersides of leaves evening-breeze blown –Shiki
Catura
Self-deprecation is a path running fast downhill into the valley of failure and despair.
Balasana
[Child's Pose]
A ♦

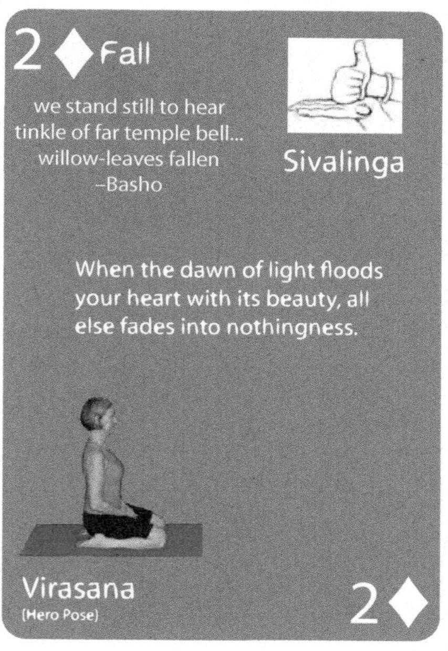
2 ♦ Fall
we stand still to hear tinkle of far temple bell... willow-leaves fallen –Basho
Sivalinga
When the dawn of light floods your heart with its beauty, all else fades into nothingness.
Virasana
[Hero Pose]
2 ♦

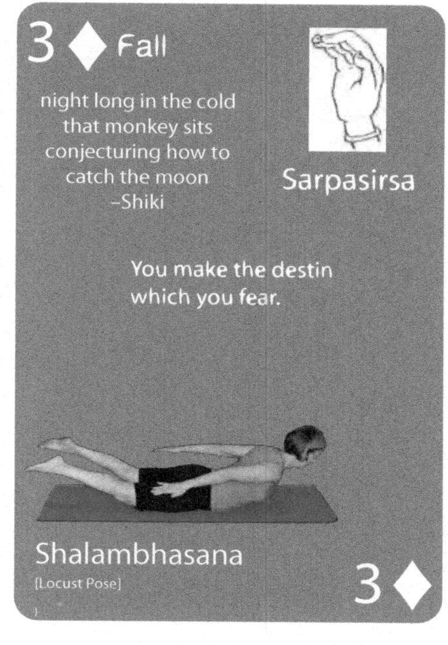
3 ♦ Fall
night long in the cold that monkey sits conjecturing how to catch the moon –Shiki
Sarpasirsa
You make the destin which you fear.
Shalambhasana
[Locust Pose]
3 ♦

4 ♦ Fall
supper in autumn flat light through an open door from a setting sun -Chora
Kapitta
Know and feel the joy of living a consecrated life of giving as an open channel to God's gifts.
Setu Bhandasana
[Bridge Pose]
4 ♦

5 ♦ Fall
on a leafless bough a crow is perched the Autumn dusk -Basho
Mahasir
See God in everything; separateness falls off, only light.
Halasana
[Plough Pose]
5 ♦

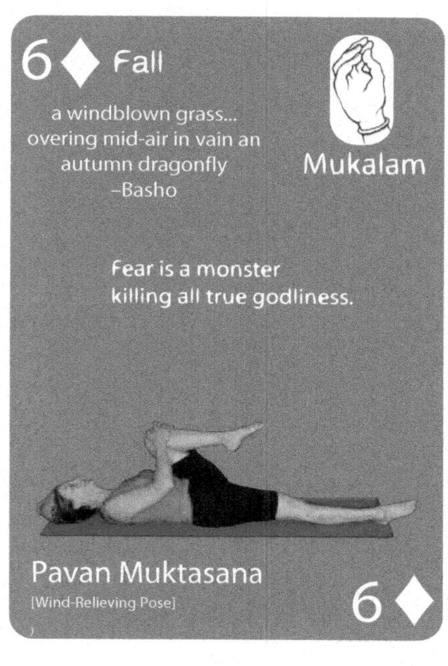
6 ♦ Fall
a windblown grass... overing mid-air in vain an autumn dragonfly –Basho
Mukalam
Fear is a monster killing all true godliness.
Pavan Muktasana
[Wind-Relieving Pose]
6 ♦

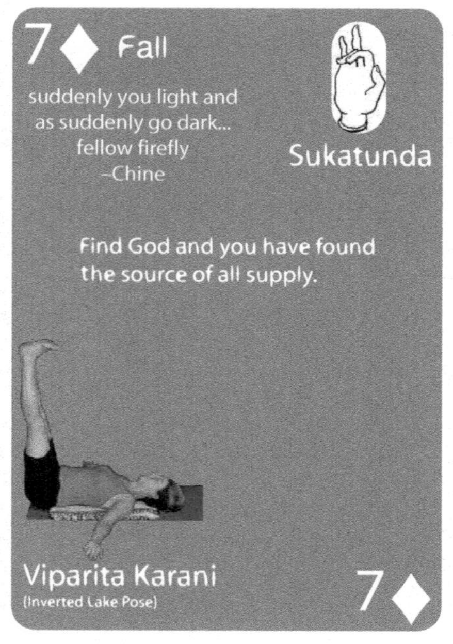
7 ♦ Fall
suddenly you light and as suddenly go dark... fellow firefly –Chine
Sukatunda
Find God and you have found the source of all supply.
Viparita Karani
[Inverted Lake Pose]
7 ♦

8 ♦ Fall
here is the dark tree denuded now of leafage... but a million stars -Seibi
Kurma
Oh, what joy to feel the vibrant pulsating life of God throbbing through the universe and through you in joyous ecstasy.
Sarvangasana
[Shoulder Stand Pose]
8 ♦

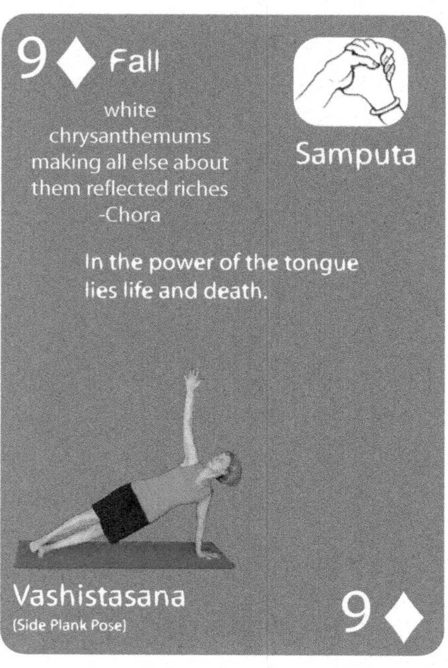
9 ♦ Fall
white chrysanthemums making all else about them reflected riches -Chora
Samputa
In the power of the tongue lies life and death.
Vashistasana
[Side Plank Pose]
9 ♦

Yoga Bent Method®

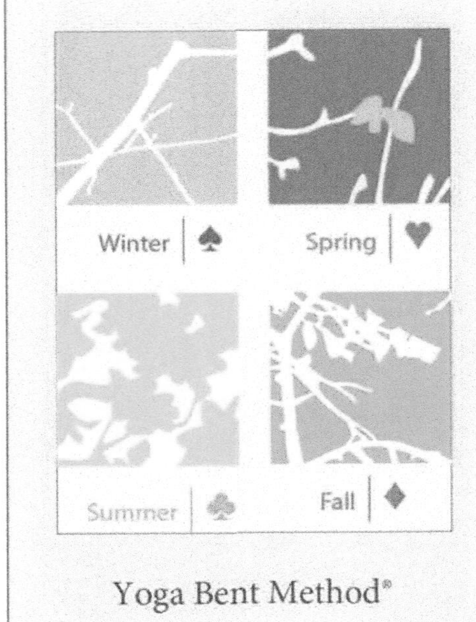

Yoga Bent Method®

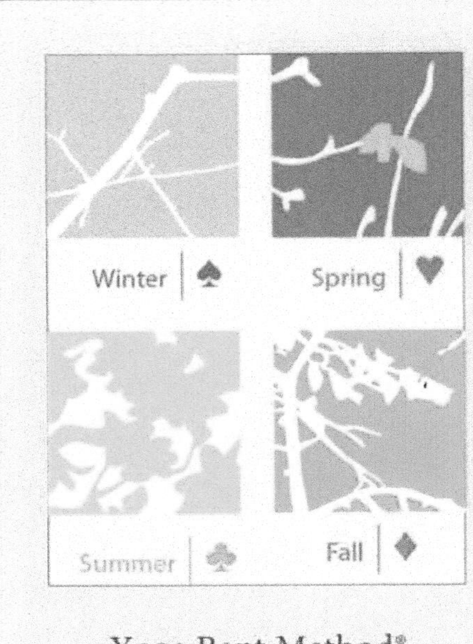

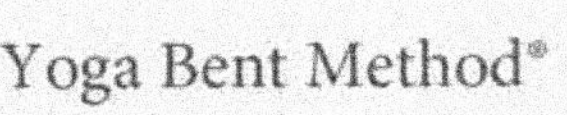

Yoga Bent Method®

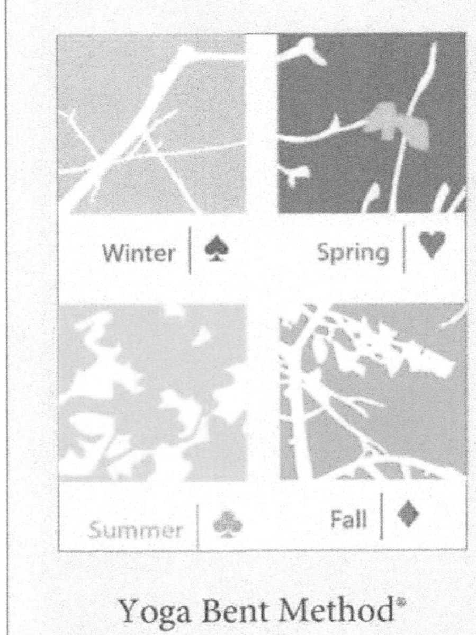

Yoga Bent Method®

Yoga Bent Method®

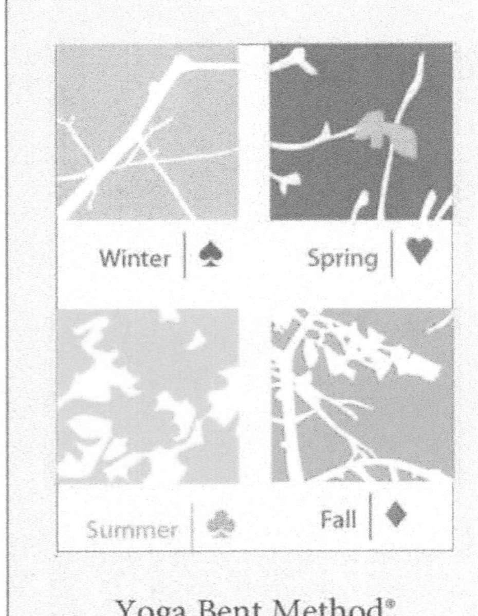

Yoga Bent Method®

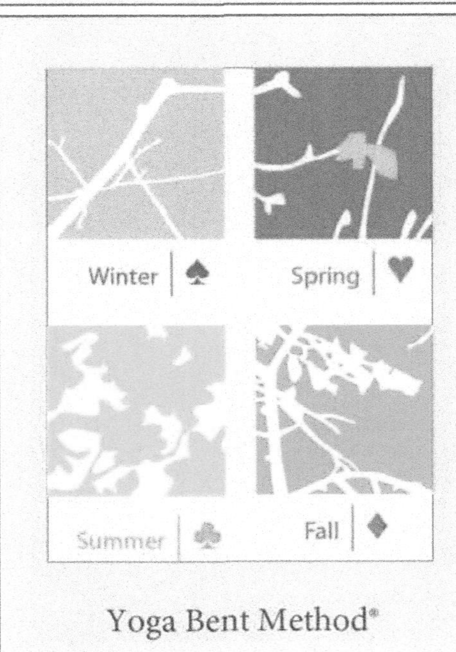

Yoga Bent Method®

Yoga Bent Method®

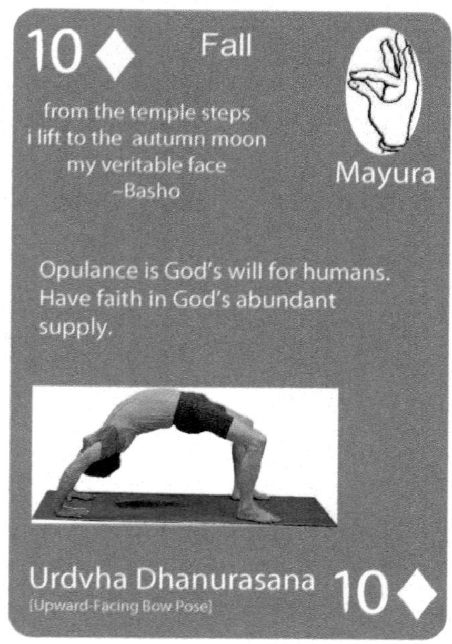
10 ♦
Fall
from the temple steps
i lift to the autumn moon
my veritable face
–Basho
Mayura
Opulance is God's will for humans. Have faith in God's abundant supply.
Urdvha Dhanurasana
[Upward-Facing Bow Pose]
10 ♦

J ♦
Fall
nights are getting cold...
not a single insect now
attacks the candle
–Shiki
Samkha
God does not choose who shall be favored those who shall be favor with Her gifts. God puts blessings on all alike. Some are wise and gather in the crop; others leave the fruit of life to wither on the vine.
Adho Mukha Vrksasana
[Hand Stand Pose]
J ♦

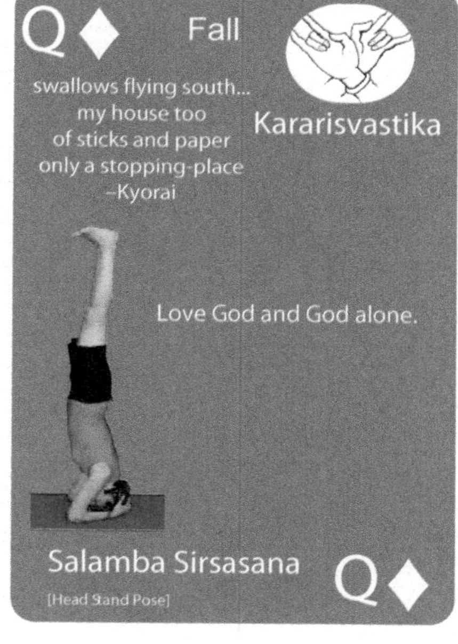
Q ♦
Fall
swallows flying south...
my house too
of sticks and paper
only a stopping-place
–Kyorai
Kararisvastika
Love God and God alone.
Salamba Sirsasana
[Head Stand Pose]
Q ♦

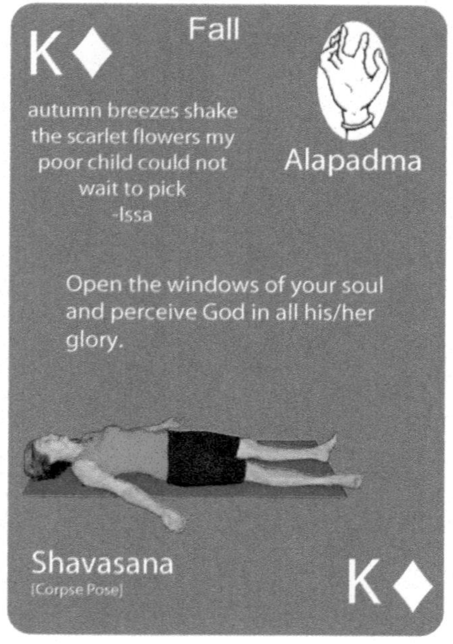
K ♦
Fall
autumn breezes shake
the scarlet flowers my
poor child could not
wait to pick
-Issa
Alapadma
Open the windows of your soul and perceive God in all his/her glory.
Shavasana
[Corpse Pose]
K ♦

Winter
Spring
Summer
Fall
Yoga Bent Method®

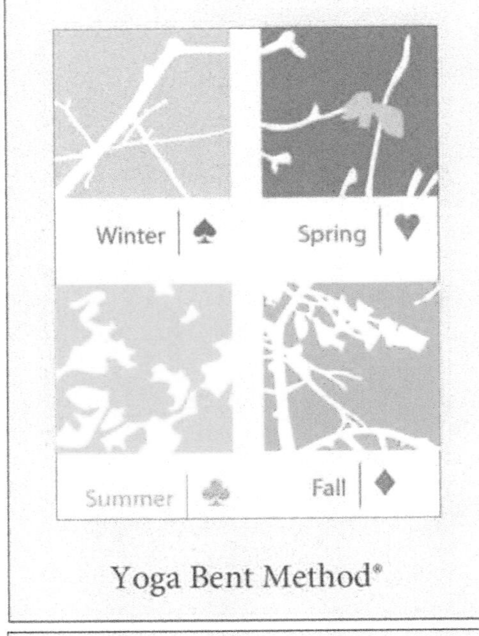
Winter
Spring
Summer
Fall
Yoga Bent Method®

Winter
Spring
Summer
Fall
Yoga Bent Method®

Winter
Spring
Summer
Fall
Yoga Bent Method®

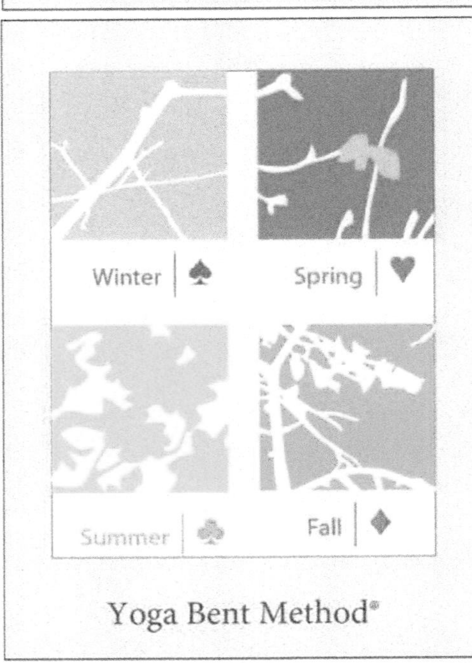
Winter
Spring
Summer
Fall
Yoga Bent Method®

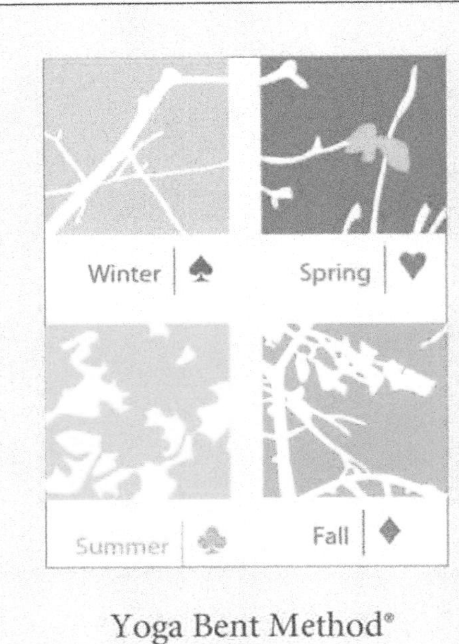
Winter
Spring
Summer
Fall
Yoga Bent Method®

Winter
Spring
Summer
Fall
Yoga Bent Method®

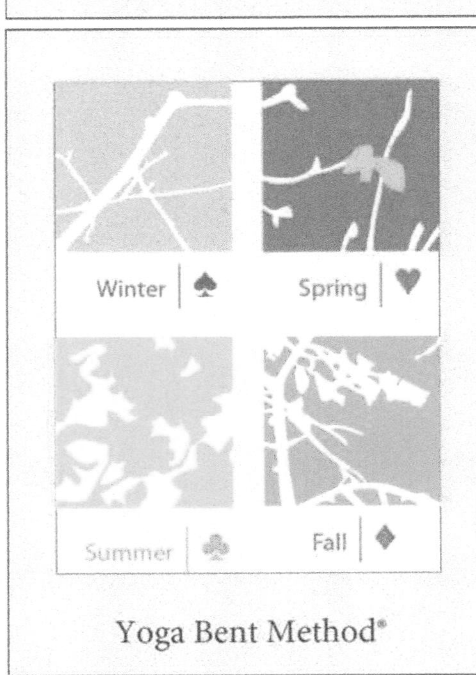
Winter
Spring
Summer
Fall
Yoga Bent Method®

Winter
Spring
Summer
Fall
Yoga Bent Method®

Sanskrit Glossary

philosophy • ethics • life

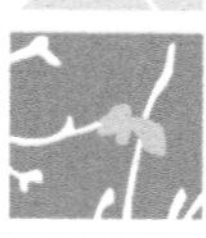

A

a
non

abhaya
freedom from fear

abhinivesa
possessiveness

abhyasa
steady effort

acharya
a religious teacher

adhah
down

adhara
a support

adharma
breach of duty

adhibhuta
the principle of objective existence

adhidaiva
the principle of subjective existence

adhikari
competent candidate

adhimatra
superior

adhimatratama
the highest, the supreme one

adhisthana
seat, abode

adhiyajna
the principle of sacrifice, incarnation

adho-mukha
face downwards

adho mukha svanasana
the dog stretch posture

adhyasa
a case of mistaken identity

adhyatma
the principle of self

adrishta
the unseen (e.g. actions of invisible entities)

adisvara
the primeval lord, a name of Shiva

aditi
the mother of the gods

aditya
son of aditi

advaita
non-duality of the universal spirit

advasana
the prone posture

agama
proof of the trustworthiness of a source of knowledge

aham
I

ahamkara
tendency to identify oneself with external phenomena, 'the I-maker'

ahimsa
non-violence

aishvarya
desire for power

ajapa
involuntary repetition (as with a mantra)

ajna
command

akarna
towards the ear

akarna dhanurasana
the shooting bow posture

akasha
ether

akrodha
freedom from anger

alabhdha-bhumikatva
the feeling that it is impossible to see reality

alamba
support

alasya
idleness

amanaska
the mind free from desire

amrita
the elixir of immortality

anahata
unbeaten

ananda
bliss

Ananta
infinite, a name of Vishnu

anantasana
Ananta's posture

anga
a limb, or body part

angamejayatva
unsteadiness of the body

angula
a finger

angushtha
the big toe

Anjana
the name of the mother of Hanuman

anjaneyasana
the splits

antahkarana
the mind

antara
within

antaranga
the practices of pranayama and pratyahara

antaratma
the inner self, residing in the heart

anuloma
with the grain, naturally

anumana
an inference

apana
one of the vital airs, controls the elimination of bodily wastes

apara
lower

aparigraha
abstention from greed, non-possessiveness

B

baddha
caught

baddhahasta sirsasana
the bound hands headstand posture

bandha
binding, a muscular lock

bandha padmasana
the bound lotus posture

baka
a wading bird, the crane

Bali
a demon king

basti
method for cleaning the intestines

bhadrasana
the auspicious posture

bhagavad gita
the dialogues between Krishna and Arjuna

bhagavan
holy

Bhairava
terrible, one of the forms of Shiva

bhajana
a hymn

bhakti
devotion, worship

bhastrika
the bellows breath

bhati
light

bhavana
concentration

bhaya
fear

bheda
a division

bhedana
breaking through, piercing

bheka
a frog

bherunda
terrible

bherundasana
the formidable posture

bhoga
enjoyment

bhoktir
one who enjoys

bhramara
a large bee

bhramari
the bee breath

bhranti-darshana
a delusion

bhu
land

bhudana
the donation of land

bhuja
arm or shoulder

bhujanga
snake

bhujangasana
the cobra posture

bhujasana
the arm posture

bhumi
the object of meditation

bhumikatva
firm ground

bhuta
a ghost, an element

bija
seed

bindu
drop or point

bodhi
supreme knowledge

Brahma
the creator

Brahmins
the highest, priestly caste

brahmacharya
control of sexual impulses

brahmacharyasana
the posterior stretch posture

brahmadvara
the door where kundalini enters the spine

brahmanda-prana
cosmic breath

Buddha
Buddha

buddhi
wisdom, reason

C

chakra
a wheel or vortex

chakra-bandha
the binding which seals all of the chakras

chakrasana
the wheel posture

chandra
the moon

chatur
four

chela
a pupil

chit
pure consciousness

chitrini
a fine cord within the spine

chitta
mind-stuff, the lower parts of mind - such as memory

chitta-vikshepa
confusion, distraction

chitta-vritti
a mode of behaviour

crore
ten million

D

Dadhicha
a sage who gave his bones to the gods, from which was fashioned the thunderbolt which slew Vrita

Daitya
a demon son of Diti

dakini
the goddess in muladhara

Daksa
a lord of created beings

daksina
the right side

dama
control of the body and senses

damani
a layer within a nadi allowing for the passage of energy

dana
giving

Danava
a demon

danda
a staff

dandasana
the staff posture

darbha
a sweet-smelling dried grass

darshama
a visit to a great person, viewpoint or vision

daurmanasya
despair

dehi
the self

deva
a divine being

devadatta
one of the vital airs, which causes yawning

devata
a divine being similar to an angel

deva-dasi
a temple prostitute

devi
a goddess

dhanu
a bow

dhanurasana
the bow posture

dharana
concentration

dharma
the law, duty, way of life

dhasanjaya
a vital air that stays in the body after death, sometimes bloating the corpse

dhenu
a cow

dhirata
strength

dhwani
a resonant sound

dhyana
contemplation

dirgha
long

Diti
mother of the daityas demons

dradhasana
the side relaxation posture

drashta
consciousness, the 'witness'

dridhata
strength

duhkha
pain, grief

dvesha
hatred

dvi
two, both

dvi-pada
two feet

E

eka
one, single

eka pada hastasana
the one leg posture

eka pada kakasana
the one leg crow posture

eka pada sirsasana
the leg-behind-head posture

ekgara
one-pointed

ekamevadvitiyam
one without a second

G

gana
Shiva's attendants

Ganapati
god of luck and wisdom

ganda
the cheek

garbha-pinda
an embryo

garbhasana
the foetus posture

garuda
an eagle

garudasana
the eagle posture

ghata
a pot, the body

ghi
clarified butter

go
a cow

gomukha
musical instrument resembling a cow's face

Sanskrit Glossary

philosophy • ethics • life

gomukhasana
the cow-faced posture

gorakshasana
the cowherd posture

gotra
family, race

granthi
a knot, obstruction in the chitrini

gu
darkness

gulma
the spleen

guna
a quality of nature

gup
guard, hide

guptasana
the hidden posture

guru
a spiritual teacher, heavy, important

H

ha
the sun

Hakini
the goddess in ajna

hala
a plough

halasana
the plough posture

hamasana
the altered peacock posture

hamsa
a swan

Hanuman
a monkey chief, son of Anjana and Vayu

hanumanasana
the splits

hasta
the hand

hasta padangusthasana
the hand-to-big-toe posture

hatha
force, against one's will

hatha-yoga
union with the supreme via discipline

himsa
violence

Hiranya-kashipu
a demon king, killed by Vishnu

I

ichchha
the will

ida
the channel on the left of the spine

indriya
organ of sense or action

indriya-jaya
mastery of the senses by controlling the desires

Isha
a form of Shiva

ishvara
a supreme being, god

ishvara-pranidhana
attentiveness to god

J

jagrata-avastha
complete awareness of the state of the mind

jalandhara
bandha where the chin rests in the notch between the collar bones

janma
birth, incarnation

janu
the knee

janu sirsasana
the head-knee posture

japa
repetition of a mantra

jathara
the stomach

jathara parivartanasana the belly-turning posture

jati
circumstances of life to which one is born

jaya
victory

jiva
a creature

jivana
life

jivatma
the individual soul

jnana
knowledge, especially spiritual knowledge

jnanendriya
an organ of knowledge, i.e. the five senses

jyotir dhyana
luminous contemplation

jyotis
inner light

kailasa
a Himalayan mountain, home of Shiva

kaivalya
spiritual independence and freedom

kakasana
the crow posture

Kakini
the goddess in anahata

kalabhairavasana
Lord Kalabhairava's posture

kali-yuga
the current, pleasure-loving age

Kama
desire for material pleasures, the god of passion

kama-dhenu
the heavenly cow

kanda
a knot, the place where the three main nadis join

kandasana
the upward ankle-twist posture

kapala
the skull

kapalabhati
a process to clear the sinuses

kapota
a dove

kapotasana
the dove posture

karma
work, action, the law of cause and effect

karmaphala
the result of an action

karma-yoga
unselfish actions

karmendriya
an action organ, e.g. the hands or feet

karnapidasana
the ear-press posture

Kartikeya
the god of war, was reared by the Pleiades

karuna
pity, tenderness

kathanta
howness

katikasana
the front-stretching posture

kaustubha
one of Vishnu's jewels

kaya
the body

kayika
pertaining to the body

kevala
whole, pure

khandapitasana
the ankle-twist posture

khechari
mudra where the tongue is inserted in the upper cavity

khyati
an outlook of knowledge

kleshas
the five sources of trouble and suffering

kona
an angle

koshas
bodies or sheaths

krauncha
a heron

krikara
one of the vital airs, causes coughing and sneezing

Krishna
the eighth incarnation of vishnu

krishnasana
the Krishna posture

kriya
cleaning

krounchasana
the heron posture

Krttikas
the Pleiades

kshatriyas
the caste of princes and warriors

kshipta
neglected or distracted

kukutasana
the cockerel posture

kumbha
a pot

kumbhaka
holding the breath

kunda
starting place of kundalini

kundala
coil of rope

kundalini
a coiled female snake, the latent energy at the base of the spine

kurma
a tortoise, one of the vital airs - controls blinking

kurmasana
the tortoise (leg-lock) posture

kutichaka
the hut-builder

L

lac
100,000

laghava
lightness

laghu
handsome, small

Lakini
the goddess in manipuraka

Lakshmi
goddess of beauty and luck

lalata
the forehead

Lanka
the kingdon of Ravana, Ceylon

lauliki
a movement of the abdominal muscles and organs

laya
absorption of the mind

laya-yoga
yoga using the latent power of kundalini

lingam
the phallus

lobha
greed

loka
a habitat

lola
swinging

lolasana
the swing posture

loma
hair

M

madhyama
average

maha
mighty

mahabandha/mahamudra
types of mudra

Mahadeva
the great god - Shiva

mahat
cosmic consciousness

maitri
friendliness

maithuna
sacramental intercourse

makara
a crocodile

makarasana
the crocodile posture

mala
a wreath

malasana
the garland posture

man
to think

manana
pondering

manas
the reasoning ability of the mind

manasika
of the mind

mandala
circle

Mandara
mountain used by the gods to stir the cosmic ocean

manduka
a frog

mandukasana
the frog posture

mani
a jewel

manipura
navel

manomani
samadhi

mantra
a prayer or sacred thought

Manu
father of the human race

marga
a path

matsya
a fish

matsyasana
the fish posture

matsyendrasana
the posture of Matsyendra

maya
illusion

mayura
a peacock

mayurasana
the peacock posture

meru-danda
the spinal column

mimansa
one of the schools of Indian philosophy

mirdu
soft, gentle

mirta
a corpse

mirtasana
the corpse posture

moha
infatuation or delusion

moksha
emancipation of the soul from rebirth

mudha
foolish, stupid

mudra
a seal

mudita
delight

mudras
muscular contractions that include the bandhas

mukha
the mouth

mukta
liberated

muktasana
the liberated posture

mukta hasta sirsasana
the freehand headstand posture

mula
root

mulabandhasana
the ankle-twist posture

mulashodhana
cleansing the rectum

murcha
mind-fainting

Sanskrit Glossary

philosophy • ethics • life

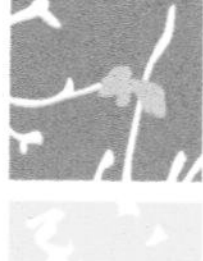

N

nabhipedasana
the upward ankle-twist posture

nada
an internal sound

nadi
a channel within the subtle body

nadi-shodhana
the purification of the nadis

naga
the vital air that causes burping

naishkaramya karma
actionless action

nakra
a crocodile

namah
a salute

nara
a man

Narasimha
the man-lion, fourth incarnation of Vishnu

Narayana
the supporter of life - Vishnu

Nataraja
Lord of the dancers, a name of Shiva

natarajasana
the Lord of the Dance posture

nauli
an abdominal exercise (lauliki)

nava
a boat

navasana
the boat posture

neti
not so

neti-yoga
cleansing of the nostrils

niddhyasana
meditation and contemplation

O

ojas
concentrated psychic power

P

pada
part of a book, the foot

padahastasana
the balancing forward bend posture

padangushtha
the big toe

padasana
the foot above posture

padma
a lotus

Padmanabha
a name of Vishnu

padmasana
the lotus posture

palmyrasana
the palm tree posture

para
beyond, higher

paramatma
the supreme spirit

parangmukhi
facing inwards

Parashurama
sixth incarnation of Vishnu

parigha
a bolt for shutting a gate

parighasana
the locked gate posture

parigraha
hoarding

paripurna
complete, whole

parivartana
revolving

parivrajaka
wanderer

parivritta parshvakonasana
the revolved lateral angle posture

parivritta paschimottanasana
the twisting back-stretching posture

parivritta sirsasana
the twisting head-knee posture

parivritta trikonasana
the revolved triangle posture

parshva
the side

parshva dhanurasana
the sideways bow posture

parshva halasana
the lateral plough posture

parshva sarvangasana
the sideways shoulderstand posture

parshva sirsasana
the headstand posture

parshvakakasana
the sideways crow posture

parvatasana
the mountain posture

paryanka
a bed

pasasana
the noose posture

pasha
a trap, noose

pashchima
west, the back of the body

pashchimottoanasana
the back-stretching posture

Patanjali
author of the Yoga Sutras

pavanmuktasana
the knee squeeze posture

pida
pain

pincha
the chin, feather

pinda
an embryo

pingala
the channel on the right of the spine

pliha
the spleen

Prahlada
a devotee of Vishnu

Prajapati
Lord of created beings

prajna
wisdom

prakasha
shining, clear

prakriti
eternal nature

pramada
indifference

pramana
authority, an ideal

prana
breath, energy, life

pranava
another name for aum

prana-vayu
a vital air that moves in the chest

pranayama
control of the breath

pranidhana
dedication

prasarita
stretched out

prasarita padottanasana
the spread legs posture

prashvasa
expiration

pratiloma
going against the grain

pratyahara
control of the senses

pratyaksha
direct evidence

punarjanman
rebirth

punya
virtue, merit, good

purakha
inhalation

purnata
perfection

purusha
the spirit or soul

purvottana
the front of the body

purvottanasana
the front-stretching posture

R

raga
anger, passion

raja
a ruler, king

raja-yoga
the yoga of mastery over the mind

rajas
mobility

Rakini
the goddess in svadhishthana

Rama
the seventh incarnation of Vishnu

rambha
plantain

Ravana
a demon king from Lanka who abducted the wife of Rama

rechaka
outbreathing

retus
semen

ru
light

Rudra
a form of Shiva

rupa
a form or body

S

Sadashiva
a form of Shiva

sadhaka
an aspirant, seeker

sadhana
practice, a quest

sah
he, that

sahaja
the karma to which one is born

sahasrara
the thousand-petalled lotus within the cerebral cavity

sakshatkara
the spirit

sakthi chalini
the nerve-power posture

salabhasana
the locust posture

salamba
supported

salamba sarvangasana
the supported shoulderstand posture

sama
equal, upright

samakonasana
the sideways leg-splits posture

sama-sthiti
standing still

sama-vritti
pranayama where inhalation, exhalation and suspension of breath are of same length

samadhi
where the aspirant is one with the object of his meditation

samana
one of the vital airs, which aids digestion

samasthiti
the upright-sitting posture

sambhava
birth

samkatasana
the dangerous posture

samkhya
one of the schools of Indian philosophy

samkhya yoga
the yoga of science

samshaya
doubt

samskaras
memories

samyama
dharana, dhyana and samadhi taken together

sannyasi
one who has renounced the world

sanjivani
a life-restoring elixir or herb

sansara
the wheel of reincarnation

santosha
contentment

sara
essence

Sarasvati
goddess of speech and learning

sarva
whole

sarvanga
the whole body

sarvangasana
the shoulderstand posture

sat
reality

sat chit ananda
bliss consciousness

Sati
mother of Kartikeya and Ganapati

sattva
orderliness, the quality of goodness in everything natural

satya
honesty

savasana
the corpse posture

savichara
investigational meditation

savitarka
inspectional meditation

sayanasana
the repose posture

setu
a bridge

setu bandhasana
the bridge posture

shabda
sound, the creative principle

Shakini
the goddess in vishuddha

shakti
female creative power, goddess

shaktichalani
one of the mudras, involves contracting the rectum

shalabha
a locust

shalabhasana
the locust posture

shama
calming the mind

shambhavi
related to Shiva

shambhavi mudra
gazing between ones eyes

Shambhu
a name of Shiva

shan
six

Shanmukha
with six mouths, a name of Kartikeya

shantih
peace

sharira
a body

shaucha
mental and bodily cleanliness

shava
a corpse

shavasana
the corpse posture

shayana
a bed

shesha
the serpent of eternity, having one thousand heads

shirsha
the head

shirshasana
the head-stand posture

shishya
the pupil of a guru

Shita
cold

Shiva
the destroyer

shmrti
memory

shodana
purification

shoka
anguish

shraddha
faith and trust

shravana
the act of listening to the doctrines

Sanskrit Glossary

philosophy • ethics • life

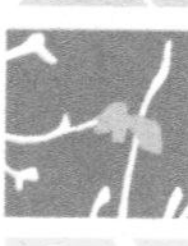

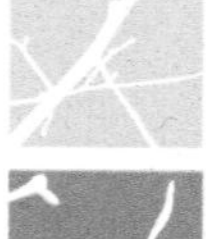

shrivatsa
the curl on Vishnu's breast

shuddha
clean, pure

shvana
a dog

shvasa
inspiration

svasa-prashvasa
heaving and sighing

siddha
a prophet or adept

siddhasana
the adept's posture

siddhi
a psychic (or occult) power

simha
a lion

simhasana
the lion posture

sirsangusthasana
the deep lunge posture

sirsasana
the headstand posture

Sita
the wife of Rama

Skanda
a name of Kartikeya, god of war

sodhana
purification

steya
robbery

sthirata
steadiness

sthiti
stability

sthula-sharira
the dense body

styana
sloth

sudras
the caste of servants and labourers

sukha
happiness

sukhasana
the easy posture

sukshma-sharira
the astral body

sumanasya
benevolence

supta
sleeping

supta baddha padmasana
the supine bound lotus posture

supta janu sirsasana
the supine head-knee posture

supta padangusthasana
the supine big toe posture

supta paschimottanasana
the supine back-stretching posture

supta vajrasana
the supine thunderbolt posture

surya
the sun

surya namaskar
the homage to the sun posture

sushumna
the spinal cord

sushupti-avastha
the state of the mind in dreamless sleep

sutra
a thread

sva
vital force, soul

svadhyaya
education through the study of the divine texts

svapnavastha
the state of the mind in a dream

svarga
heaven

svarupa
one's true nature

svasamvedana
the understanding of oneself

svastikasana
the prosperous posture

T

tada
a mountain

tamas
darkness, inertia, ignorance

tan
to stretch

tandava
violent dance of Shiva

tanmatras
the five potentials or senses

tantras
treatises on ritual, meditation, discipline, etc.

tap
to burn, shine, suffer

tapas
austerity, purification

tara
crossing over

Taraka
a demon slain by Kartikeya

tat
that

tattva
an element, the twenty-four categories of thatness

tejas
radiant energy, majesty

tirieng
horizontal

tittibha
a firefly

tittibhasana
the firefly posture

tola
a balance

tolangulasana
the balance posture

tolasana
the scales posture

trataka
an exercise to clear the vision

tri
three

trikona
a triangle

trikonasana
the triangle posture

trishna
thirst, desire

Trivikrama
fifth incarnation of Vishnu, who filled the earth, heaven and hell with his three steps (krama)

U

ubhaya
both

ubhaya padangusthasana
the buttocks balance posture

udana
the vital air controlling the intake of food and air

uddiyana
a fetter or binding involving the raising of the diaphragm

ugra
powerful, noble

ugrasana
the posterior stretch posture

ullola
a large wave

Uma
Shiva's wife, Parvati

unmani
samadhi

Upanishads
the philosophical parts of the Vedas. 'upa' (near) 'ni' (down) sad (to sit) - the act of sitting down by one's Guru to receive instruction.

upavishtha
seated

upeksha
disregard

urdhra prasarita ekapadasana
balancing forward posture

urdhva
raised

urdhva hastattanasana
the up-stretched arms posture

urdhva-mukha
face upwards

urdhva-retus
a celibate

ushtra
a camel

ushtrasana
the camel posture

utkata
fierce

utkatasana
the the hunkering posture

uttana
an intense stretch

utthita
stretched

utthita eka pada sirsasana
the balancing leg-behind-head posture

utthita kurmasana
the balancing tortoise posture

utthita lingamasana
the balancing on the phallus posture

utthita padangusthasana
the balancing big toe posture

utthita parsvakonasana
the stretched lateral angle posture

utthita paschimottanasana
the balancing back-stretching posture

V

vacha
speech

vaikuntha
Vishnu

vairagya
uncolouredness, not desiring physical objects

vaisesika
one of the schools of Indian philosophy

vaisyas
the caste of merchants and professionals

vajra
one of the channels in the spine, a thunderbolt, diamond

vajrasana
the thunderbolt posture

vajroli
the thunderbolt contraction

vakra
bent

vakrasana
the curved posture

valakhilya
a class of tiny entities, about the size of a thumb

vama
the left side

vamadevasana
Vamadeva's posture

Vamana
Vishnu's fifth incarnation

vamaprakasha
lovely shiningness

vasana
longing

Vasnata
the deity of Spring

vasti
internal cleansing

Vasuki
a name of Shesha

vatayana
a horse

vatayanasana
the horseface posture

vayus
the vital airs

veda
the sacred scriptures of the Hindus

vedana
feelings

vedanta
one of the schools of Indian philosophy

vedas
the sacred scriptures of the Hindus

vibhuti
divine power

vichara
continued thought

vidya
knowledge, science

vijnana
comprehension

vikalpa
imagination, fancy

vikshepa
confusion

vikshipta
mental aggitation

viloma
against the natural order of things

vipakas
the distressing results of karmas

viparita
reversed, inverted

viparitakarani
the upside-down posture

viparyaya
a mistaken view

vira
brave, a hero

virabhadrasana
the arrow posture

Virancha
name of Brahma

virasana
the hero posture

Virochana
a demon prince

virya
vitality, enthusiasm

vishama-vritti
uneven or strained movement whilst breathing

vishesha
particular

Vishnu
the preserver of life

vishudda
pure

vitarka
discernment

viveka
discrimination

vriksha
a tree

vrikshasana
the tree posture

vrishchika
a scorpion

vrishchikasana
the scorpion posture

vrit
to turn

vritti
a vortex, an idea, behaviour

vyadhi
illness

vyana
one of the vital airs, circulates energy all over the body

vajna
a sacrifice

Yama
the god of death

yamas
the five moral commandments

yantra
a design used in meditation

yastikasana
the stick posture

yoga
union, from 'yuj' - to join

yogadandasana
the yogin's staff posture

yogasana
the anchor posture

yoga-nidra
the sleep of yoga, where the body is resting but the mind is awake

yogi/yogin
one who practices yoga

yoni
vagina, womb, or source

yuga
an age

yuj
to yoke, join, concentrate on

yukta
joined with, one who has attained the communion with the supreme spirit

CPSIA information can be obtained
at www.ICGtesting.com
Printed in the USA
LVOW06s2357190916
505350LV00049B/589/P

9 780988 631618